Saving Victoria's Breasts

Exposing America's Shameful Breast Biopsy Scandal

This is the true story of
Victoria Case

as told to

Fred Hughes
Veteran radio broadcaster,
newspaper publisher, investigative journalist,
medical researcher and certified clinical thermographer

Research by:
Victoria Case and Fred Hughes

Website:
www.SavingVictoriasBreasts.com

[handwritten note:] I am delighted your idea helped to see the light — Victoria

Front cover designed by:
Gabrielle Taube

Gabbi Taube is the founder and host of the multi-speaker transformational seminar series CoachingWithTheMasters.com. She is known by many as the 'Queen of Connecting.' Gabbi has a background in journalism, advertising, and marketing, and is the CEO of her own advertising agency, Effective Media Consulting, in Michigan. Gabbi faced two battles with breast cancer, one in her 20s and again in her 30s after giving birth to her second child.

Cover Photo image credit: © OJO Images / www.fotosearch.com

Back cover designed by:
Morgan Meddaugh

Editing by:
Brett Blofield

Page layout by:
Katie Fitzgibbons
Morgan Meddaugh

Photographs by:
Victoria Case
Fred Hughes
Dr. Gary McCown

Digital Infrared Thermal Images by:
Brenda Kinder

Website videos by:
Medianetwork, LLC

First Edition
August 2013

Published by
Victoria Case, LLC
All rights reserved
Printed in the USA

Library of Congress Control Number: 2013946688

**Printing, distribution, website, marketing,
and social media development by**
Spectra Integration
Columbia, South Carolina

Disclaimers

Number One:

When Victoria moved from North Carolina to California at age 19, her business career took off. She became a computer programmer, and got involved in real estate developments and home-building. Her technical and administrative skills enabled her to manage large office staffs and large amounts of money. She was successful in the business world in large part because of her organization and documentation skills. Her interest in personal health led her to become a Qigong instructor, and all of her life experiences enabled her to become a medical researcher to be taken seriously. This is Victoria's true story with no apology to any health, cancer or humanitarian organization, doctor or dentist that might be offended.

Number Two:

This book is not intended to diagnose, treat, cure, or prevent any disease or medical condition. For diagnosis or treatment of any special medical problem, consult your own physician. The publisher and author are not responsible for any specific health needs that may require medical supervision and are not liable for any damages or negative consequences from any treatment, action, application or preparation, to any person reading or following the information in this book. References are provided for informational purposes only and do not constitute endorsement of any websites or other sources. Readers should be aware that the websites listed in this book may change.

Number Three:

The author is primarily a radio broadcaster, newspaper publisher, investigative journalist, and researcher. Although a Certified Clinical Thermographer, the author is not a medical doctor, dentist, nutritionist, or health professional, and is not practicing medicine. While this book is intended to offer broad consumer understanding of new discoveries and technologies, it should not be construed as providing medical advice.

Number Four:

This book is intended to inform, educate, inspire, stimulate, motivate and offer hope and encouragement to those who are in search of the truth. Anticipated side-effects may include – but are not limited to – shock, anger, and righteous indignation, once the truth is known. No warranties or guarantees are expressed or implied. Neither the publisher nor the author shall be liable or responsible to any person or entity for any physical, psychological, emotional, financial or commercial damages, alleged to have been caused, directly or indirectly by the information in this book, including, but not limited to, special, incidental, consequential or other damages. Our views and rights are the same: You are responsible for your own choices, actions, and results.

Number Five:

To the best of our knowledge, this book is truth, from cover to cover, even though it has not been evaluated or cleared by the U.S. Food and Drug Administration (FDA), or America's medical monopoly. This book does not carry a "Seal of Approval" from any cancer organization, or any dental or medical association.

Graphic Content:

Graphic Content of Six Photos Unavoidable

Prior to final editing, more than 20 people, mostly professionals, read draft copies of this book's content without seeing photographs. Based on verbal descriptions alone, not one person grasped the gravity of the situation that Victoria was dealing with until they were shown the graphic pictures. The six breast images may be disturbing for some readers. Victoria is a very private person. She did not want the images published but the reality is that the true story of her long battle to save her breast can't be comprehended without them. The only image in the book that shows both breasts is a post-ablation photo. Its purpose is to allow women to see the outcome of a breast-saving ablation procedure as compared to a mastectomy.

Table of Contents

Victoria's Dedication

My name is Victoria Case. This is my true story. After more than five years, it does not have the ending I desired, but as with all things, it can be what I make it.

The first thing I want the reader to learn is that a cancer diagnosis is not a death sentence, especially if the diagnosis is ductal carcinoma in situ (DCIS). This is a stage zero precancerous condition of the breast.

Many experts believe DCIS should not even be classified as cancer. There are many reasons you could have a lump in your breast and it may not be cancer. In the medical community this is now being treated as dramatically as a staged cancer.

The best thing you can do for yourself with any cancer diagnosis is remain calm. Stress and fear are your number one enemies. Most doctors will rush you to make a decision. The first decision, most likely, will be for you to have a breast biopsy immediately. Please **DO NOT** consider having a biopsy until you read this book. You need to know all the facts so you can make an informed decision, and do what is best for YOU.

Every situation has a source that creates the problem. You need to have a Digital Infrared Thermal Image and see what is going on in your mouth that is creating infection. You need to analyze the foods you are eating and make sure they are healthy foods that are going to help your body function properly. You need to start moving and get some exercise. If you have toxic situations or a toxic person in your life, get rid of them. Life is short and all of us deserve the best life has to offer.

I do want to thank my family – Mother, Teresa, Allen Wood Jr., and Gregory. My love for you kept me strong.

I also want to thank the people that supported me – Fred Hughes, "Buzz," Brenda Kinder, and Ronda Lutfey.

My dedication is to all people that get a cancer diagnosis; remain calm and make a wise decision regarding your treatment. Please let my story give you knowledge and information, so you can make life or death decisions that will result in you having a long and healthy life.

If this book had been available in 2007, I would have made a completely different decision concerning my health and well-being, and be telling a very different story.

Be blessed and stay healthy,
Victoria

This book is In Honor of
Beverly Hughes Crummey &
Patricia Hughes Bagdan

My first book was dedicated In Memory of my mother, Sarah Bedsole Hughes, and In Honor of my father, Al Hughes. Both parents are now deceased.

This book is dedicated to my two younger sisters who have loved me, encouraged me, and stood by me through thick and thin.

Both of them have had extensive dental work. Patty's dental procedures appear to have been done to a high degree of excellence. Bev's dental procedures were anything but excellent, until she met Dr. Gary McCown in Knoxville, Tennessee in 2012.

There's no gentle way of describing Bev's dental work. Over the years, she was butchered, ending up with 24 root canal-treated teeth and seven implants. At least four of her root canals had to be retreated at different times, from six to 15 years later.

I realize the claims about oral pathology in my two books seem bizarre, perhaps absurd, and to many people, unbelievable. That's why I so much appreciate my sister, Patty, providing me with a quote to incorporate into this dedication.

"To go against the dominant thinking of your friends, of most of the people you see every day, is perhaps the most difficult act of heroism you can perform" (Theodore White, 1915-1986, American journalist, historian and author).

My sister, Bev, is especially fond of this quote: "The problems of the world cannot possibly be solved by skeptics or cynics whose horizons are limited by obvious realities. We need men and women who can dream of things that never were" (John F. Kennedy, 1917-1963, American president).

Patty and Beverly, I love you dearly,
Your brother, Fred

Introduction
Conspiracy theory or truth?

By Fred Hughes

What you are about to read is not a conspiracy theory crafted by an aging Right Wing fanatic. I've always considered myself a typical hard-working, blue collar American who happens to have extensive white collar skills and experiences.

Real medicine has always been the last thing on my mind, except for authoring a book about a new technology that has applications for both the medical and dental fields, and I had to suffer through my own medical crisis before putting it on paper.

I basically ignored a heart attack in 2000 but a second one in 2005 altered my life. I met a researcher who was using Digital Infrared Thermal Imaging to prove the connection between oral pathology and cancer and many degenerative diseases. This same technology has many diverse applications, such as revealing periodontal disease when there's no hint of it during an oral exam or in a dental x-ray, and showing developing thyroid issues and inflamed carotid arteries long before there's a medical symptom.

The connection between oral pathology and diseases has been known since the days of Weston Price, an American dentist and researcher in the early 1900s, but suddenly there was a technology – inexpensive and non-invasive – that could be used to give a dentist more diagnostic information about a patient than a typical dental x-ray could possibly reveal.

And the technology could painlessly capture heat signatures in a woman's breasts suggesting developing pathology as much as 10 years earlier than a mammogram.

In the hands of a dentist who understood the capabilities of combining a digital Panorex with thermal imaging, patients would no longer be walking out of the dental office with a life-threatening anaerobic infection that neither the dentist nor hygienist could see.

As of today, the oral pathology connection with cancer is iron-clad, although heavily suppressed in 'respected' medical journals and the media. Every woman with breast cancer should expect to find an anaerobic infection in her mouth, and she should always look on the same side as the tumor. Apart from high doses of radiation or chemotherapy drugs and environmental toxins as a direct cause, no exceptions have been found. When did a doctor or nurse working on a breast cancer team tell you that?

I published a book about this discovery in 2007 *(Am I Dead? ... or do I just feel like it. Cancer cured ... the coming storm)*. The year before, I published the first newspaper story that explained how thermal imaging was being used to screen for oral pathology and diseases. My 2005 heart attack only accelerated my retirement from the newspaper business.

I had agreed to sell my North Carolina newspaper to Gannett, a media giant that now owns 23 TV stations, 200-plus weeklies, magazines and trade publications, and 82 U.S. daily newspapers, including *USA Today*, which has the country's largest print circulation.

Gannett had exclusive rights to give this story international exposure. It never happened. Gannett reporters never even challenged the published claims. Why not? Are the media biased?

As I was driving down an interstate, a man in Oregon posed that question to Rush Limbaugh on his syndicated radio show on Sept. 18, 2012. The man specifically asked if The Associated Press is biased. They've all been trained the same way, answered Limbaugh. "It's the kids of the Sixties grown up. They live and work in the same place ... it's a collective ... it's a commune."

In the largest sense, I have Gannett to thank for the inspiration to tell the story and self-publish the 350-page book complete with two dozen pages of color photos and thermal images. My first book was not technical and the story wasn't complicated.

Saving Victoria's Breasts is basically the same as far as the technical aspect, but the story itself is very complicated. It's a true story from cover to cover and positive proof that truth can be stranger than fiction.

And that brings us to Victoria's story. I well remember the day I finally confessed that very point to her. "Your story is stranger than fiction. You could not make this stuff up."

The seed for Victoria's book may have been planted in January 2009, but it wasn't until after her right breast cryoablation procedure in

April 2009 that we realized how Victoria's story could change the lives of millions of women who live in absolute fear of getting breast cancer. But she would need a forum, and that outlet would not be the mainstream media whose drug and medical coverage seems to be dictated directly or indirectly by pharmaceutical companies, the American Medical Association (AMA), and the U.S. Food and Drug Administration (FDA).

Besides, these groups have no history of seriously promoting any treatments for breast cancer that don't involve surgery, radiation and chemotherapy. They don't even want women to have the freedom of medical choice. There's too much money involved. The truth is that breast cancer is not to be feared; it is to be prevented. However, lifelong prevention is very difficult if women do not address the root cause – oral pathology.

Cancer is a cause and a symptom. It's a warning sign that the body is out of balance.

Can a person get cancer and not have oral pathology? Absolutely! It's no secret that radiation and chemical toxins, regardless of their source, can cause cancer. There is, however, a documented connection between cancer and oral pathology.

Victoria's story gives new meaning to the phrases: medical abuse, gross incompetence, and blind ignorance.

How did this happen?

Breast cancer has become a pink pawn to be shuffled around on a game board so doctors and so-called foundations, research programs, and charities can use the 'fear factor' to rake in billions of dollars in fees, grants, and donations. The promise of a pharmaceutical cure is always on the horizon. The cure was 'on the horizon' when I was a teenager.

Along the way, these charlatans spread around a few crumbs under the guise of promoting awareness and prevention and promising assistance to women, and all the while they buck every natural, non-invasive, and alternative approach to preventing or curing breast cancer.

R. Webster Kehr, an ex-marine, who developed a cancer research website about 10 years ago, CancerTutor.com, has stated that alternative treatments are so good that many thousands of people cure their own cancer without any medical help.

In the most recent Pink Madness of October, not one word was spoken in the mainstream media about anaerobic infections in the jawbone and their link to breast cancer. Yet, the *Wall Street Journal* published a detailed article in December 2012 linking oral health issues to serious diseases.

I am not a doctor – never will be. It worked out that I was in the right place at the right time in the right circumstances with the appropriate skills and experiences to understand the oral pathology connection, and to be able to put it into words.

Over the past six years, I have evaluated thousands of thermal images and compared them to oral histories and dental x-rays, especially digital panoramic x-rays of the mouth. The findings are astounding. There are dentists scattered around the country whose own experiences with their patients' histories are equally incredible.

As you read Victoria's story, you're likely to chuckle one moment and be in tears the next. You will be happy that she's alive, and angry at the dozens of doctors who ignored and abused her.

Most of all, you will be appalled at the breast biopsy scandal that is operating with impunity in the United States, protected by a catch phrase in the medical industry called Standard of Care.

- If you are a woman who had a mammogram- or ultrasound-guided breast biopsy since 1998, there's a 99% probability that you have a foreign object in your breast – a metal clip or marker, a piece of wire, or even a piece of plastic.
- If your biopsy was before 2010, there's an 80% probability that you don't know about it. You were never informed and you never gave your consent, either written or verbal.
- If your biopsy was in 2010 or more recently, there's a 50% probability that you don't know about it. You were never informed and you never gave your consent, either written or verbal.

Why did the probability of a woman 'knowing' about a clip or marker in her breast decline in the past two years? Doctors are being more cautious about getting a signed release, but women are still not being told the truth about the potential dangers. In fact, few women are being told about any risks or dangers, and virtually no woman is being told about the malfunction history of biopsy devices.

Are the clips or markers going to harm women?

Medical doctors who do these procedures will tell you no, it's nothing to worry about. These same doctors demand that the marker is absolutely necessary, although it only came into use in the late 1990s. It was Adolf Hitler who said, "If you tell a lie loud enough and long enough, the people will believe."

So far tens of thousands of women are not having a problem with the markers. Does that make them safe and totally harmless?

Try convincing women who are already suffering that the markers are harmless. Many of these women went months or years before figuring out why they're suffering. Seldom did their doctors help them. They still are struggling to learn what to do about it. Before finishing this book, women will know what to do.

Although started over four years ago, the completion of *Saving Victoria's Breasts* was stalled by the discovery in 2010 that the placement of tiny pieces of metal in the breasts of most women who have a core biopsy had become routine, yet full disclosure was being hidden. Where's the outrage from women?

The medical claim is that these 'permanent markers' are completely safe. The same safety claim was made for silicone breast implants, and we know the rest of that story.

The evidence shows that breast biopsy clips or markers are not as safe as advertised. On the contrary, they are being blamed for triggering all sorts of pain, infections, and possibly even prohibiting breast cancer recovery in some women who refuse radical surgery. There is no protocol for safely removing these foreign objects without further damaging breast tissue, the very reason many women refuse surgical options.

Even when cancer is not present, a woman could still lose her breast because of the foreign object. She would be hard pressed to find a doctor to help her, and eventually the woman could no longer tolerate the pain and infection.

Every woman from age 17 to 70 needs to read Victoria's story. Every father, husband, uncle, fiancée, and boyfriend needs to read it, too.

About the Prologue

By Fred Hughes

Bill Irwin is the first and only blind person in the world to thru-hike the full length of the Appalachian Trail with a Seeing Eye® dog – 2,167.9 miles. He is totally blind, only able to distinguish night from day. His trail journey started March 8, 1990 at Springer Mountain, Georgia and ended in Maine on November 21, 1990.

Why did he do it?

The answer to the "why" began a long time ago, says Bill. "It had more to do with the blindness that afflicted my soul than with the physical blindness," he wrote in his best-selling book, *Blind Courage.*

How did he do it?

He met other hikers, north- and southbound, but most of the time he was alone with his dog, Orient. He had to find shelters, water, and the trail itself, marked only with white blazes on trees. The "how" is an amazing story that you will want to read in the 222 pages of his book.

Bill Irwin endured incredible pain on the trail, but he was accustomed to pain – pain from divorce, pain from alcoholism, pain from estranged children.

He also had endured the pain of a misdiagnosis by medical doctors; not once, but twice. Both times he was given a death sentence.

In his early 20s, Bill was hospitalized for nine months after a preliminary diagnosis of liver cancer. The diagnosis was later changed to a common bile duct obstruction. "So the docs blew it," he said, "but this time I thought I was really going to bite the dust."

At age 28, he was told for the second time that he had cancer and was going to die. Doctors said a malignant melanoma in his left eye was fast spreading and immediate surgery was required.

"Dying was not something I was remotely interested in, nor was I prepared for it, mentally, emotionally, or spiritually," he wrote in *Blind Courage.* "From what I knew of God at that time, He certainly would not be pleased with my lifestyle. I didn't want to explain it to him anytime soon."

Meanwhile, one alert physician examined Bill's eye tissue and offered a dissenting opinion. Bill did not have cancer; he had a degenerative disease and faced a fifty-fifty chance of losing the sight in his right eye.

Doctors made another mistake, but he had already lost his eye. Bill actually had chorioretinitis (inflammation of the thin pigmented vascular coat of the eye) "which was not even named at the time I had it."

Five years later, the disease would surface again resulting in total blindness. Forty-four years would pass before Bill began pondering a probable connection between oral pathology and the disease that led to his blindness.

Today, Bill travels extensively as a professional motivational speaker and uses the phone and monthly wellness meetings in Dover-Foxcroft, Maine, which are simulcast as free webinars, to help others find cures for cancer and degenerative diseases. Read more about Bill, and order an autographed copy of his book from his website (BillIrwin.com).

Bill Irwin conquered the Appalachian Trail with commitment, perseverance, information, and the will to survive. He conquered prostate cancer the same way. Many people who face a cancer diagnosis have all the ingredients to win, except correct information. Please allow *Saving Victoria's Breasts* to change that.

Prologue

By Bill Irwin

Fred Hughes has authored two books that taught me what I needed to learn about my own cancer, and I believe that they will help save thousands of lives, whether someone is diagnosed with breast cancer or a malignant tumor in another part of the body.

If you don't have a cancer diagnosis, you are very fortunate, but it may not always be that way. Cancer is a very insidious thing. Reading these books may keep you from hearing those dreaded words, "You have cancer!"

Victoria lived in excruciating pain and in pure hell for a long time due to the lack of knowledge that could have saved her numerous sleepless nights as well as a huge amount of money that she spent unnecessarily! She encountered so many obstacles and people that could have helped her, if only they had been willing and informed, but ignorance is no excuse!

The Bible says, quoting God, "My people perish due to lack of knowledge."

Then God sent Fred to intervene in Victoria's life. It made a huge difference in the outcome of her treatment regimen and the ultimate result of Victoria being completely healthy.

A Texas researcher, who did extensive studies on root canal teeth (38,000 patient records), uncovered one critical bit of information that directly impacted Victoria's ability to recover from a breast cancer diagnosis. In his massive study, Bob Jones found that 94% of root canal-treated teeth had positive pathology (some type of active infection).

Fred's research and writing made a profound impact on my life as well. One statement he quoted put the final critical touch on his work: "Your dentist is your most important doctor." I have come to believe that is true, much to the chagrin of the conventional allopathic medical and dental communities.

At age 72, I am busier than I have ever been in my life. I have enough energy to run three ministries, two businesses, spend an hour each day doing rigorous exercise – sometimes even two hours – plus doing whatever God lays on my heart each day I live.

Sometimes that is a pleasure and sometimes it is a real chore, especially when it requires me to get out in the middle of a winter storm and remove several feet of white stuff from our half-mile driveway in north central Maine where my wife, Debra, and I have been living now for nearly 17 years. This can be a stretch for a blind man.

In January 2012, on a very snowy day, I had to hustle to get the snow out of the way so our rural postal delivery person could deliver our mail.

As I made a 360-degree turn in a turn-around near our home I did so full throttle with my snow-blower and when I was in the middle of the turn I experienced an excruciating pain in my right hip. At first, I just tried to ignore it, but it got worse.

Weeks passed and it didn't get better. So, I made an appointment with my orthopedist and upon his examination he discovered a fracture in the head of my right femur. He suggested that I continue to stay off of it for another month since I was not interested whatsoever in the surgery he may have suggested if he hadn't known me so well.

I have been a primarily raw vegan for over 15 years and have fervently adhered to that discipline. I am a certified health minister by an internationally known provider of information and products that promotes wellness from a biblical perspective.

(Hallelujah Acres at hacres.com offers concise information about supplements, nutrition, recovery diet for cancer, health tips, recipes for main dishes plus juicing and smoothies, and instructions on how to prepare them.)

In that capacity I have very strongly proclaimed that my wellness lifestyle would ease my mind about ever coming down sick with any of the horrible diseases that most Americans are vulnerable to. I guess I said it with a little righteous indignation or as I like to say it, "audacity on steroids."

I never did worry about diseases like diabetes, arthritis, cardiovascular incidents like strokes and heart-attacks, multiple sclerosis, Parkinson's disease, and especially cancer that took the lives of many of my ancestors.

I agreed to obey my doctor's suggestion to stay off my feet for another month.

At the end of that month one of the ministries I direct as the presiding officer had a scheduled board meeting three hours away from our home.

During that weekend I had to climb two flights of stairs to get to our room and had to do so several times and the pain became unbearable. I spent both nights going from one room to the next seeking comfort to no avail. The most comfortable position I could get into was just standing up; not a thing one would be inclined to choose in the middle of the night; I got no rest!

On our way home I told Debra that something terrible was wrong with my hip and I thought it must be cancer since a blood clot had already been ruled out. That is exactly what the diagnosis was that next Thursday when my orthopedist called me with my MRI results.

He called me at home at the end of the day and asked me if I was sitting down at the time. I was. I knew that he must not have great news, but I already had in mind what he was going to say, something that no one ever wants to hear: "You have cancer!"

There was a long pause. He was devastated to have to tell me that I had stage four prostate cancer with metastatic involvement in both my hips, legs, and throughout my pelvis.

He tried to get his urologist to see me but since it was so late stage the doctor refused by saying, "I am retiring soon and don't want to take on a difficult case like yours." In fact, no urologist that was contacted in the entire state of Maine would take my case.

A friend called from southern Maine, and in our conversation I discovered that he had a son who lived in Burlington, Massachusetts. It was near Lahey Clinic, the Mayo Clinic of the northeast.

Soon after that my son-in-law, who is head of medicine at Walter Reed Regional Naval Hospital at Bethesda, Maryland, called and said that his urologists and oncologists met with him to discuss my case. They all recommended either Harvard or Lahey Clinic for an immediate referral.

Then I connected the dots and decided to choose Lahey Clinic so Debra could stay near the clinic if and when I had to be hospitalized.

This came very soon and on May 17, 2012 I was at Lahey Clinic getting my pre-operative work-up and we were invited to stay with our friend's son. I had my surgery to place a titanium rod in my right hip from the knee all the way through the head of the femur on May 20 as my hip was severely compromised by the tumor. The surgery was a resounding success. In fact, it took away all my pain and my convalescence was uneventful.

The following week I had an appointment with the oncologist at Lahey Clinic and the meeting was certainly what I expected. He first told me, "You can expect to live a year and a half if you begin taking chemotherapy and radiation right away, and if you don't you won't live even a year!"

He then looked at my record and saw that I drink eight, eight-ounce glasses of freshly juiced, carrot juice daily and boldly proclaimed "and if you don't stop drinking that carrot juice you are going to die much sooner than I said as it is feeding your cancer." I asked him where he heard that and he ignored my question.

I then told him that my health was my responsibility and that I would never submit to any of those very toxic protocols of treatment. I politely left and never returned.

I began to think of how in the world could I have possibly gotten cancer on the lifestyle that I had been living for such a long time; I hadn't even had as much as a common cold in all those years, let alone cancer. I thought I was in perfect health!

I was embarrassed, very confused, and devastated.

I got in touch with the American Anti-cancer Institute (AACI) and got a copy of Robert G. (Bob) Wright's book, *Killing Cancer – Not People* (AmericanAci.org). Wright is the founder and director of AACI who says, "Cancer is nearly 100% preventable and reversible when people have precise knowledge on what to do." This book revealed things to me that boggled my mind.

I had never in my long career as a clinical chemist heard of such things as a toxic jaw, dental cavitations, or trapped emotions, and I thought I had heard it all.

I began to investigate all of this and learned that the cause of my cancer had to be from the 24 root canal-treated teeth that I had over my lifetime. Furthermore, I recently had eight dental implants that potentially had to be removed as well as all of the root canals.

(Bill's first root canal was done at age 15; he had several root canals by age 19. We'll never know the exact teeth involved in the early root canal treatments; all of his early dentists are deceased, and Bill had never scrutinized his dental history before October 2012. Adding insult to injury, most of Bill's root canal-treated teeth were crowned and the packing material under most of the crowns was half mercury.)

I was facing a trip to Mexico to have extensive dental surgery since it was so expensive to have it done in the U.S. I was informed that only about 50 dentists in this country had been specially trained to perform this highly specialized surgery. That is what makes it so expensive. None of them got this special training in any dental school.

In fact, in Fred's first book (*Am I Dead? ...or do I just feel like it. Cancer cured ... the coming storm*), I learned that neither the American Dental Association nor the American Medical Association acknowledge any of this information as being good science.

At this point, I began thinking about my dentist at home in Maine whom I have known for over 16 years. I know he is an honest and very caring man. If he had known that he was doing anything to me that was harmful, he would not have done it, regardless of what it would cost him.

I began to realize that God's hand was in the whole scenario in a very powerful way. Through Caring Bridge, where I was chronicling my journey treating my cancer, I was contacted by a friend, Olin Idol, a fellow health minister. He wanted me to call a man in North Carolina named Fred Hughes, who was intensely involved in thermal imaging research as it relates to oral pathology, and he works closely with Dr. Gary McCown, a holistic dentist in Knoxville, Tennessee.

Talking with Fred was like talking with an old friend that I hadn't seen in a long time; we immediately struck up a friendship of spiritual and emotional connectedness and both of us became aware of it.

On July 4, 2012, Debra and I flew to Knoxville and I was seen by Dr. McCown the following day. He was so knowledgeable and personable I immediately knew that I had been sent to the right dentist to do my surgery.

Since I had been previously told by a biological dentist in Maine that I was going to lose all my teeth, including my implants, I was dreading hearing the same assessment from Dr. McCown. I had spent a small fortune getting dental work in recent years and was facing losing it all, but if that is what it would take to cure my cancer, I became willing to do it.

To my amazement Dr. McCown did a careful examination on my mouth and decided that all but one of my implants was "solid as a rock," as he put it, and I was elated. The surgery to remove four contiguous, infected root canals and one infected implant went well.

(Bill's infected root canal teeth were all connected on the Tooth Meridian Chart to his prostate cancer; 24, 25, and 26 have a urogenital connection and 27 a gonads connection as well as hips. The infected implant 29 has a 'hip joint to the knee' connection. Although the dental implant was the worst of the infections, it was the combination of all the individual infections in his lower jaw that overpowered Bill's tumor suppressant genes.)

We went home to Maine and returned to Knoxville in mid-September for the B.R.A.T. (Bike Ride Across Tennessee) that had been on my calendar for over two years.

I really was beginning to see God at work in this whole story that was being revealed to me one little step at a time.

I first activated all the prayer chains that I was connected with worldwide including the one at my orthopedist's church upon his behest. People from around the world were praying for me daily and letting me know about it. What a wonderful blessing prayer can be.

I intensified my health regimen to include seven different modalities of proactive alternative treatments that had proven to be effective in curing numerous people's cancer in a relative short period of time.

In early May 2012, my PSA test was 568 mcg/dl and I agreed to try a GRNH inhibitor generically called Degerelix, which would cut off my testosterone which could be feeding my tumor. My son-in-law assured me that the worst side effects were that it made a person feel better and their hair and beard may grow slower.

I knew that I could live with these side effects easily.

By mid-July, my PSA test had dropped to 168 mcg/dl and I knew that I was on the road to recovery. God is so good! By the end of July my tumor marker had dropped to a mere 3 mcg/dl, and by the time of this writing it was 1.3 mcg/dl, which is normal for a healthy 20-year-old man.

I remembered that I had a speaking engagement in Tennessee and was going to have to cancel it. After praying about it and getting assurance that I was recovering from my cancer I decided not to cancel the speaking commitment, but get ready for it by beginning to work out daily to re-gain my lost strength and endurance.

My plan of training began with five minutes a day on my stationary bicycle in my garage. After a month I had worked up to an hour a day and I asked my wife to join me by taking our tandem bike to the road. We began increasing our ride a little each week until we could easily do 70 miles a day.

The Bicycle Ride Across Tennessee is a tour sponsored by the Tennessee Department of Transportation. I was to be the keynote speaker for the event that began on Sunday morning and ended on the following Saturday afternoon.

We climbed most of the steep mountains in Eastern Tennessee – imagine riding up and down over a figure eight – and averaged 5,500 feet daily of vertical gain, for a grand total of 40,000 feet of vertical altitude in six days. We rode nearly 500 miles and it was a blast! My son, Billy, joined me and rode with me on our tandem bike for the last half of the journey. That was also God at work; we hadn't had that much time together in over 30 years.

During the ride on the last evening, we were having dinner and a man came up to the table and said that he wanted to talk with Bill Irwin. I turned my head in his direction and to my astonishment it was Dr. Gary McCown, my Knoxville dentist. "I am delivering your new partial tonight so you will have a chance to wear it before our appointment on Monday morning," he said. Has your dentist ever given you curb service?

And on Monday morning, guess who else showed up? Yes, it was my friend Fred Hughes whom I had never met, except over the phone and the internet. My dental visit was a first meeting that seemed like a reunion with Fred and Gary that I hadn't expected at all.

Now you can easily see that each of these encounters were divine appointments orchestrated by our Lord God; no one else could have possibly put this all together.

I am now learning so much about dental toxicity and cavitations and all that goes along with this entirely new area of health that I was never informed about. I learned in Fred's book how bacteria can get into one's jawbone. Any tooth extraction site, traumatic event involving the head or mouth, and root canal-treated teeth are problematic for these infections.

These little toxin-producing cavities are called cavitations and that is where Fred comes in, as he has become an authority in interpreting thermal (heat sensitive) scans of the jaw using Digital Infrared Thermal Imaging (DITI).

The toxins are acidic in nature and one of the criteria for a tumor to flourish is that it be in an acidic environment. In jawbone infections, bacteria become anaerobic – capable of living without oxygen – and produce toxins which can be deadly. Tumors also like sugar, which should be eliminated from the diet of anyone who has cancer.

All of this information is what eased my mind about the root cause of my cancer; it had to be in my mouth.

When Dr. McCown saw me a couple of months after my dental surgery, he couldn't believe how much better I looked and I substantiated that with the fact that I also felt much better as well. A dying man could not come close to being able to ride a bicycle 500 miles in six days while climbing eight miles vertically in that brief period of time.

I pray that you will use the information in this book to help yourself or someone else know what to do if faced with the diagnosis, "You have cancer."

Cancer is a three billion dollar industry and the authorities that run such a huge business are not about to let anyone come up with a cure. All the billions of dollars donated to cancer research eventually go to Big Pharma to develop more and more chemotherapeutic, pharmaceutical and radiological agents to poison people in an effort to 'kill their cancer' to little avail.

The real statistics are astounding: 97% of those diagnosed with cancer that receive conventional medical protocols, like surgery, chemotherapy and radiation, die before five years. For those who do nothing but go home to die, 28% survive the five years. Of those who take the natural approach, God's way, 80% survive five years.

So which will you choose if you are diagnosed with cancer? I think I know what your answer will be after you read this book and learn what Victoria and I learned.

Chapter 1

Not every cancer diagnosis is accurate

At age 53 and seemingly in excellent health, Victoria heard the four most dreaded words a woman can hear: "You have breast cancer." She wasn't dreaming; her world was shaken.

Born in the foothills of the Blue Ridge Mountains in 1954, Victoria did experience vivid dreams as a child; however, they were not your typical dreams, and she never dreamed of being diagnosed with cancer.

Both her parents were native North Carolinians: a father in construction and a stay-at-home mother who raised two boys and two girls and had to return to work when Victoria was six. Except for her sister, Teri, who is five years older, Victoria and her two younger brothers were born in a three-year window prompting her mother to tell everyone she saw, "I have three kids in diapers."

Her baby brother, Greg, was born in 1957, a breech baby. In the 1950s medical doctors were like gods. You didn't question what happened in the delivery room. Instead of choosing a Caesarian birth, the doctor elected to remove the baby boy with forceps, and damaged parts of his brain.

"I learned compassion by having him as a brother," Victoria says. "People always made fun of him when we were kids, especially children." Woody, her closest sibling growing up – 18 months apart – and Victoria were "always getting in fights protecting him."

Playing with dolls in frilly dresses when she was a little girl didn't promise much of a future for the North Carolina native. Victoria's fantasies were much more mature, well beyond mythical childhood dreams like marrying a loving prince who would carry her away on a stately white stallion. She "always" dreamed of being a businesswoman.

In high school, she lived 30 minutes from the fabled 469-mile long Blue Ridge Parkway and less than 90 minutes from the Appalachian Trail that stretched over 2,100 miles from Georgia to

Maine. She readily admits that her idea of roughing it was a hotel that doesn't have room service.

Not once did she ever set foot on the Trail, although she visited the Parkway numerous times, especially in high school when family picnics were fashionable. Victoria was focused academically, and displayed a love for history and a talent with numbers. She has always loved calculators and computers, a "real left brain person."

Maybe that's why she worked afternoons in high school for an accountant and never enrolled in home economics.

"I got tired of seeing Southern girls treated the way they were and I wanted to be there with the 'big boys' making business decisions. That was really my fantasy," she concedes. "My mother was a very strong woman. I got a lot of strength from her."

The family doctor once said that Victoria "burned more energy sitting than most people do walking." Those who knew her personally viewed her in one of two extremes: energetic and motivated, or just plain hyper.

While taking tests at the end of 7th grade, she was the shortest young lady in her class. When she enrolled three months later in the 8th grade, she was one of the tallest students. Everyone marveled at her incredible growth spurt as she quickly reached five foot seven.

"I was always skinny," Victoria chuckles, apparently a by-product of rapid metabolism. In high school, she couldn't break a hundred pounds soaking wet, but it wasn't because she didn't try. "I just couldn't."

"Mother, when are my breasts going to blossom?" Victoria asked. "Oh, sweetheart, you will next summer," her mother would reply.

"But I was looking good when Twiggy came out," Victoria quipped, thinking back to the early 1960s arrival of the small-breasted English super model and fashion icon who brought new meaning to the word "thin." Twiggy's popular appeal seemed to reflect the attitude that less is more.

Instead of the curvaceous Marilyn Monroe and Jane Mansfield look, young girls were taken with the stick figure. Twiggy ushered in a new era of self-confidence for thousands of young women. This acceptance of the "thin look" made Victoria very comfortable in her own skin.

She never fretted about having small breasts. But having Twiggy on the scene probably emboldened her some when it came to the acceptance of her own size and shape.

Victoria wore her dark brunette hair several inches below her waist, well past her teen years. She was 25 when her long hair was finally cut by her sister, who operated her own hair salon in New Orleans.

"My sister said we've got to get rid of this Woodstock look," a reference to the biggest rock festival of all time in 1969 that gave rise to a new pop culture known as the "Woodstock generation."

Prior to her own diagnosis, Victoria's closest cancer connection was her strong-willed mother, who had squeamos cell cancer on her lower right leg at age 74. Nine years after the medical diagnosis, following a successful natural treatment protocol, Victoria describes her mother as being in "extremely good health and very active."

Her alcoholic father had a heart attack and died in 1996, the same day an abscessed tooth was extracted. The dental visit was in the morning. He was dead by dinner time. "We think that's what killed him." Victoria can't remember a time when her father was not an alcoholic except for the last two years of his life.

Her emotions get the best of her at times, and she resorts to humor, about the only thing that kept her going during her diagnosed cancer crisis. "My dad was a drunk, not an alcoholic, because he didn't go to any meetings."

Her father was a soft-spoken, kind-hearted guy when he wasn't drinking. One drink, however, is all it took, sort of a Jekyll and Hyde personality change. Victoria's parents divorced in 1963 when she was seven.

Her father's unsavory habits created serious strife within the family. It was a time in history when alcoholism was not discussed outside the immediate home. It was also a time when no medical doctor or dentist ever discussed how stress is a killer, and no medical doctor or dentist ever hinted that an oral infection could harm a person, much less kill them.

Victoria was soon to learn that she had an oral infection but no pain or other symptoms.

The U.S. Food and Drug Administration (FDA) reports that more than 75% of adults over age 35 suffer from some type of periodontal (gum) disease – an oral infection. It has long been known that people with diseased gums are at higher risk of heart disease. The last few years have brought a rash of studies suggesting periodontal disease is also related to other serious diseases, one in particular.

In a study published September 18, 2012, in GUT (International Journal of Gastroenterology and Hepatology), researchers identified particular types of mouth bacteria, some of which are found in gum disease, and concluded that the presence of these microbes may double your risk of pancreatic cancer.

It shouldn't be surprising to learn about a direct correlation between mouth bacteria and other diseases.

An active bacterial infection caused by unhealthy gums can be even more alarming when you consider there's probably something else going on in your body that's not good.

In March 2007, the *Washington Post* reported the death of a boy as a result of complications from a tooth abscess. Despite undergoing two operations and spending six weeks in a hospital, the 12-year-old died after bacteria from the infection spread from his jaw to his brain.

A tooth abscess is nothing to fool around with, and who can withstand the pain? Victoria would learn this the hard way.

In the 4th grade, Victoria came down with the flu, became dehydrated, and was hospitalized on Valentine's Day. "I knew I never wanted to go back to a place like that again," she said. "I hated it. I was so sad and so depressed."

That experience, coupled with her brother's trauma-induced mental challenges, influenced Victoria's choice to not have children. That one hospital experience "scared me," she confessed. She was also too busy with her career to give a child proper attention.

At age 19, Victoria moved to California and spread her wings. It was 1973. [Grateful Dead bass player, Phil Lesh, was busted for drugs, actress Betty Grabel died, Ronald Reagan was governor, a gallon of gas and a dozen eggs cost about the same – between 40 and 45 cents. The Miami Dolphins beat the Washington Redskins in Los Angeles 14-7 to win the Super Bowl, and the Oakland A's defeated the New York Mets 4 games to 3 in the World Series.]

In the movie world, the iconic film "American Graffiti" opened in theaters nationwide. The cast included a bit-part for Suzanne Somers, the mysterious 'blonde in the car,' a role later expanded for the film's reissue after she became famous.

In addition to playing the ditzy blonde in the television series Three's Company, Somers found success as a poet, entrepreneur, spokeswoman, nightclub performer, and talk show host. Like Victoria, she was the daughter of an alcoholic father.

Little did Somers suspect that she would hear the four awful words, "You have breast cancer."

At the time Somers was diagnosed, she lived in Palm Springs, California, the same city as Victoria. "I remember people were afraid she was going to die, and I was rooting for her because she was going to reject chemo. By not doing the harmful drugs, I thought she would have a much better chance of living with a higher quality of life."

As a breast cancer survivor, Somers authored the 2009 book, KNOCKOUT. It includes interviews with a dozen doctors who are curing cancer and tips about how to prevent getting it in the first place.

In the first chapter, Somers tells about her early morning race to an emergency room in 2008, gasping for air. Her entire body was covered in welts. Perhaps she had been poisoned or was suffering an allergic reaction to something.

Suzanne Somers was soon told that her previous breast cancer had metastasized to her liver and innumerable tumors were in her chest. She was also diagnosed with a blood clot and pneumonia.

She described a shocking scenario as various doctors appeared in her hospital room.

The oncologist had the "bedside manner of a moose" and showed no compassion or tenderness. She quoted the doctor as saying, "You've got cancer. I just looked at your CAT scan and it's everywhere … your lungs, your liver, tumors around your heart … I've never seen so much cancer." She wrote that both a lung cancer doctor and a surgeon agreed.

Somers was offered the best treatment solution an orthodox oncologist could provide – full-body chemo.

Meanwhile, her daughter-in-law told her, "I looked up your symptoms and it could be something called valley fever, and it's found in the soil in the desert of the Southwest." The daughter-in-law added, "You work in your organic garden all the time, and you dig regularly in the ruins in New Mexico. It makes sense."

The symptoms of valley fever were eerily close to the diagnosis of a team of cancer doctors who were offering chemo as her only hope for survival.

Somers agreed to the surgical removal of some lung tissue for lab analysis and, after four days of drama and trauma, found out that she had been misdiagnosed. She did not have cancer, and she was not going to die.

Had she taken the chemo, the outcome might have been different. It could have been somewhere between devastating and deadly. There's another lesson in this story; not every cancer diagnosis is accurate.

Have you ever wondered why we're even having this discussion in the 21st Century? After all, the federal government's War on Cancer is entering its fifth decade. Shouldn't the battle be won by now?

Victoria was a sophomore in high school when President Richard Nixon officially declared war on cancer. "In 1970, the American people made clear their desire for a cure for the second-leading cause of death in the United States." This declaration of war is stated on the website of the federally-sponsored National Cancer Institute (NCI).

In her own way, Victoria was declaring generational war on immaturity. Although she was studious and a regular on the honor roll, she managed to hold down a weekend job selling tickets at the local movie theater, and enjoyed being around older people.

She wore long hair and bellbottoms, liked a boy who was "geekish," found leather vests and jackets to be fashionable, and was comfortable wearing platform shoes so high they required straps on the heels to keep them from falling off, but she wasn't a 'stick in the mud' either. She remembers her cheerleader uniform with pleated skirt, V-neck vest, and pom-poms, and to this day describes it as "hot."

"In this town you had to be a redneck or a hippie. I was a hippie, but I had a lot of good redneck friends."

President Nixon responded to the nation's call for a cure during his January 1971 State of the Union address.

"I will also ask for an appropriation of an extra $100 million to launch an intensive campaign to find a cure for cancer, and I will ask later for whatever additional funds can effectively be used. The time has come in America when the same kind of concentrated effort that split the atom and took man to the moon should be turned toward conquering this dread disease. Let us make a total national commitment to achieve this goal."

If we dissect Nixon's statement, we can give our attention to some catch phrases like "find a cure," and "time has come," and "make a total national commitment." Fifty years later, a new generation is hearing those same catch phrases. That's all they've ever been – catch phrases – and repeating the same old phrases has become a trademark of the cancer industry.

Mention Richard Nixon's name today, 43 years later, and the only subject that comes to mind for most people is Watergate. The political scandal erupted after the June 1972 break-in at the Democratic National Committee offices in Washington, DC, and the attempted cover-up leading to Nixon's resignation in August 1974.

The Federal Bureau of Investigation connected cash found on the burglars to a slush fund used by the Committee for the Re-Election of the President, a fundraising group for Nixon's campaign. Eventually, Nixon's White House staff and the President himself were implicated in the crime, because of the money trail.

Cash found on the burglars?

What is there about following the money trail that leads to the truth? The phrase itself has become part of the national lexicon, wrote Kee Malesky on National Public Radio's website (npr.org), because it was supposedly whispered to reporter Bob Woodward by Deep Throat as a way to cut through the lies and deception and find the truth about the Watergate scandal.

There's evidence that the "follow the money trail" legend didn't actually happen that way, but, there is much truth in the idea of finding the motivation and then seeing who stands to profit.

Before reading Victoria's story, think about the colossal failure of the War on Cancer. Where's the promised cure?

Billions of dollars over decades have been spent in research, building cancer institutes, establishing cancer wings at hospitals, and lining the pockets of non-profit organizations like the American Cancer Society and the Susan B. Komen Breast Cancer Foundation – organizations that can't afford to see cancer cured.

The National Cancer Institute's 2012 budget request was $5,869,857,000. That's nearly six billion dollars. The 2013 budget request is about the same and it comes on the 75th anniversary of the founding of the NCI. This is only *one* organization collecting 'cancer cure' money! The money being dumped into the "War on Cancer" could fill up a black hole in outer space.

In a paper published in 2003, cancer researcher R. Webster Kehr said the war in medicine is different than a war with guns, tanks, planes, and soldiers. The War on Cancer is a war of information. "The American people know exactly half of all truth; the half that is most profitable," he said.

Chapter 2

Does the definition of 'cured' matter?

Five years after arriving in California, Victoria was hired by a large developer, Falcon Lake Properties, to take over their data processing department where she wrote all the software packages for financial statements, accounts payable and receivables, and job costing.

The developer primarily built condos with associated country clubs that included golf courses. Big projects. Big money. Big stress. The boss was her biggest stressor.

When she resigned April 30, 1999, she was vice-president of Finance and Administration and administrative assistant to the president. By this time, the group had divided into a parent company with 12 affiliated companies. Victoria's tenure was exactly 21 years from age 23 to age 44.

Over the span of 19 years, from 1986 to 2005, Victoria experienced two failed marriages. Both husbands were in the construction business; one of them is past history, and she's on speaking-terms with the other. But both ex-husbands introduced unique stresses into her life.

Did stress play a role in Victoria's cancer diagnosis? If so, how much of one? When trying to maintain whole body wellness, is stress even a consideration? What about the role of stress in preventing cancer? Is there a connection?

If a physically fit and highly trained astronaut can succumb to stress, how vulnerable are the rest of us? And what exactly is stress?

Dr. Vladimir Bernik, MD, a board certified psychiatrist, published an article called "Stress: The Silent Killer."

To make his point, he referred to an event in July 1997, when the world was taken by surprise with the news that the Russian spaceship Mir (which means "peace") had a sudden failure of its power supply, due to a wrong command issued by Commander Vladimir Tsibliev.

The physician who was in charge of the crew, Dr. Igor Goncharov, explained that "the mistake resulted from the commander's high level of stress."

Being isolated from her close-knit family was just another one of the stressors that Victoria had to deal with and she had not yet celebrated her 20th birthday.

Dr. Bernik said there is still no clear definition in the medical pathology textbooks, but one dictionary defines stress as "the set of all organic reactions to physical, psychic, infectious, or other, aggressions," which are capable of disturbing homeostasis (the internal body equilibrium).

Dr. Bernik also quoted Canadian physician Hans Selye, the creator of the modern concept of stress, who once stated that stress is the result of a civilization which man himself "no longer can withstand."

Dr. Selye, as a pioneering endocrinologist, even reported that dental infections such as abscessed teeth or infections present in "dead" root canal teeth can contribute to systemic (affecting the whole body or at least multiple organs or systems) inflammation and symptoms.

Dr. Michael Jacobson, DO, wrote the book, *The Word on Health.* He told the story of Egyptian tablets found in the ruins of Nineveh dating back to 650 BC that described a terrible disease suffered by the king. No treatment known at the time was of any help. When the royal patient had his teeth extracted, all his troubles immediately disappeared.

Victoria's mother was quite upset when her daughter moved to California in the early 1970s. "In her mind, my mother thought I was going to be corrupted. If it was west of the Mississippi, according to my mother, they're out there nude and running around on drugs. It was just another planet."

Victoria was nearly 2,300 miles from home. "It was a hard move, but I'm a rebel," she confesses. "And it was very enlightening." But there is no overstating the obvious. She was homesick, but she did not relate the separation from family for the first time with stress. Neither did she correlate the data processing challenges or her boss with stress.

Her younger brother loves French toast. One day, Victoria fixed French toast for her breakfast. Suddenly, she found herself crying, and the emotional outpouring went on all day. "I just missed my family very much. I couldn't eat that French toast. It reminded me too much of him."

It was a trying time as the mother-daughter relationship didn't heal until her mother flew to California nearly three years later. She saw firsthand that Victoria had an established career, appealing apartment, new car, pleasant friends, and lived in a beautiful city with more sunshine and warm weather than her mother had ever seen on a winter day.

On the radio, the Mamas & the Papas were singing, "All the leaves are brown and the sky is gray." The classic song "California Dreamin" took on a new meaning for Victoria who says she does a pretty cool rendition while taking a shower.

It's known that certain events in our lives are so severe in terms of stress, that they are characterized as a trauma of a psychic origin. Stress can cause or worsen a great number of disease conditions.

Those who don't remember the Russian spacecraft incident will surely be familiar with the anxiety syndrome, Post-Traumatic Stress Disorder (PTSD), which affected so many veterans of the Vietnam, Iraq, and Afghanistan wars.

A non-profit, non-partisan rehabilitative effort for veterans is the Wounded Warrior Project® (woundedwarriorproject.org) that reports one in five soldiers returning from Iraq and Afghanistan has PTSD.

But you don't have to be in a war to have post-traumatic stress. What about people who must deal with a cancer diagnosis? What is the stress level? Is it even measurable? What about the people who are diagnosed with cancer, and they don't have cancer?

Vietnam was much like today's War on Cancer. There was no clear purpose; American troops were handcuffed by politicians and bureaucrats, and there was no intent to win.

The Vietnam Era statistics are grim.

More than 58,000 U.S. soldiers were killed in action (KIA), more than 303,000 were wounded (WIA), nearly 1,700 were missing in action (MIA), and nearly 800 became prisoners of war

(POW). The tallies do not reflect the mental and emotional carnage. An untold number of families had their lives destroyed.

It's the same way with cancer. Innocent people are dying and somebody is making a ton of money.

Cancer deaths are estimates. According to the American Cancer Society, it's estimated that one person dies every minute from cancer, even after undergoing conventional cancer treatments.

As startling as that number is, punch this number into your computer or phone calculator: A new cancer case is diagnosed in the United States every 30 seconds. That means more than one million new cancer cases are being diagnosed annually.

How many cases are misdiagnosed?

The World Health Organization predicts that cases of cancer will increase by up to 50% worldwide by 2020.

Who benefits?

The only people who benefited from Vietnam were the industrial military complex including the manufacturers of the instruments of war and the contractors who supplied the support mechanisms, plus the bankers, and political cronies.

How can a politician, of all people, resist the temptation to profit from war?

Maybe we should be asking another question: How can a politician, of all people, resist the temptation to profit from cancer?

The investment folio of many politicians is liberally blessed with stocks and stock options of pharmaceutical companies – the same corporate entities that profit from cancer drugs, heart disease drugs, and diabetes drugs. Well, you get the picture.

Candidate John Edwards received campaign soft money from pharmaceutical company employees and owned stock in several drug companies. That's nothing unexpected for members of Congress nor is it wrong, but Edwards was campaigning for the highest office in the land, and making political hay as his wife, Elizabeth, confronted breast cancer.

An insider's account of John Edwards's pursuit of the presidency and the scandal that brought him down is detailed in the book, *The Politician,* by Andrew Young, John's longest serving and most trusted aide. The book was published in 2010, the same year Elizabeth died.

Elizabeth was diagnosed with breast cancer in 2004. She and John were both well heeled; they had enough money to buy the "best" medical care and go anywhere in the world to get it. The conventional treatments allegedly brought her cancer into remission.

In March 2007, the cancer had returned with a vengeance and had spread to other parts of her body. In her limited interviews, Elizabeth was quoted as saying that living with stage four cancer is like dancing with a partner who keeps changing.

CNN announced her death at age 61 on December 8, 2010. "My job is to stay alive until they find a cure. I don't think there's any way to live with this diagnosis than to have that kind of optimism," Edwards told a reporter. "Fortunately with the research, it looks like there may be a new drug for me down the line," she said.

It's tempting to be callous and ask how that worked out for her. But Elizabeth's death was unnecessary. Although she was an attorney, best-selling author, and driving force behind John's political career, her view of cancer was like looking at a stranger through the peep hole in the front door.

Her treatment decision was dictated by a lack of honest knowledge on the subject of cancer, including the hundreds of non-mainstream treatment options and thousands and thousands of personal testimonies of cures, and influenced by a medical system that wants to keep it that way.

One of her four children was killed in a car wreck in 1996. Ten years later, after her initial cancer diagnosis, she wrote *Saving Graces: Finding Solace and Strength from Friends and Strangers,* which chronicled the aftermath of her son's death and her battle with cancer. About this same time, she apparently learned of her husband's infidelity.

I wonder how many of her physicians offered a serious talk about the stress in her life and how that might affect her body's ability to survive, much less recover.

I also wonder if, during her extensive education, she ever read the famous treatise of surgical maladies that dental decay can produce which was written in the 17th century by French surgeon, Gene Louise Petit.

I know she had the opportunity to learn about the oral pathology connection because her secretary sent me a canned response thanking me for sending a copy of my first book (*Am I Dead?*). A former North Carolina sheriff, a personal friend, was concerned enough about Elizabeth's health that he obtained her private mailing address for me.

I was listening to the radio the day she died and heard a news broadcaster proclaim that Edwards "fought a good fight." No, she didn't! She didn't have a chance. She had the 'best' insurance, the 'best' doctors, and the 'wrong' information.

Compared to cancer, the Vietnam payout was peanuts. Today, the number of people and institutions that thrive because of cancer has exploded.

The obvious beneficiaries are cancer hospitals, cancer doctors, and the corporate giants that manufacture cancer drugs. The not so obvious beneficiary is the Pinkwashing Campaign, and all the for-profit entities and not-for-profit foundations that rake in hundreds of millions of dollars under the guise of creating public awareness and discovering a cure for cancer.

For the pharmaceutical companies, the money's in the medicine, not the cure. For the cancer foundations, the money is not in the medicine but the notion that we'll find a cure if everyone donates some more money.

Watch a little TV, and you'll soon hear a commercial asking for money. "We're almost there, but we need your help," a typical advertisement says.

The website, cancer-treatment-tips.com, has an interesting take on current cancer statistics. They cite alternative treatment, natural treatment, and holistic treatment protocols as having cure rates as high as 90% or better.

In contrast, the website reports that the American Cancer Society (ACS) listed some of their cancer cure rates as high as 55%. Yet other sources are stating that the cure rate for conventional cancer treatment is less than 3%.

41

Who is telling the truth? Here's how the significant discrepancy is explained.

The ACS and other cancer groups use a "five-year survival" rate (ability to live for five years). The five-year number is an arbitrary figure and there is no scientific basis for choosing five years rather than six or eight years.

If a woman has breast cancer, and after five years, she has no breast cancer but does have metastasized lung cancer, she is still considered cured and her "successful" treatment is added to the cure rate.

If a woman survived breast cancer for five years, but she died from the cancer treatment after five years and one day, the cancer industry considers her to be cured, according to their statistical reporting.

If a woman survived conventional treatment for breast cancer, and due to the destruction of her immune system caused by the toxic treatment, she caught a cold or pneumonia, and she died, she is still considered "cured" of cancer and her name is added to the cure rate.

Of course, the motive behind this is the profiteering of billions of dollars that the medical and pharmaceutical industries get from existing and potential cancer patients. The money is in the medicine, not the cure, and good cancer statistics bring in more business. Cancer is big business as well as a global epidemic. According to the World Cancer Report, global cancer rates could increase to 15 million new cases by 2020.

Chapter 3

Mammography is oversold to women

As an adult, at age 39, Victoria wore braces. The funds for correcting her crooked teeth when she was a teen-ager were simply not in the family budget, regardless of how hard her mother worked.

Because of her 'business instincts,' she was already accustomed to connecting the dots to solve problems. She could remember as a child, drawing straight lines between numbers or dots on a piece of paper and watching an image slowly emerging. The fun of the game was solving the puzzle before all the dots were connected.

Now she's an adult and she's still connecting the dots.

She was beginning to recognize a connection between the mouth and whole-body wellness. It wasn't something that her orthodontist told her about. It was her personal experience. "I'd have a rash all over my face. He'd change out the adjustment wire, and then it would go away."

But the dentist denied any connection between her mouth and the rash. "No, it couldn't be that," he insisted.

What is there in the American psyche that causes a professional, like a well-trained dentist or doctor, to deny the obvious?

Let me refer to an article written by Judy Converse, MPH, RD, that was published on the website of VRAN, aimed at pediatricians. VRAN is the Vaccination Risk Awareness Network (vran.org). You probably could substitute any other medical discipline – doctors, dentists, specialists – and arrive at the same conclusion.

"It's 2006, and for the first time in history, U.S. children are sicker than the generation before them," wrote Converse. "They're not just a little worse off, they are precipitously worse off physically, emotionally, educationally and developmentally. The statistics have been repeated so often, they are almost boring."

Converse went on to describe the appalling statistics on childhood health issues like obesity, juvenile diabetes, autism, asthma, life-threatening food allergies, and attention-deficit disorder.

Perhaps the increasingly aggressive vaccination schedule is partly to blame, Converse pointed out. There is some compelling evidence to support the claim.

However, the problem is much deeper and less complicated. What happened to the fundamentals? If you're old enough, think back to the 1950s or the early '60s. In the classroom, students learned the Three R's – reading, writing and arithmetic. Students were also taught by the example of their parents to eat whole foods and drink plenty of clean water.

What happened to the fundamentals? Nutrition and hydration lost their importance. They were replaced by processed foods and sugar-laden soft drinks.

"With our children's very lives at stake, why do parents and governments remain loyal to the medical culture that may have led them to this?" Converse asked. Read her answer at least twice, and meditate on it. Let it sink in.

"And as the ship sinks beneath their feet, how do pediatric providers manage to deny the obvious: Many children in their highly vaccinated practices are sick a lot, don't develop normally, can't sleep, can't tolerate or won't eat a typical diet, become overweight, acquire preventable nutrition problems that cause lifelong damage? Worse, how do they defend that they have virtually nothing to offer, other than symptom-masking drugs?"

All this is leading to a point: Low-tech skills have faded from pediatric practice, and from most other medical disciplines.

A doctor needs to spend more than three minutes discussing questions, said Converse. The doctor should be listening to parents, completing a thorough exam for signs and symptoms of nutrient deficiencies, and interpreting the growth chart rather than just adding a dot to it.

"Every child I met had nutritional failure issues," wrote Converse. "Not one of their pediatricians noticed."

Victoria's mother only breast-fed one child, and it was Victoria. It was a matter of circumstances. Victoria's body never had to attempt to process a lot of high-fructose corn syrup which dominates infant formulas and has led to much childhood obesity.

Of course, Victoria was not exposed to GMO (genetically modified) foods, either, as a child.

Victoria had always eaten healthy. Her mother and her maternal grandmother were excellent cooks. "I should have paid more attention," Victoria admits. "My grandmother said if I'd weed her garden, I could pick whatever I wanted and she would cook it for me. I loved green beans, carrots, potatoes and vine-ripened tomatoes."

Victoria's friends say her mother's bran muffins with nuts and cranberries are to die for.

Victoria had never worried about her diet. "I made the connection early on that whatever you ate determined how you felt." Although she did have a 'sweet tooth,' she never had to worry about weight gain. So she enjoyed her sweets, not excessively, but definitely pleasurably.

Although she could handle one "s" word, she could not handle two of them. Sugar was okay, but stress had been with her since childhood. And it had not been kind.

Before age 40, she began to form an association between stress and poor physical health. She was connecting some dots, but she couldn't solve the puzzle yet.

If Victoria was going to be sick, it wouldn't be because of poor eating habits. After all, she couldn't get the image of a second grade friend out of her head: the young girl was so heavy set that she often got stuck in the one-piece metal and wood desk – the kind with an ink well, hinged top, and non-adjustable seat attached.

"I felt so bad when other children laughed at her. She didn't look healthy. She couldn't run and play the way the rest of us did. I made up my mind I would avoid such a condition at all cost."

Two failed marriages on the West Coast – one husband she described as a sociopath – and the stress of being so far away from her kid brothers with whom she had always been very close, were weighing heavy on her spirit.

"When I was married to my first husband he had an affair. So I guess it was fitting that I had him sign the divorce settlement on January 17, 1994, the day of the Northridge, California earthquake.

We lived in Palm Springs and could feel it at our home. The earth was shaking under us as he was signing."

"I know I don't pick husbands well. Anyway the divorce was very upsetting and I felt a lump in my right breast about the same place the lump was found in 2007."

Victoria didn't think about the 1993 incident with a lump until 2011, a full 18 years later. Nor did she remember the paperback book that her sister mailed to her from New Orleans in 1987, *You Can Heal Your Life,* by Louise Hay (hayhouse.com), a noted metaphysical counselor and publisher of self-help, inspirational and transformational books. Hay draws a correlation between health issues and a person's thought processes.

For example, Hay connects breast problems with the "mothering and nurturing" instinct, a trait that Victoria is all too familiar with because of the life challenges faced by her younger brother.

Fifty years ago medical mind-control was in its infancy. Cancer had not developed into a trillion dollar industry in America. There was no need yet for daily brainwashing, persuasion, thought control, and manipulation.

The statistic that one in eight women will have breast cancer was not being reported 50 years ago on an almost hourly basis because it had not happened yet, unlike in October 2012 when the bold headline in the women's magazine *SELF* proclaimed in their 12-page 'cancer handbook,' that "790,740 women will get breast cancer this year."

This cancer epidemic happened in spite of the billions of dollars already spent on cancer research. Make no mistake; cancer is big business in this country. The breast cancer industry is by far the worst offender, especially as it disseminates its propaganda. Information and misinformation are being touted by a constant blitz from the media, cancer foundations, and charities.

The misinformation campaign involving breast cancer started with the advent of x-rays.

- 1913 – X-rays had only been around about 18 years when German physician Albert Solomon began to use x-ray technology to study breast tissue that had been removed by mastectomy. He's generally considered to be the inventor of breast radiology.

- Mid-1930s – Raul Leborgne of Uruguay identified the need to compress the breast for a more accurate screening.
- 1956 – Houston-based radiologist Robert Egan developed a special film for mammograms.
- 1966 – The first mammogram machine was introduced.
- 1976 – The mammogram had become the standard test for breast cancer detection.
- 1994 – Federal government adopted national standards for mammography.

Mammography is a cash cow in the breast cancer industry, and it isn't going away in spite of a steady stream of new research and technological advances.

"Mammography is one of the most oversold and understudied technologies in medical history," according to Devra Davis, PhD, the founder of Environmental Health Trust. She published an article in the huffingtonpost.com in November 2009 citing hard numbers that confirm "the sorry truth – mammography regularly used in women under age 50 produces more harm than good."

All mammograms are not created equal.

"A large proportion of test sites use substandard equipment, are staffed by inadequately trained technicians and radiologists, or are rarely if ever inspected to be sure the equipment is working properly at a minimal dose of radiation," *New York Times* science reporter Gina Kolata reported in 1990.

It was another four years after the newspaper's revelation before the federal government adopted national standards for mammography.

Even so, the allusion of a mammogram's credibility had been created between 1966 and 1994. Millions of women falsely believe in its invincibility.

Like the Japanese attack on Pearl Harbor in 1941, this is one of the unintended consequences of mammography. The Japanese underestimated how America would respond. Admiral Yamamoto's famous quote stated it best in the movie "Tora! Tora! Tora!" when he said the attacks would only serve to "... awaken a sleeping giant and fill him with a terrible resolve."

Will women ever wake up and resolve to stop being abused?

Will women ever stop believing in a mammogram's invincibility?

Chapter 4

Did you throw up pink? I did!

"And don't even get me started on the pink ribbon cancer non-profit groups, which are a total fraud." Those are the words of Mike Adams in a NaturalNews.com article published October 1, 2008. "Their focus is to trap women in a system of cancer screening that actually causes cancer: Mammography!"

Adams is the same writer that said, "Chemotherapy is merely a very expensive form of physician-assisted suicide."

What is all the pink hype really about? That's a loaded question. Some people think the pink hype is magnificent; others see it for what it has become – commercialization of a dastardly disease that is causing women to suffer the ravages of radiation, chemotherapy and radical surgery that results in breast disfigurement, or complete loss of the breast.

One thing is for sure, says Victoria. "Most people give with a kind heart and a genuine belief that their donation will actually help. Sadly, that's not the case."

In October I walked out the contractors' exit at Lowe's and bumped into a large cardboard box filled with pink "project aprons," or nail aprons as they were known. The sign said: Susan G. Komen for the Cure Project Apron, $2.98.

Contractors could choose an all-pink apron with black letters or an off-white apron with black letters and a pink ribbon.

How many aprons must the building supply company sell in order to make a meaningful contribution to breast cancer awareness and research?

Here's a more specific question. How many aprons must the building supply company sell in order to fund the total $684,000 pay package in 2012 of Nancy Brinker, founder and CEO of the Susan G. Komen foundation.

Considering the level of independent breast cancer research I have personally been associated with over the past six years, I probably have a more repulsive reaction to this sort of marketing than the average male. And I was repulsed.

But I find the National Football League's adoption of pink to be the crowning insult to my intelligence and, more specifically, to every woman in America who is dealing with breast cancer. The NFL's use of pink is nauseating: sweat bands, shoes, ribbons tied to the waist, gloves, ribbons imprinted on jerseys and shirt collars, coaches on the sideline wearing light gray caps with a pink bib, and the referee sporting a pink whistle.

And after you watch all the pink being displayed in an NFL football game, you can bid on game-worn NFL products. The money trail is endless. If the pink marketing campaign has been so successful, why are more women having breast cancer issues?

Players think they're making a great contribution. In fact, they're being used.

Have you ever asked yourself what the "portion of proceeds" amounts to in real dollars? How many dollars are used for meaningful research and assistance programs and why isn't it fully disclosed? Meaningful is the key word in this question. Brick and mortar overhead and administrative salaries are not meaningful to a woman who has been told she has breast cancer.

Why are people who blindly donate to pink campaigns not asking the hard questions about where the money goes and how effective it is? Victoria wants to know.

I'm not trying to create a tempest in a teapot with this example, but the illustration speaks to the point being made. The Teapot Museum in Sparta, North Carolina was being envisioned before 2005 to spur tourism in the small community and replace some revenues from lost manufacturing jobs.

Long before the $14.5 million project was deemed to be unfeasible, the state of North Carolina had earmarked $400,000 in taxpayer money and another $500,000 was earmarked by Congress. The appropriation was part of more than $226 million in excessive North Carolina spending and $29 billion spent by Congress on similar 'pork' projects.

A new plan was developed to build a smaller museum facility costing only $3 million. State taxpayer money was given to the project but the federal money was never delivered because a national watchdog group criticized the pork barrel spending and gave the Teapot Museum a special "Oinker of 2006" award.

Did North Carolina citizens benefit from this pork spending? If so, how? Victoria did not benefit. Every dime spent on her five-year ordeal came from one of two pockets: hers and her insurance company's. In round numbers, Victoria spent $70,000 from her own pocket and paid the insurance company premiums of about $24,000 over the five years.

No one answers these questions on pork spending, and no one even asks these questions when it comes to 'pink ribbon' purchases.

As I see it, the pink referee's whistle is the ultimate insult, unless some medical doctors and independent researchers get together and blow the whistle on fraudulent breast cancer screenings and treatments. In that case, I'll be okay with the whistleblowers using pink whistles.

Matthew Zachary, founder of the I'm Too Young For This! Cancer Foundation, a survivor-led, advocacy, support, and research organization, is more expressive than I when it comes to "breast cancer pink nausea."

"This month, it begins," he wrote in a 2008 article, referring to the month of October. "The torrential onslaught and ceaseless marketing." His assessment is ridiculously funny and incredibly accurate.

"At the stroke of midnight on October 1," Zachary said, "everything that has a pulse, a price tag or both will magically pumpkin-ize itself into a pink-colored cause-branded premium with 'a portion' of the proceeds going to none other than our friends at the omnipresent, megalithic establishment known as the Susan G. Komen For The Cure Foundation."

Zachary calls October's Breast Cancer Awareness Month, "the end of rational consumption as we know it."

Zachary is not an outsider in the cancer info wars. He was a concert pianist and composer when diagnosed with pediatric brain cancer during his senior year in college.

Zachery founded Stupid Cancer™ in 2012. The organization works exclusively on behalf of survivors and care providers under the age of 40 (StupidCancer.org). Its mission is to end isolation and improve quality of life for young adults affected by cancer.

The history of the Pink Campaign over the past two decades is clouded in controversy as well as many shades of colors, and some of the colors are not pink; some of the colors are used in crazy places.

Take the pink ink used for the letter "e" in the word "Times" in the masthead of the October 2012 issues of the *Asheville Citizen-Times* (North Carolina). The banner or flag of a newspaper is almost sacred to most publishers. The newspaper also used space in the right corner above the fold to mention Breast Cancer Awareness Month.

Was the use of pink on the front page an effective approach to combating breast cancer, or was it a marketing ploy?

Why wouldn't a Gannett-owned newspaper do a little investigation and tell its readers what I'm telling you? It's called the sin of omission.

The *Citizen-Times,* owned by Gannett, never once published a serious story about Digital Infrared Thermal Imaging as an alternative breast screening plan for women, or reported on the book (*Am I Dead? ... or do I just feel like it)*, much less questioned an oral pathology connection with cancer. Why?

To be clear, this is my personal opinion: A reporter asked some local doctors about thermal imaging and local dentists about an oral pathology connection, and they were told it is all fake science and worthless, so they dropped it. Of course, the doctors knew nothing factual about thermal imaging and the dentists knew nothing factual about oral pathology apart from their dental school training.

It might be easier to list companies that are not profiting from pink than to list those that are. Don't kid yourself into thinking you are helping to find a cure for cancer. It's a racket.

Pink has provided awareness, no argument there. In fact, at its inception, Estee Lauder makeup counters distributed 1.5 million ribbons in 1992, each accompanied by a laminated card describing a proper breast self-exam. That was a meaningful contribution.

Anyone at least 45 years old remembers the yellow ribbons of the late 1970s that became a national folk symbol for the return of imprisoned heroes. That was the year that Penne Laingren, wife of one of the U.S. Embassy hostages in Iran, U.S. charge d'affaires Bruce Laingren, was inspired by a song to tie yellow ribbons around the trees in her front yard.

The yellow ribbon became a message of hope and solidarity as Americans all over the country wrapped yellow ribbons around trees to focus attention on the 52 Americans held hostage in Tehran, half way around the world.

In the early 1990s, AIDS activists utilized bright red ribbons, "the color of passion," to frame their cause.

There were many causes and many colors of ribbons. The use of ribbons became so prolific that the *New York Times* declared 1992 as "The Year of the Ribbon." However, there was a brief interlude before the pink ribbon hit the national stage.

Since late 1990, The Susan G. Komen Breast Cancer Foundation has been handing out bright pink visors to breast cancer survivors running in its Race for the Cure. In the fall of 1991, the foundation also gave pink ribbons to all participants in the New York City race. The ribbons were only an item in the big picture, not the big picture itself.

The pink ribbon's status as an American icon was about to change. A national magazine's second annual Breast Cancer Awareness Month issue was in its design phase, under the direction of Alexander Penney, then the editor-in-chief of *SELF*.

Victoria subscribed at the beginning and remembers reading the first issue. She is still a subscriber and has always enjoyed the magazine. "Their heart is in the right place," she says. If the magazine's writers read Victoria's story, they'll have to face a new reality; all the known facts about breast cancer are not necessarily all the facts.

The first issue, which was inspired and guest edited by Evelyn Lauder, a breast cancer survivor and senior corporate vice president of Estee Lauder, was an amazing success. In the publishing business, that means readership rose dramatically, market impact was exceptionally positive, and advertising revenues made executives blush green.

Lucy Schulte Danziger is currently editor-in-chief of SELF. In her Editor's Letter, she wrote in the October 2012 issue: "When Alexander Penney, then editor of SELF, and the late Evelyn Lauder cofounded the pink ribbon in 1992, to raise awareness of breast cancer, they were fearless in bringing national attention to a taboo subject. Today, the ribbon is ubiquitous, its message obvious: Get screened [with a mammogram] and see a doc if anything is awry."

How did that work out?

A radio news report on November 2, 2012, stated that 2.5 million women are affected by breast cancer each year. Is anyone asking why?

According to news reports, Evelyn Lauder died November 12, 2011 at age 75 from nongenetic ovarian cancer. She survived an early stage breast cancer in 1987. How tragic that no doctor ever got to the source of her cancer and cured her completely.

We now have an internationally published story that there is such a thing as over treatment. The Associated Press released a story on this subject on November 21, 2012 under the byline of chief medical writer Marilyn Marchione.

"Mammograms have done surprisingly little to catch deadly breast cancers before they spread," a big U.S. study finds. "At the same time, more than a million women have been treated for cancers that never would have threatened their lives, researchers estimate."

According to the AP story, "Up to one-third of breast cancers, or 50,000 to 70,000 cases a year, don't need treatment, the study suggests."

It's the most detailed look yet at "over treatment" of breast cancer, reported the AP, "and it adds fresh evidence that screening is not as helpful as many women believe."

Whether you agree or disagree, the study "spotlights a reality that is tough for many Americans to accept: Some abnormalities that doctors call 'cancer' are not a health threat or truly malignant."

As with every study that challenges the status quo, defenders mystically appear and throw darts at the new research. This happened immediately with the AP report.

Here are some other statements in the Associated Press story:

53

- Breast cancer is the leading type of cancer and cause of cancer deaths in women worldwide. Nearly 1.4 million new cases are diagnosed each year.
- Mammograms are an imperfect screening tool – they often give false alarms, spurring biopsies and other tests that ultimately show no cancer was present. The new study looks at a different risk: Over diagnosis, or finding cancer that is present but does not need treatment.

Lucy Schulte Danziger's commentary in *SELF* does not address the early history of the pink ribbon, nor would I expect her to. But the pink campaign is so engrained in American culture now, that its early history has been lost.

How many people remember that Florence Nightingale, who died in 1910, was instrumental in changing the role and perception of the nursing profession?

Most folks who are in the know attribute the origin of the breast cancer awareness ribbons to a California woman named Charlotte Haley, but the color she had chosen was peach rather than pink.

My first introduction to this 68-year-old activist was an article written by Robyn Stoetzel, RN, former oncology nurse and a member of Breast Cancer Action (bcaction.org). "Charlotte Haley should be one of the most famous women in the world," said Stoetzel. "Everyone touched by breast cancer should know her story."

Haley was a 1990s activist, the granddaughter, sister, and mother of women who had battled breast cancer. In 1990 she began hand-making peach-colored loops in her dining room. Each set of five came with a card saying: "The National Cancer Institute annual budget is $1.8 billion, only 5% goes for cancer prevention. Help us wake up our legislators and America by wearing this ribbon."

Her distribution network was face-to-face on sidewalks and supermarkets, letter writing campaigns to First Ladies and Dear Abby, word of mouth in beauty parlors and over backyard fences. It was the essence of a non-commercial grassroots campaign.

In 1992 Charlotte Haley declined overtures from *SELF* and Estee Lauder to use her peach ribbon as the magazine's promotional focus for Breast Cancer Awareness Month. Stoetzel described what happened next: "Unable to get Charlotte's permission, they found another color for the ribbon, a color that was 'soothing, comforting, quieting' – all the things breast cancer is not."

Haley's peach ribbon was now a target. Lawyers advised the magazine and the cosmetics company that they should choose another color. They chose pink.

To learn why it was critically important to use Haley's peach ribbon concept, we need look no further than a maxim espoused by Ralph Waldo Emerson, American poet, essayist, and lecturer: "A good symbol is the best argument, and is a missionary to persuade thousands."

"Pink is the quintessential female color," according to Margaret Welch, director of the Color Association of the United States. "The profile on pink is playful, life-affirming. We have studies as to its calming effect, its quieting effect, its lessening of stress," wrote Sandy M. Fernandez on the website, thinkbeforeyoupink.org.

The *SELF* commentary stated: "Companies have recently come under fire for 'pinkwashing' – using the ribbon to burnish their image while marketing products that endanger women's health or give only a token of the proceeds to the cause."

The commentary in *SELF* continued: "The ribbon helped lead to more and better testing, and it fueled millions of dollars' worth of research to find better treatments and a cure."

Many critics find that to be an argumentative statement and many analysts would dispute the statistics quoted by Danziger in her commentary. One reason her statistics are flawed is that they do not address the DCIS issue, and how these precancerous cases are being used to manipulate the glowing statistical outcome that suggests progress, which is not the case in real life.

Imagine what could happen if *SELF* used a little space to explain the connection between oral pathology and breast cancer. There are dozens of books and research articles supporting this connection. They aren't hard to find; they are simply ignored.

When *SELF* and Estee Lauder approached Charlotte Haley, that was akin to food critic Duncan Hines listing the restaurant of Harlan Sanders, founder of Kentucky Fried Chicken, in his famous guide to restaurants in the U.S.

In hindsight, we know that Sanders was on to something big.

As Sanders developed his distinct appearance, including his trademark mustache and goatee, and white suit and black string tie, he had the tools needed to attract a partnership of businessmen that purchased the KFC corporation and expanded its impact globally. Colonel Sanders became a household name.

Here's the difference.

Harlan Sanders was selling chicken, and it became hugely profitable. It was appropriate – and good business – for Sanders to sell KFC and to collect franchise and appearance fees.

Pink ribbons were selling breast cancer awareness and, on this point, they were phenomenally successful. Like the KFC brand, the pink ribbons became hugely profitable for hundreds of products and services that got on the pink bandwagon.

But the profits were ill-gotten gain because the pink-promoted research and cure angle is fraudulent.

There has been no full public accounting of the money raised by pink campaigns – hundreds of them – or the research that the unknown funds allegedly spawned. And everyone knows there is no conventional, medically-controlled cure! The pink bandwagon has glamorized radical breast cancer surgery and toxic chemo and radiation treatments that produce horrible and long-lasting side effects.

Are women really proud to show their scarred breasts and bald head? Has breast augmentation surgery become so advanced that women consider bald heads and breasts implants trophies and a badge of honor?

The fairy tale by Hans Christian Anderson speaks to the glamorization of the Pink Ribbon campaigns.

Two weavers promised an Emperor a new suit of clothes that would be invisible to those that are stupid, incompetent, or unfit for their positions. When the Emperor paraded before his subjects, a child cried out, "But he isn't wearing anything at all!"

Children understand basic concepts. Why do most adults not see what's happening in the cancer industry?

Charlotte Haley must have sensed that the corporate overtures to enlist her partnership or cooperation in promoting breast cancer awareness with her peach ribbons were a venture that was too commercial. Based on everything that has been published about her, that's exactly why she rejected the offers.

Even if *SELF* and Estee Lauder initially grasped the financial implications of pink, there is no doubt that their attempt to provide Charlotte Haley with national exposure was genuine, and their interest was focused on the stated purpose – breast cancer awareness.

No one could have known how nauseating the pink campaign would become.

Danziger is correct on one point: There's a backlash – like the sound of a distant tidal wave coming toward you – against the commercialism of pink.

"It's an Epidemic, Stupid" is the title of the Think Before You Pink® campaign sponsored by Breast Cancer Action.

"Breast cancer requires more than awareness, and pink ribbons, and screening," according to the campaign, which also blasts the government "for outsourcing its responsibility for public health and breast cancer to large-scale philanthropic organizations, like Komen and Avon, which are beholden to corporate funders."

But I disagree wholeheartedly with their conclusion that the government should initiate and support independent research and strong regulation "to turn the tide on this epidemic." It is the medical industry's stranglehold on non-toxic and non-surgical treatments, with the support of government regulators, which prevents known cures from being used.

To quote Ronald Reagan from his first inaugural address in 1981, "In this present crisis, government is not a solution to the problem, government is the problem."

If we lived in a country where health freedom was practiced, people could go to any medical doctor and choose any medical treatment, and surrender their life to the doctor and his drug therapies, if that's what they wanted to do.

But people should also be allowed to choose non-invasive diagnostic procedures and treatment protocols, and be guided in their choices by health practitioners from many disciplines, whether medical doctors or not, if that's what they want to do. That is precisely what Victoria wanted.

The people who choose a more natural approach should not be intimidated, ridiculed, or threatened, and neither should practitioners who try to help them. This includes licensed medical doctors and dentists who desire to be healers and not drug pushers. Insurance companies should be paying for alternative treatments, just as they do for slash, burn, and poison treatments.

The editor-in-chief of *SELF* acknowledged that the first 20 years of the pink ribbon campaign centered on detecting and treating cancer. The next 20, she wrote, need to be more focused on prevention – "doing all we can to stop cancer before it starts."

If that's the case, *SELF* better get serious about reporting on Digital Infrared Thermal Imaging technology as a screening tool for both breast cancer, and the proper analysis of oral infections as they relate to breast cancer.

How does Danziger's statement relate to the commercialized use of the pink ribbons? Breast Cancer Action has developed a "Think Before You Pink® Toolkit." In the kit, you'll get some of the resources, information, and tools you need to:

1. Take action to hold pinkwashing corporations accountable.
2. Deepen your understanding of the politics of breast cancer.
3. Ask questions to be certain your valuable dollars go towards addressing and ending the breast cancer epidemic.
4. Help others learn the truth about breast cancer and pink ribbon marketing.

Chapter 5

Your breast lump may not be cancer

Thirty, 40, or 50 years ago women were not being pressured like they are today to have annual mammograms or even biopsies just because there seemed to be an out of the ordinary symptom appearing in the breast.

"Women did not panic back then," observes Victoria. "Women applied common sense."

A woman knew that her breast sensations could be hormone-related, allergy related, or connected with inflammatory foods, fibrocystic tissue, toxic overload, and any number of other reasons that did not include the "c" word. Women interacted with each other, shared information, and concluded that most of these issues simply disappeared in time.

"Women were rational." If the issues didn't go away, then a visit to a doctor was considered.

Today, all the breast cancer awareness hype has displaced common sense. A woman constantly hears that one in eight women will develop breast cancer. This establishes the fear factor resulting in an immediate trip to the doctor the moment anything 'different' happens involving her breasts.

A woman hears the well-rehearsed mammogram speech that, by its very nature, is intended to cause a fear reaction. Suddenly, she's easy prey and will agree to an invasive biopsy with little or no thought.

"I think they have women believing you must get the lump out of your body at all cost before the sun goes down and not just take one breast but take both. That is another part of the propaganda machine. If you get cancer in one breast, you will get it in the other."

It's not true. This is more politics and marketing than science. Playing politics with mammograms may increase media ratings but it doesn't serve the interest of women.

As a country, we originally got into this cancer mess because of our sickly diets, dependence on processed food, and exposures to environmental toxins, all contributors to our malnourished bodies where cancer thrives. The size of our mouths became smaller as we stopped eating wholesome, non-toxic foods – a lot smaller than people who live in undeveloped countries and eat nothing but wholesome unprocessed foods. Our teeth became crowded. As a result, dentists routinely recommend the removal of wisdom teeth to 'make room' for the remaining 28 teeth.

There's a certain irony in this suggestion. The American Association of Oral and Maxillofacial Surgeons – the wisdom teeth experts – published a four-page advertising supplement in *USA Today* that cited 10 reasons to remove your wisdom teeth. Wisdom teeth that seem to be problem-free "remain a breeding ground" for oral infection and inflammation, according to Reason #3. "Research supports the concept that such inflammation may enter the bloodstream and contribute to the development and/or progression of a variety of diseases, including diabetes, cardiovascular diseases, and stroke."

Cancer should be added to the list, but dentists are just as afraid of the "c" word as medical doctors who are not oncologists.

Because of our poor nutrition, people in developed nations began having more tooth and gum issues. And a huge dental industry emerged to respond to this crisis.

Efforts to cure cancer and to prevent it in the first place will remain elusive until doctors, dentists, and insurance companies accept the oral pathology connection. That's not going to happen in the mainstream, but there's nothing stopping a cancer victim from addressing their oral pathology on their own.

Well, there is something stopping a private citizen from addressing their oral pathology: the shortage of dentists who understand the relationship between a person's mouth and the rest of their body, and are trained and willing to do something about it.

With cancer, like most problems in life, you must get to the source. "Your breast is not the source of the problem." Victoria knows this all too well.

She was so exhausted after the stressful decision to divorce her first husband in 1993, when she felt the lump she thought, "I will deal with that later. It is just too much right now. When I moved out of our house and got settled, away from this man after the divorce, the lump went away."

She and her second husband built a new house on the West Coast. "I cleaned, organized, worked very hard…and we moved in August 7, 2005. On the morning of August 29, 2005 as Hurricane Katrina slammed into New Orleans, her husband stated that he wanted a divorce.

"This man thought he could take the business we had both worked so hard for and the new house that I had worked so hard on and dismiss me because he was greedy and wanted everything for himself."

Victoria found herself in a quandary, hundreds of miles away from her family. "He told me I had no rights," she said, but what she remembered most was "what I saw in his eyes scared me and I thought it best I pack all my things and move back to North Carolina."

"I was already stressed because my only sister lived in Orleans Parrish, several miles from the French Quarter. I told my Mother not to tell Teri I was getting a divorce; my sister was about to lose her home."

"At the end of the day on August 29, 2005, we both lost our homes, just in different ways," Victoria reflected.

In fact, the date August 29 became an unforgettable day in Victoria's life. Her ex-husband finally settled a monetary lawsuit exactly one year later on August 29, 2006, and a contractor who was supposed to build Victoria's new house in North Carolina settled on August 29, 2007 for failure to perform. He couldn't fight Victoria's chronological, almost hour-by-hour, 'stop-notice' documentation.

"To say the least, it was very painful," she said. "After I got back to North Carolina where I felt safe, I had to hire an attorney and worked with her day and night on a lawsuit against my ex-husband for months. This is where my documents came in so handy for me. It was very stressful, but something had to be done for unjust behavior."

The over-achiever that she is, Victoria acquired her real estate license and set about clearing a forest, doing site preparation, digging a well, installing a septic system, and putting in a road and grading for her new house. "As always I was on overdrive and exhausting myself." As with most women, she expected no consequences from total exhaustion.

Victoria does a lot of reading and listening in the early morning each day. One of her calendars offers daily quotes. "Contrary to popular belief, we feel wasted when we continually do too much. We don't feel exhilarated by our successes or expanded by our accomplishments. We feel drained. There are other ways to be productive."

Little did Victoria know that her frustrations in finding a contractor to build a quality home in a timely manner were going to nearly drain her life energy.

"After numerous meetings with one builder, I hired them to build my new home." After the drywall was hung, she fired the builder. "To give you an example of how bad they were it took five inspections to get their framing passed." She said the builder presented a "great sales presentation," but was unable to deliver performance.

Dawn to dark, day after day, Victoria was on the new home job site, cleaning, inspecting "and being so upset. I couldn't believe this was happening now." She was gravely shocked and disappointed in the absence of a work ethic among these Southern boys she had hired.

Between the house construction issues and her second divorce, stress was building to a dangerous level. Tragically, she was not doing anything to cope with this hidden challenge to her body.

Victoria received her final inspection as owner-builder (certificate of occupancy) on November 16, 2007. For practical purposes, her house was completed in early December 2007. She was 53 years old. "I thought now I can get my life back on track and enjoy life again." Sadly, this feeling was short-lived.

On December 15, 2007, Victoria's sister had her first Christmas party in her rebuilt home in New Orleans. Back in North Carolina, there was no furniture in Victoria's house on Christmas Eve. She blew up an air mattress and slept in front of her fireplace.

It was pleasant and chilly, but not bitterly cold on Christmas morning when Victoria discovered a lump in her right breast, "and for the first time I felt pain in the right breast."

"Merry Christmas, I thought to myself."

Chapter 6

Is DCIS cancer?

With the noticeable discomfort, Victoria was alarmed. She had felt a lump in the same spot in the same breast 14 years earlier, when she was going through her first stressful divorce at age 39. With all the stress she did not remember the first incident until long after her Christmas morning 2007 discovery. Somehow, in her mind, the first lump faded into oblivion.

Reflecting on this memory failure, Victoria realizes she might have remained calmer in the face of the Christmas morning revelation. Rather than falling prey to panic, if only she had remembered that a lump was there years before, and had disappeared on it's own.

Victoria is blessed with a photographic memory. Normally, she can quote dates, names, and events faster than they can be located in a computer file. What happened? Her memory briefly became a victim of stress and the draining affect it had on her entire body. "I was so overwhelmed."

The original lump disappeared without any treatment.

In 1994, as Victoria was trying to put her first failed marriage behind her, she had agreed to a doctor's insistence that she have a baseline mammogram.

While already health conscious, she was not fully aware of the radiation and compression dangers imposed by mammograms, nor with the ineffectiveness of the uncomfortable and painful procedure. Although Victoria had previously found the lump through self-examination in October 1993, the mammogram detected nothing, but she was blasted with ionizing radiation. "I thought to myself, 'I don't want to do that again. It was so painful and barbaric.'"

That's why mammography is a brilliant business model for the cancer industry, readers of NaturalNews.com were told in November 2012. "If women get annual mammograms, sooner or later they'll find a tumor caused by the mammography! (And then the doctors will say, good thing we caught it early, huh?)"

The baseline mammogram procedure was done at a Palm Springs, California imaging center located in the same complex as her doctor's office. "I really liked that doctor."

The mammogram's negative finding left Victoria with a false sense of security. Besides, the lump had disappeared completely.

According to Victoria, "He did go by the 40-year-old rule. When you're 40, you should get your baseline mammogram. I was 40 and that's what he wanted me to do."

Some months later, Victoria learned that her family doctor, who was pushing her to have the mammogram, also owned part interest in the imaging center. "What a racket! Is this cancer prevention or padding the bottom line?" she wondered. "Is there a conflict of interest?"

Call me old-school, but it seems to me that full disclosure by the doctor and his ownership in the imaging center would have been appropriate for all of his patients.

Today, because of what she has learned, a police detail could not force Victoria to have a mammogram.

Why?

The American College of Physicians (ACP) has recommended women in their 40s consult with their doctor before undergoing routine annual mammography screening. An expert panel from the ACP, which represents 120,000 internists, made this recommendation in the journal *Annals of Internal Medicine*.

After reviewing 117 studies conducted between 1966 and 2005, the panel found the data on mammography screening for women in their 40s are so unclear that the effectiveness of reducing breast cancer deaths could be either 15% or "... nearly zero."

The dangers of mammography are also recognized in the medical field. According to Dr. Samuel Epstein of the Cancer Prevention Coalition (PreventCancer.com), "Screening mammography poses significant and cumulative risks of breast cancer for pre-menopausal women."

The routine practice of taking four films of each breast annually results in approximately one rad (radiation absorbed dose) exposure, about 1,000 times greater than that from a chest x-ray. The pre-menopausal breast is highly sensitive to radiation.

Researchers at the Nordic Cochrane Centre in Denmark examined the benefits and negative effects of seven breast cancer screening programs on 500,000 women in the United States, Canada, Scotland, and Sweden. The study's authors found that for every 2,000 women who received mammograms over a 10-year period, only one would have her life prolonged, but 10 would endure unnecessary and potentially harmful treatments.

However, the UK's National Health Service (NHS) breast screening program – which provides free mammograms for women over the age of 50 every three years – cited different statistics in defending its program. An NHS statement said the Department of Health's advisory committee on breast cancer screening had conducted its own evaluation of the program, and found that screening prolonged the life of five women out of every 2,000 over a 10-year period.

Did you get that? Allow this to sink in! Instead of mammography prolonging the life of one out of every 2000 women, the UK is proud to claim the archaic technology will prolong the life of five out of every 2,000 women over a 10-year period.

Either statistic is outrageous!

An estimated 41,000 women in the U.S. will die this year from breast cancer. Is this less of a concern to us than dying in battle?

Breast cancer is preventable and curable. And we know the trigger. It's in the mouth! Why don't you know about it? That's 41,000 women. Dead! Why aren't you outraged?

Consider the outrage that lingered for years after the Battle of the Alamo. Using the highest estimates, fewer than 900 Texans and Mexicans were killed or wounded, according to eyewitness accounts and most Alamo historians. We can't bring back those valiant soldiers who died at the Alamo, but if there's enough outrage we can save the lives of thousands of women.

Will enough women become outraged to make a difference?

It's a fact: the high radiation (1-10 rads depending upon the exam) burns tissue, as all direct radiation does. Since mammographic screening was introduced, the incidence of a

form of breast cancer called ductal carcinoma in situ (DCIS) has increased by 328%.

In the second edition of her book, *Outsmart Your Cancer,* Tanya Harter Pierce writes that DCIS "now comprises about 30% of all breast cancer diagnoses in the United States and is included in the cure-rate statistics for life-threatening breast cancer as well," although many experts believe that DCIS is a pre-cancerous state and should not even be classified as cancer. It is said to be 99% curable.

Here's why the classification of DCIS is significant. It affects mainstream medicine's statistical breast cancer analysis, making it appear that cure rates are getting better.

Pierce puts it this way, "But these statistics are achievable only after gross statistical manipulations have been done, and after key terms like 'cure' have been re-defined."

Pierce cites six specific ways that official cancer cure-rate statistics are often fudged so that conventional methods for treating cancer can look better than they really are. The first one, she says, is re-defining "cure" as meaning a person is living five years after diagnosis, instead of using the word's real meaning, which is "cancer-free."

Whatever you do, don't confuse a five-year survival statistic with a cure. They are not the same. A little interpretation is in order.

- You are cured if you have an apparent lack of symptoms after five years.
- If, on the other hand, you die a day after five years from the effects of the treatment, you are still counted in the 'cured' statistics, sort of cured and dead at the same time.

A good line for a cancer victim's tombstone is: I wouldn't have been cured if I hadn't lived that additional day.

Getting back to the DCIS scandal.

Due to the considerable pressure placed on the woman's breast during the procedure, a mammogram can actually help spread existing cancer cells. According to some health practitioners, this compression could cause existing cancer cells to metastasize from the breast site.

Research has also found a gene, called oncogene AC, which is extremely sensitive to even small doses of radiation. A significant percentage of women in the United States have this gene, which could increase their risk of mammography-induced cancer. Research indicates that 10,000 oncogene AC carriers will die of breast cancer each year due to mammography.

The National Cancer Institute released evidence that, among women under 35, mammography could cause 75 cases of breast cancer for every 15 it identifies. A Canadian study found a 52% increase in breast cancer mortality in young women given annual mammograms.

This is outrageous. But where's the outrage?

The truth about mammograms can't be reported without the threat of reprisals. Why? As I've already stated, the procedure is a money maker in the medical industry. It will be protected at any cost. There is an alternative, and it's called thermal imaging. In recent years, this non-toxic, non-invasive and totally painless breast screening procedure has drawn thousands of women away from mammography.

Millions of women could and should be using thermal imaging to monitor breast health. Why aren't they doing this? Thermal imaging was available to Victoria. She could have been using it, but she didn't know about it. She never heard a single message about thermal imaging during Pink Ribbon Month. However, she could have purchased hundreds of products that were packaged in pink. How helpful!

Many have never heard of thermal imaging, and others have been told that it's quackery. The orthodox medical establishment has total control over nearly everything a woman hears. The establishment is aided and abetted by well-funded U.S. government agencies like the FDA, National Institute of Health, the National Cancer Institute, and wealthy non-profit groups that reinforce the establishment's propaganda.

What's the real reason that thermal imaging technology has been suppressed? It's about money. Breast thermal imaging poses a real financial threat, and the medical industry is viciously fighting back.

Look at what happened in Canada after CBC News, the country's largest news broadcaster, ran a hit-piece November 27, 2012, on thermal imaging. The next day, Health Canada warned Canadians and their health-care providers that thermography machines are not approved for use in Canada for breast cancer screening.

The Canadian press promptly reported, "The department says it is not aware of any scientific evidence that supports use of the thermal imaging machines as a screening tool for early detection of breast cancer."

And the senior manager of cancer control policy at the Canadian Cancer Society was also quoted as saying there is no proof thermography actually works as a diagnostic tool for breast cancer. "It's not effective at detecting breast cancers," Gillian Bromfield told CBC News. "It misses the large majority of breast cancers and, on top of that, it also detects cancers when there actually are none."

Bromfield's statements are a complete contradiction to the facts as published in medical journals. His statements also exude arrogance and ignorance. Thermal imaging is promoted as a screening device for monitoring breast health. It is not promoted as a diagnostic tool. However, in the hands of a trained practitioner – an expert in thermal imaging – it can reveal obvious indicators of cancer.

Secondly, thermal imaging will not "detect cancers when there actually are none," as Bromfield claimed. Thermal imaging sees inflammation and inflammatory patterns. If inflammation is present, thermal imaging will see it. The presence of inflammation does not necessarily mean cancer. The statement that thermal imaging is detecting cancers when there are none present is totally ludicrous.

But notice who writes his pay check – the Canadian equivalent of the American Cancer Society.

Why didn't the Canadian press question this assertion? The answer involves money. Like their American counterparts, they rely on advertising revenue from Big Pharma. If anything truthful is reported about alternative medicine, the money dries up.

There was method in their madness. The broadcast story was a one-sided 'investigation' that was aired just weeks after other international reports surfaced describing the dangers and ineffectiveness of mammograms.

Let's be honest. Any investigative reporter should be able to surf the internet with at least the same skills as a 12-year-old. Any middle school student with a laptop could tap into a search engine during their lunch break and find numerous peer-reviewed articles including the report, "Breast Thermography and Cancer Risk Prediction."

Michel Gautherie, PhD, and his colleagues reported in 1981 on a 10-year study, which found that an abnormal thermogram was 10 times more significant as a future risk indicator for breast cancer than having a family history of breast cancer.

Yet, we are to believe that Health Canada is unaware of this research.

William Amalu, president of the International Academy of Clinical Thermography (iact-org.org), examined samples of the 800 peer-reviewed studies on thermography – some of which spanned 12 years and tens of thousands of subjects – and reached the same conclusion.

The study's authors were either PhD's with doctorates in a representative field, or physicians primarily in the specialties of oncology, radiology, gynecology, and internal medicine.

It was 13 years after publication of this research that a medical doctor was pushing Victoria to have her first mammogram. She had good reasons to avoid them prior to age 40, and she knew what those reasons were. Nothing was ever said by her doctor about the existence of an optional technology for monitoring her breast health.

Twenty-seven years would pass after the 1981 thermal imaging study was published before Victoria would learn about breast thermography. That was criminal.

The study summarized a total of 13 points, four of which need to be heavily emphasized:

- Breast thermography has undergone extensive research since the late 1950s.
- A persistent abnormal thermogram carries with it a much higher risk of future breast cancer – 22 times higher.

- An abnormal infrared thermal image is the single most important marker of high risk for developing breast cancer.
- Breast thermography has the ability to detect the first signs that a cancer may be forming up to 10 years before any other procedure can detect it [and this includes mammograms].

The last point was emphasized by Dr. Christiane Northrup (drnorthrup.com) in an article posted on the HuffingtonPost.com. "The most promising aspect of thermography," she said, "is its ability to spot anomalies years before mammography."

As for mammograms, "You would be surprised by how many women tell me their doctors make them feel guilty for not having a mammogram," said Dr. Northrup.

The Canadian medical industry may be viciously fighting thermography, but Canadian women and thermographers have started their own rebellion. A website petition (Change.org) was posted by the Professional Academy of Clinical Thermology (PACT), which claims to be the world's largest petition platform with 20 million users.

Women are not pulling their punches either. Some examples of comments posted by petition signers:
- "This kind of journalism makes the CBC look like the propaganda wing of Health Canada."
- "If I can track vascular changes in my body without exposing myself to harmful radiation, that seems like the safest choice for me."
- "Experts that read mammograms are not experts at reading a thermography report. It's like asking an expert plumber to fix your TV. Insanity! Don't let them take your right for a second opinion."
- "I want to take control of my own health and thermography is part of my plan, not mammography which causes what I am trying to prevent!"

The online petition refutes disinformation being presented in the media, asks for thermography to be paid by Canadian health benefit providers, and urges creation of regulations in Canada supporting its use. Someone needs to start a petition drive in the United States.

Chapter 7

Why does cancer return after a mastectomy?

Victoria was 47 before she ever encountered a friend who had diagnosed breast cancer. The woman had surgery in Palm Springs, California on September 11, 2001. She was checking into the hospital about the same time as the first plane struck the Twin Towers. This particular acquaintance accepted the Medical Establishment's most forceful remedy – mastectomy. It was the first time that Victoria sensed the horrors of the popularly accepted radical surgery technique for dealing with breast cancer.

It had not yet occurred to Victoria that many women still have cancer after their breasts have been butchered. It shows up soon after the surgery, or it might wait five years, 10 years, or more.

Why are there so many cases of breast cancer coming back after a mastectomy? Isn't that why the breasts are being surgically removed, to keep that from happening?

The American Cancer Society has a name for this event – cancer coming back after treatment. It's called a recurrence. The ACS breaks recurrences down into three categories.

- If the cancer comes back in the same breast or near the mastectomy scar, it's called a local recurrence.
- If the cancer comes back farther away, it's called a distant recurrence.
- "Rarely, the cancer comes back in nearby lymph nodes," the ACS says. This is called a regional recurrence.

Victoria would eventually connect the dots. She was on a journey now. Nothing would stop her from uncovering the truth. In the course of her five-year battle, she would find the truth, and all the dirty little secrets that came with it.

Meanwhile, it was Tuesday, October 2, 2012. I was trying to outline a disclaimer for this book, you know, the special wording that is supposed to help absolve an author from inadvertently practicing medicine without a license and being hauled away to prison.

71

I heard a 'ping,' and checked my email. It was a forwarded message announcing Monday as World Cancer Day. Fact checking the claim, I learned that it had already been observed on February 4, 2012, and the next World Cancer Day would not happen until Monday, February 4, 2013.

Even so, I had to shake my head as I read the short message: "Dear God, I pray for a cure for cancer. Amen." Doctors rarely talk about "curing" cancer. Instead, doctors judge a treatment's success by how long a patient lives, usually five years. It's all about statistics, "damned lies and statistics," said Mark Twain.

The money is in the medicine, not the cure. How many times do we have to repeat this statement? We may already have the only 'cures' for cancer that we'll ever be allowed to have.

Next was a photo of a burning candle and these words: "A candle loses nothing by lighting another candle." I was being told to pass the email on to someone else, as if my action could lead to a cure.

I wanted to scream. Praying for a cancer cure might make us feel better, but we already have cures for cancer. Patients just don't know about them. Instead of praying for a cure, as though it will come in a magic pill, why aren't people praying to remove man-made obstacles that prevent using or knowing about known and effective – but non-pharmaceutical – cancer treatments?

There's too much money in diseases. I heard someone telling the story of a friend who was diagnosed with diabetes and he attended a big seminar put on by a diabetes awareness organization, complete with 'experts' and 'medical leaders' promoting it. At the meeting, he was served soft drinks, donuts, and all kinds of sugary snacks.

Do you think the man's diabetes will ever be cured?

Sometimes we can't fix stupid, and many times a person with a cancer diagnosis is better off doing nothing.

The incidence of thyroid cancer has been increasing 6.6% per year since 2004. Doctors don't know why, but the suggestion has been made that it's the result of more diagnostic tests using better imaging equipment.

Some or all of the thyroid gland is removed during surgery, leaving a two-inch scar, and some patients are required to swallow radioactive iodine to wipe out stray cancer cells. Of course, if the thyroid is removed, the patient must take synthetic hormones for the rest of their life.

An article in the April 2013 issue of *SELF* magazine reflects a novel new approach for dealing with thyroid cancer. "Finding and treating small thyroid cancers may do us more harm than the cancer itself ever would."

Victoria did the right thing in 1993 when a lump first appeared in her right breast. She didn't run to the doctor, and the lump disappeared. It was before the days of cancer hype – a lump in your breast will kill you by tomorrow if you don't act today. She intuitively knew how to remain calm. That's all she did, and the lump went away because the stress of her first divorce had slowly faded away.

The lump appeared for the second time at Christmas in 2007. Fourteen years earlier, Victoria's advice to any woman in a similar situation would have been to not panic, change lifestyle and nutrition, dump the stress, then monitor the situation to see what happens.

Victoria deeply regrets not taking her own advice in 2007. Instead, she saw a doctor and life as she knew it would change forever.

Chapter 8

My stud must be 14 carat

In 1968 at age 15, Victoria was an 8th grader in junior high when she and a girlfriend conspired without Victoria's mother's knowledge to pierce her ears. It wasn't nearly as dramatic as Oprah Winfrey's agonizing piercing session taped for her television show in 2005.

Oprah had dreamed of having her ears pierced for years, but feared it would be too painful. Once it was done, Oprah was delighted at the results, in spite of the pain. "Other people want to climb mountains and jump out of planes," Oprah said. "I wanted to get my ears pierced because you can wear cooler earrings."

For Victoria, it wasn't about cool earrings or rebellion as much as it was a right of passage – the first step to being grown up. Okay, there probably was some peer pressure. The piercing was not done in a physician's office, jewelry store, or department store. It was done at her friend's home, after school, and the method was somewhat crude, but it worked.

Truth be known, hundreds of thousands of young girls have done the same thing.

After using an ice cube to deaden her earlobes, her school buddy held a sliced chunk of white potato behind the earlobe and pressed an alcohol-sterilized sewing needle through the flesh into the potato. "I have small ear lobes so it made it easy. But my Mom wasn't too happy about what I had done."

All was good when Victoria inserted a pair of 14-carat gold studs during the first week as the puncture healed. But when she eventually inserted a cheap pair of earrings, her body's sensitivity to metal reared its ugly head. The earlobes swelled, became red and sore, and sometimes produced a crusty discharge. "It was a mess and very painful."

Only when she wore 14-carat gold or sterling silver earrings was Victoria able to avoid pain and suffering.

That same year a family dentist performed a root canal on her upper right front tooth, tooth #8 on the Tooth Meridian Chart, the first incisor.

Saving the tooth seemed paramount at the time. Victoria was grateful to have the tooth intact, but she was intimidated by the name of the procedure. "What is a root canal tooth?" she wondered. The dental procedure was expensive and it produced another strain on the family budget. At that age, what teenager wants to lose their front tooth?

This root canal procedure was especially important to Victoria's mother, a one-sport varsity athlete in high school, who lost a front tooth playing basketball. There were eight kids in her family, and there was no money for expensive dental work.

"She grew up with no natural front tooth," said Victoria. "After what I learned, I told her it probably saved her life."

The Chinese have known for hundreds of years that the mouth and body are interconnected. Over time these 'connections' or 'associations' between teeth, organs, and systems in the body have been charted, hence the name Tooth Meridian Chart (meridians are energy channels or pathways in the body).

Although she was good at solving puzzles, this mouth connection was way over Victoria's head in the late 1960s. In fact, it was way over the head of nearly every dentist in America.

Besides, she was young and naive and she believed that no dentist or doctor would cause harm to a patient, either accidentally or on purpose.

She never dreamed there could be a problem with a root canal, a procedure that requires the severing of the tooth's blood supply and nerve. The process utilizes a special stainless steel dental file. Little did Victoria know that following her own procedure, her face would be blemished 41 years with a red spot the size of a pencil eraser on her upper lip, directly above the root canal tooth.

It became a vanity issue. Every time she looked in the mirror, there was this strange red spot. "What is it?" she thought. It was fruitless to try and conceal the marking with makeup. It was too close to the mouth.

If the ugly spot wasn't enough, every time she sneezed she experienced pain between the nose and upper lip. It wasn't an excruciating pain, but more of a discomfort. It never went away.

Like many Americans, Victoria has a small jaw – generally the result of dietary deficiencies in childhood – and tooth crowding became an issue in her early teens.

Her teeth were especially crowded in the upper right, so much so that her permanent upper right canine, tooth #6, was unable to erupt properly. In an attempt to correct the problem, the family dentist instructed her to use a Popsicle stick regularly to press on the front side of the partially exposed tooth, in the hope that it would fully emerge.

"It worked," she said.

It wasn't until January 2009 that Digital Infrared Thermal Imaging suggested the upper right front tooth root canal (tooth #8) was infected. X-rays and dental exams never indicated a problem and there were no symptoms.

Victoria would soon learn about the real danger of a root canal.

She would also learn about a breast screening procedure that was non-invasive, painless, accurate, and inexpensive – Digital Infrared Thermographic Imaging (DITI). She would also learn why she didn't already know about it. Its use was being suppressed by the traditional medical world, and its practitioners were constantly being harassed.

It would be 43 years before a respected national mainstream newspaper used the word cancer in a compelling article that connected the mouth with the rest of the body.

On December 27, 2011, *The Wall Street Journal* published a story with the headline, "If Your Teeth Could Talk." The subhead stated: The mouth offers clues to disorders and disease; dentists could play larger role in patient care.

The piece was under the byline of WSJ 'Personal Journal' Senior Editor Melinda Beck, who explained that one's teeth and gums hold a lot of details about the body's overall health.

"The eyes may be the window to the soul, but the mouth provides an even better view of the body as a whole," wrote Beck.

"Some of the earliest signs of diabetes, cancer, pregnancy, immune disorders, hormone imbalances, and drug issues show up in the gums, teeth, and tongue – sometimes long before a patient knows anything is wrong."

She added, "There's also growing evidence that oral health problems, particularly gum disease, can harm a patient's general health as well, raising the risk of diabetes, heart disease, stroke, pneumonia, and pregnancy complications."

Beck quoted Anthony Iacopino, director of the International Centre for Oral-Systemic Health, which opened at the University of Manitoba Faculty of Dentistry in Canada in 2008. He said: "We have lots of data showing a direct correlation between inflammation in the mouth and inflammation in the body."

As Victoria would come to find out, there was a Cleveland dentist in the early 1900s, Dr. Weston A. Price (1870-1948), who clearly established the connection between oral pathology and systemic diseases. He spent 25 years of his career performing research on pulpless and endodontically-treated teeth. His theory was that infected teeth should be treated by dental extraction rather than root canals.

By the 1950s, however, Dr. Price's dental studies had been marginalized. In 1951, a special review issue of the *Journal of the American Dental Association* confirmed the shift of Standard of Care from extraction back to endodontic dentistry.

Dr. Price's research involved more than dental practices. He wondered why Americans were developing so many health and dental issues. He authored an epic study demonstrating the importance of whole food nutrition, and the degeneration and destruction that comes from a diet of processed foods.

Price's 1939 book, *Nutrition and Physical Degeneration*, is published by Price-Pottenger Nutrition Foundation (ppnf.org), in an expanded 8th edition. Price-Pottenger is a non-profit education foundation committed to reversing the trend of declining health in the modern world.

According to a review on amazon.com, for nearly 10 years, Dr. Price and his wife traveled around the world in search of the secret to health. Instead of looking at people afflicted with disease symptoms, this highly-respected dentist and dental researcher chose to focus on healthy individuals, in an effort to learn how they achieved such amazing health.

Another researcher, Sally Fallon, who is a journalist, chef, homemaker, and community activist, wrote a nutrition book based on Price's principles, *Nourishing Tradition: The Cookbook that Challenges Politically Correct Nutrition and the Diet Dictocrats.*

As president of The Weston A. Price Foundation (westonaprice.org), Fallon wrote on the organization's website that Dr. Price "turned from test tubes and microscopes to unstudied evidence among human beings" in his search for the causes of dental decay and physical degeneration that he observed at work.

"The world became his laboratory," she said. "As he traveled, his findings led him to the belief that dental caries and deformed dental arches resulting in crowded, crooked teeth and unattractive appearance were merely a sign of physical degeneration, resulting from what he had suspected – nutritional deficiencies."

Dr. Price found the answer he was searching for among indigenous people groups around the world, people who ate their traditional diets of mostly raw, uncooked food, and had never been exposed to the Western diet consisting mostly of dead, processed food.

When it comes to food, sometimes we often don't know whether to laugh or cry. Buddy Hackett, American comedian and actor, once said, "As a child my family's menu consisted of two choices: take it or leave it."

English lawyer and philosopher Francis Bacon, Sr. wrote: "It's not what we eat but what we digest that makes us strong."

If we are what we eat, then there's a huge disconnect between modern medicine and a typical doctor's understanding of nutrition.

According to a 2006 study published on the website of the National Institute of Health (nih.gov), students received 23.9 contact hours of nutrition instruction on average during medical school. Most hours were taught in the first two years, and three-quarters of nutritional instruction occurred outside of a dedicated nutrition course. In other words, the bulk of nutrition education was being mixed in with the basic science courses.

A contributing writer at *The New York Times Magazine,* Michael Pollan, published an essay with an interesting premise. If you are what you eat, and especially if you eat industrial food, as 99% of Americans do, what you are, is "corn," he said.

"During the last year I've been following a bushel of corn through the industrial food system. What I keep finding in case after case, if you follow the food back to the farm – if you follow the nutrients, if you follow the carbon – you end up in a corn field in Iowa, over and over and over again," Pollan concluded.

The sweet corn grown in your backyard garden can be pretty healthy and very tasty, but not all corn is good for you. Most farmed corn goes to concentrated animal feed operations or processing facilities to create products like high fructose corn syrup or ethanol.

High fructose corn syrup is less expensive to produce than sugar from sugar beets or sugar cane, but fructose contains no enzymes, vitamins or minerals, and leeches micronutrients from the body.

The question becomes very basic: Why don't doctors understand the association between good nutrition and good health? They know all about the latest drugs.

For the most part, medical schools have failed to put the proper emphasis on nutrition. They simply don't teach it in a coordinated curriculum. But there's an ever greater obstacle. In the past 50 years, so much has been discovered that medical students can't possibly absorb it all. It's a time management challenge like trying to cram a square peg in a round hole. It doesn't fit.

Your medical doctor is not a god. He doesn't have all the answers. There are not enough hours in the day for your doctor to learn everything. There were insufficient hours in medical school for him to learn much of anything about nutrition.

Chapter 9

Is your doctor drunk?

Prior to January 2009, Victoria had two thermal breast studies. Neither time was her face scanned to identify possible oral pathology. On January 23, 2009, she was having full-body thermal imaging as well as imaging of her face.

Although it was the third time her breasts had been thermally imaged, January 2009 was the first time her face had been scanned to identify oral pathology.

It wasn't until July 2009 – six months after her full-body thermal imaging that included face scans – that the bad root canal tooth (#8) was extracted and Victoria got the shock of her life.

On the basis of her thermal imaging, Victoria could anticipate having cavitations in her wisdom teeth extraction sites on the lower right and upper right. Otherwise, her perfect mouth was unremarkable except for tell-tale heat signatures precisely over her upper right front tooth (#8) and a second root canal tooth issue at tooth #14.

After reading the book *Am I Dead? ... or do I just feel like it*, Victoria had already connected the dots. It was her right breast and she only had wisdom teeth extractions on the right side and she had a right front root canal. She knew that she was living a healthy lifestyle and eating nutritious food. Everybody in her family was very healthy. Why did she have a lump in her right breast? Now she knew the source of her problem.

"I was always so puzzled why I had a lump in my breast. I just couldn't figure it out. However, after reading the book, anybody with half a mind would know why it happened. It's nothing I'm doing wrong. It's my teeth."

"I heard the dentist say, 'Look at this!'"

The dentist, Dr. Gary M. McCown, DDS, who maintains a private practice in Knoxville and is an assistant professor at the University of Tennessee Dental School, placed her extracted dead root canal tooth (#8) on a white paper-covered tray.

As Victoria turned her head to the left, her eyes fastened on her bloody tooth, and a short needle-like object. It was a quarter-inch long piece of metal. Dr. McCown identified the object as part of the stainless steel file used in the root canal procedure more than four decades earlier.

This was shocking news to Victoria. She had never heard of a piece of metal being left in the jawbone of a dental patient.

Are you packing metal in your root canal tooth and don't know it? It's estimated that one million patients leave a dentist's office each year with a broken file tip in their jaw. The tip of the tiny reamer (root canal file) was left in this patient's tooth (stainless steel is black in the photo) and it protruded into the jawbone.

Finding metal in root canal teeth "is pretty common," the dentist explained. "It usually happens in the crooked canals of the molars."

Not in Victoria's case. It was a front tooth, one of the Big Four, the first thing other people see when she smiles.

It is not a violation of Standard of Care "as long as you inform the patient that it happened," Dr. McCown noted. Neither Victoria nor her mother were informed many years earlier that part of a dental instrument broke off during the procedure and the tip of the file was left in her jawbone.

As with any profession, patients have both legal and moral expectations of their dentist when they sit down in a chair in the exam room. It isn't like this is Greek to a dentist. There are organizations devoted to this subject, like the American Society for Dental Ethics, a section of the American College of Dentists.

In my mind, the ethical obligations of a dentist or medical doctor should exceed their legal obligations. Medicine and dentistry are, after all, Hippocratic professions – Do No Harm.

Victoria's dentist had an ethical obligation to tell the mother of his underage patient that this incident occurred. He accidentally left a piece of metal in her jawbone. How many times does this happen and patients are not informed?

Victoria was stunned.

"Well, that explains why I've always had this red spot on my lip, because I know I'm allergic to metal," Victoria exclaimed. The red spot gradually appeared in the two months following the 1968 root canal procedure, along with the weird sensations.

A nickel-iron alloy is used to manufacture stainless steel, according to the American Osteopathic College of Dermatology, and nickel appears to be a very common cause of allergic skin rashes. The AOCD also reports that a nickel allergy is more common among women than men.

For sensitive people, the best thing to do is to discontinue exposure to nickel and nickel-containing items, the AOCD reported. It appears that this is the closest thing there is to a cure.

It's hard to 'discontinue exposure' when you have nickel in the jawbone and don't even know it, says Victoria. "How many people have an allergic reaction to nickel and it's coming from a broken file tip and they don't know it?"

Victoria was not allowed by her mother to wear makeup before the 8th grade. She was a 7th grader. How would she cover up this blemish? Compared to losing her front tooth, Victoria considered the ugly red spot to be a minor concession, a walk in the park, to going toothless. When she began wearing makeup, she was upset to discover that the beige "concealer" she was using would not completely disguise the ugly mark all day because one wipe with a napkin and the mark was exposed again. "It was embarrassing."

"You go to a dentist. You get a root canal. They tell you it's safe. I should have correlated the root canal procedure with the gradual appearance of the red circle. But I didn't. I was too happy about not losing my front tooth. I was very happy that my mom did that for me."

"At that time in my life, I had complete faith in my dentist. Who was I to question his actions?"

As a teen, Victoria had no idea what the dentist was doing in her mouth during her first root canal procedure. She believed her tooth was going to be 'saved,' and she thought that was all she needed to know.

Most patients leave a dentist office after a root canal procedure with no idea about what was done to them. "The root canals can be very tiny and usually are the tiniest at the tip of the root" requiring a tiny reamer to be used, explains Dr. Frank Jerome, a minimally invasive, biocompatible dentist in Columbus, Indiana, who is also the author of the book *Tooth Truth,* a dental primer written primarily for the consumer (Dentistry-ToothTruth.com).

One of the challenges of the procedure is to ream the tooth to the tip without going through it into the bone. It is more common than not to over enlarge the tip allowing filling materials to get into the bone, Dr. Jerome says.

"The reamers are turned by hand so the dentist can stop if there is too much resistance and try again. If the reamer gets turned too tightly it will bind in the canal and the instrument can snap off leaving the end plugged with part of the stainless steel reamer often protruding from the tooth into the bone."

Dentists are not supposed to leave a broken instrument in the tooth but it happens a lot, according to Dr. Jerome, and removal of the broken tip "can be difficult and time consuming."

Victoria is not alone when it comes to Americans who have a broken file tip in their jawbone. Among the millions of Americans who might be in harm's way, there could be thousands or even hundreds of thousands of people like Victoria living with allergic reactions caused by metal in their mouth and they don't know it's there.

When an instrument is new it is sharp and cuts well. Each time the instrument is used, it gets duller. It is hard to know how many times an instrument has been used. "A new one rarely breaks," says Dr. Jerome.

There are two primary reasons that breakage occurs: Heat sterilization deteriorates the metal and dentists are trying to avoid extra costs – to avoid replacing a $5 or $6 instrument.

The real cost of the broken tips can be to the patient's health. In Victoria's case, it was devastating. Not only was she allergic to stainless steel, but the dentist was using a file to clean out an infection, and the infected file tip was left in her jawbone.

How frequently does this occur?

"If there are 30 million root canals done per year, many with several roots, it is possible that a million instruments are broken off in the canals every year. There could be more," says Dr. Jerome. "Root canals became more common beginning in the 1970s so there may be 40 or 50 million root canalled teeth with broken instruments within."

Dr. Jerome says, "Unless the dentist wishes to incur more costs by using new instruments each time, they will keep using them until they feel bad and are then discarded. By then it may be too late."

There is one website (RealSelf.com) where 10 dentists are answering an inquiry about possible harm from a broken file tip left in a root canal tooth. The files are either stainless steel or nickel-titanium. Every dentist played down any danger of a piece of metal being left in the jawbone and shrugged it off as 'not a problem.'

For most of her life, Victoria remained isolated from America's medical system although she still painfully recalls "a drunken doctor" botching the insertion of a contraceptive device at age 19. "He really hurt me ... he scared me to death," she remembers.

"I was terrified." Realizing the pain he had caused, the doctor said, "Don't worry, I won't charge you for that. You're too small for an IUD (intrauterine device)."

Victoria didn't realize that the medical professional who had vowed "to do no harm" when he took the Hippocratic Oath was actually inebriated. Two weeks later, she learned that the doctor's license had been taken because of alcoholism.

Before this experience, for practical purposes, Victoria had rarely been sick. Her encounter with her drunken doctor "sort of snapped me out of thinking that doctors were gods." There was a natural response from Victoria; she started keeping records of every dental and medical appointment, and accumulating hard-copy documentation of everything that happened to her, and everyone who was involved.

She has been writing in her journal in detail on a daily basis since 2000.

About journals, Victoria says they'll "snap you back to reality faster than anything. It's in your own handwriting. You wrote it. You can't deny it."

Several weeks later another doctor inserted the IUD and almost overnight she began having cramps, constant vaginal discharges, chronic infection, and a loss of appetite. After losing weight and experiencing severe pain, the IUD – which contained stainless steel in the metal ring, and a combination of metallic plastic – was removed about six months later.

This was the third time that Victoria would be able to associate a striking physical reaction to an exposure to metal. It would not be the last.

Chapter 10

Drill, fill, and bill

Prior to her 20th birthday, Victoria was given a battery-powered wristwatch with an all-metal band. The back plate of the round-shaped timepiece was imprinted with the words "stainless steel." After wearing the watch a few days, her left wrist began itching, and she'd break out in a bright red rash.

She noticed that the rash went away when she wasn't wearing the watch.

For 22 years, her sensitivity to metals became a background issue. She had no awareness of any further reactions to metals, although she knew not to wear cheap earrings or metal watches.

In September 1995, at age 41, after a botched attempt by a dentist to esthetically fill a tiny cavity in her upper left front tooth (incisor #9), Victoria finally decided to have her crooked teeth fixed. She had little choice.

She looked in the mirror after her front tooth was filled with a 'white' composite, and saw too much filling material and a mismatch with the color of her natural teeth. "It was kind of a yellowish tint. It was terrible. It made my tooth look longer than the others."

Before seeing the dentist, she already knew that her bite was off and she was experiencing a bad case of TMJ (temporomandibuler joint), a disorder that causes jaw pain. It was the crowded teeth that affected her self-esteem. Her divorce was finalized and she didn't need the burden of ugly front teeth. "I was going to do what made me feel good!"

For more than two years, she wore upper and lower braces. The part of the braces that could be seen when she talked or smiled was clear. "I was vain," she admitted. The hidden part of the braces was metal.

Her body seemed to tolerate the metal in the braces. However, within hours of regular adjustments that required the use of metal adjustment wires, she would break out in a red rash all over her face.

She complained to her renowned orthodontist, Dr. Jeffrey Schantz, in Palm Springs, California, about the facial reactions, but the complaints fell on deaf ears. However, on May 20, 1996, her dental records reflect an entry that acknowledges "possible allergic reaction referred to as contact dermatitis."

Victoria's orthodontic chart on May 20, 1996 identifies allergic reaction to an adjustment wire and was diagnosed as contact dermatitis. The rash on her face disappeared within an hour after the offending metal was removed.

She wasn't happy with the dental office atmosphere as most of the patients were children and she was an adult patient. "I wondered what kind of pain they are suffering and they can't express themselves like I can." But her financial investment was simply too great for her to walk out. She took the position, grin and bear it.

When it came time to fit her permanent retainer on March 19, 1998, the dentist walked in to install a device that was made of both plastic and metal, but the plastic was impregnated with tiny gold flakes that looked like glitter.

"The part that went around my teeth was metal. They knew I was allergic to certain metals."

Fourteen years later, during the research for this book, Victoria was confronted with the discouraging probability that the 'gold' flakes themselves were actually harmful toxins, and possibly metallic.

Nevertheless, Victoria's orthodontist would not verbally acknowledge a connection between the rashes and any metal, no matter how many times he was confronted.

Victoria was allergic to the metal in this retainer. It caused extreme dryness in her mouth and eyes and a rash on her face. It was years later that she discovered the imitation gold flakes embedded in the plastic were contributing to her allergic reaction.

Nor would he acknowledge a connection between her dry eyes and dry mouth and the metal. "My eyes were drying out so bad I couldn't even cope with life. I was constantly using eye drops."

However, Victoria's orthodontic chart on June 9, 1998, contained an entry that stated again, "allergic response" to the specific metal in the retainer. This despite what the dentist was verbally telling her.

"Since I couldn't get any satisfaction from the orthodontist, I wasted a lot of money seeing various eye doctors."

One female ophthalmologist told Victoria, "Oh, this happens to a lot of women your age ... dry eyes. And she just told me to keep on with the drops."

Dr. Schantz insisted nobody was allergic to stainless steel. Victoria angrily told him: "Why would I make this up?" She proceeded to show him the infamous stainless steel watch and tell him the story of the rashes it produced.

The orthodontist steadfastly refused to admit there could be a connection. "He did nothing more than attempt to pacify me." But he conceded, "I can make you a retainer out of plastic."

On her last visit, Victoria spoke with the receptionist as she paid the extra $200 for the all-plastic retainer, and mentioned her persistent reactions to metal. "The receptionist told me the truth. 'Yes, some of our kids are allergic to metals.'"

Victoria would eventually realize that receptionists in medical and dental offices are always more willing to tell the truth than the doctor. This would become a critical observation in her search for the truth about her diagnosed breast cancer.

On May 28, 2002, at age 47, Victoria accidentally swallowed a large 'silver amalgam' filling while sitting in the dental chair at Pahrump Family Dental in Pahrump, Nevada during a routine replacement of a cracked filling in her first molar in the lower left, tooth #19.

Allowing a patient to swallow an amalgam filling – much less breathe the mercury vapor while drilling on the old filling – is considered sloppy dental work in some circles, and should not be considered acceptable. However, it's not the position of the American Dental Association.

Using a rubber dam in the mouth to prevent swallowing an amalgam filling would be the safe way to do the procedure. Unfortunately, doing it without the rubber dam is considered to be the right way or the "Standard of Care," meaning at least 51% of dentists are doing it this way.

So, the definition of Standard of Care in the dental industry for any procedure is based on the fact that more than half of the dentists are following the same protocol. This is what makes a procedure acceptable to the ADA, but it doesn't make it right.

What if a few dentists find a better way to do a procedure? It doesn't matter. Their better way will not become Standard of Care until more than 51% of the dentists agree to use the new procedure.

Even more alarming is the fact that Standard of Care can prevent a dentist from being a healer, and doing a procedure that a patient needs and is requesting, but the procedure does not meet Standard of Care. It's a vicious circle.

Using the words "Standard" and "Care" in the same phrase is simply deceitful. It could be said that criminals follow a "standard of care" in that what they do is nothing more than the average behavior of what they do.

The world of civil and mechanical engineers is ruled by exacting and tenacious "standards" and specifications. Codes, designs and plans are strictly adhered to. If these engineers operated with the same 'standard of care' definition used by medical doctors, there would be no specifications, no standards, and no accountability. Bridges would fall, balconies would collapse. If someone dies because of an engineer's error, he would be prosecuted to the strictest possible standard.

So why do doctors get a free pass? Doctors are rarely held accountable when a patient dies.

Doesn't this make you want to pull your hair out?

Then there's the matter of the silver amalgam fillings, which contain 50% or more of mercury.

Dr. Boyd Haley, when he was chairman of the chemistry department at the University of Kentucky, told a Tucson-based medical society Doctors for Disaster Preparedness, that millions of dollars were spent tracking one Canadian cow with "Mad Cow Disease," but blamed the American medical and dental professions for not following the science and speaking out about a far more devastating epidemic.

Dr. Haley's message was reported by Vin Suprynowicz, nationally syndicated Libertarian columnist and author. Psychiatrists call it attention deficit disorder, autism, autism spectrum disorder, or pervasive development disorder. "Dr. Haley calls it Mad Child Disease and thinks that its various forms represent different levels of mercury toxicity," Suprynowicz reported.

Dr. Haley argued that the ADA has never tested or funded a test on an amalgam filling to determine whether it actually releases mercury.

The organization DAMS (Dental Amalgam Mercury Solutions) says on its website (dams.cc) that amalgam fillings "act as a time-release poison – the poison being mercury." The amalgam fillings debate is more complex, however, as mercury is not the only threat to an individual's health. DAMS says, "The other metals in amalgam, namely copper, tin, silver, and zinc also have some toxicity in their elemental forms, adding to the hazard of amalgam."

According to Dr. Haley, the epidemic of Mad Child Disease started at the same time as the mandated vaccine program in 1982-1985. "The first case of autism, for a time a uniquely American disease, was described in 1941. Thimerosal had been patented in 1928 and was added to various American drugs in the 1930s," reported Suprynowicz.

Haley reported that boys are much more susceptible to mercury toxicity than girls because testosterone potentiates (increases) toxicity while estrogen is protective.

Victoria's life was bogged down at this time trying to survive in the hectic environment of a successful development and construction company. The business and personal stresses were almost more than she could deal with. As health conscious as she was becoming, the fact that the dentist placed more metal in her mouth went unnoticed.

Her dental chart indicates the crown was "porcelain fused high noble metal." The metal was used to add strength to the porcelain. Three categories of metal are typically used for a crown's foundation.

Base metal contains nickel and chromium, and less than 25% of the noble metals, which are gold, palladium, and platinum. Metal sensitivity can become an issue with base metal. For example, it's estimated that 5% of the population is allergic to nickel. Victoria knows this all too well.

Noble metal contains between 25% and 60% gold, palladium, and platinum.

High noble metal must contain more than 60% of any combination of gold, platinum, and palladium. Although more expensive, porcelain fused to high noble metal crowns will, allegedly, cause no allergic reactions.

Victoria knows differently.

How was Victoria affected by her new dental work?

For two or three days, she remembers, "I was just dragging. I was exhausted. I wasn't feeling myself. I was sick. At that point I didn't know about the proper removal of mercury or the repercussions of swallowing mercury."

For several weeks her tooth was protected by a temporary crown, and eventually replaced with a permanent ceramic crown. There was one big problem. The dentist used a ceramic crown with a metal inlay on the back side.

Within a couple of weeks, Victoria developed another strange rash. This time it was on the left side of her face, and it would "come and go."

She did all the accounting in the family's residential and commercial construction business. She did the selling, and would help clients pick out all their colors, their carpet, window coverings, all the decorating. "We did turn-key jobs," she explained. "I used to say, 'Bring your toothbrush. We've got everything else in there, including the washer and dryer.'"

Stress was formidable. "Even when we went home, he sat in a cushiony chair with the remote control while I cooked and cleaned."

"I was so busy and my ex-husband was so difficult to deal with, I thought I had a stress rash." You can get too bogged down with life and you don't notice the obvious.

What is a stress rash? A website that provides clear answers for common questions (WiseGeek.com) stated: "As stress levels rise, so can inflammation and histamine levels. Essentially, some people may be having an allergic response to stress."

But, in Victoria's case, it wasn't a stress rash. It was a reaction to the metal in the crown. "This is how I figured it out. I had bought some fluoride-free toothpaste at the health food store that was in a metal tube. After using the toothpaste for a couple of days, I had a red rash that went around my entire mouth. I looked like Bozo the Clown."

"One morning when I was brushing my teeth, I finally realized that the tube was metal. I knew it was metal, but I had been too distracted with life to make the association. When I observed metal shavings coming out with the toothpaste, I suspected the shavings were being caused by screwing the cap on and off."

"Then I had my 'ah ah' moment." Victoria opened her mouth wide and looked in the mirror and was horrified at the obvious shiny, silver-looking strip of metal on the back side of the crown touching the tongue.

This went on for nearly two years … an on-again, off-again rash on the left side of her face. Enough was enough. Victoria was determined to lose the metal crown. She was convinced it was the sole cause of the rash.

But who would know what she was and was not allergic to? "I researched and researched to find a dentist. I tried to find out what I would not be allergic to."

During her research, Victoria soon discovered one product that kept her teeth pearly white and did not cause any allergic reaction. She began using cinnamon-flavored Tooth Soap® (toothsoap.com).

Victoria endured the rash until July 2004, when a different dentist in Pahrump located in the same building replaced the crown on #19 for a second time "at my insistence," to get rid of the metal, but it was not done correctly. "The bite was off and it was painful. The dental office made me pay a second time, mainly because they didn't believe me [that I was allergic to the metal in the crown]."

Victoria's stress level was bumped up another notch.

"But it was worth it. The rash on the left side of my face went away and has never come back."

In her mouth were a total of nine silver amalgam fillings. She did not know at the time that a silver amalgam filling is at least 50% mercury in composition.

This fact is a well kept secret by the official organization that controls American dentists – the American Dental Association (ADA). The ADA and individual state dental boards work in tandem to regulate and control dentists from dental school to the grave.

Had the dentist originally offered to fill the cavity with a compound that was half mercury, and told her about its contents, Victoria would not have needed to know anything about amalgam fillings. She would have recoiled in horror at the idea of placing mercury in her mouth.

But the American Dental Association asserts that mercury is perfectly safe in the mouth. They're so confident of this fact that they call a mercury amalgam filling a "silver amalgam" filling. Ever wonder why?

Again, we refer to Vin Suprynowicz, who interviewed Dr. Richard Fischer, dentist and past president of the International

Academy of Oral Medicine and Toxicology. Suprynowicz quoted Fischer as saying:

"The American Dental Association says it's unethical for me to recommend that you get them (amalgam fillings) removed. Dentists will do it as long as they're not the ones doing the recommending. They say it's unethical to recommend the removal of amalgam fillings to people who are not allergic to them, for the alleged purpose of removing a toxic substance from the body. So what they're saying is that an amalgam that contains one of the most toxic elements on the planet is only 'allegedly' toxic."

Suprynowicz's commentary was published in the Pahrump *Valley Times*, in Nevada. Victoria had clipped the article and saved it with her dental records.

Victoria finally took time to do some toxic research on her own. She found the website (ToxicTeeth.org) of Consumers for Dental Choice that promotes mercury-free dentistry and safe dental amalgams. Consumers for Dental Choice and the organization DAMS are two of the nation's leading opponents of mercury amalgams.

So, knowing the risks of mercury, why do half the dentists in America continue to use the filling material so readily accepted by their parents and grandparents? One reason that Medicaid only pays for a mercury alloy filling is because, historically, they have been cheap.

It's the profits. "Amalgams are quick and easy," says Consumers for Dental Choice. "Dentists make more money per chair per day implanting mercury. For factory-style dentistry, where the teeth represent dollar signs instead of part of a human being, dentists drill, fill, and bill."

The Toxic Teeth website says the term "drill, fill, and bill" is a joke aspiring dentists learn in dental school. "Only the joke is on us and our children: they count their money, and we have a vaporous neurotoxin implanted an inch from our brains or our children's brains."

The website adds: "And of course, since amalgam damages tooth structure and cracks teeth, pro-mercury dentists will continue to profit from amalgam long after its initial placement. Teeth with amalgam require more dental work in the long term. So for the pro-mercury half of dentists, amalgam is the gift that keeps on giving."

Ninety-five percent of dentistry is re-doing previous dentistry. If a mercury alloy filling is placed in a child's mouth, it can eventually lead to more fillings, a crown, a root canal, and finally an extraction, easily costing $4,000 to $6,000 for the tooth's life cycle.

Victoria submitted email questions to the Toxic Teeth website and received an immediate reply from Freya Koss, director of development, who had personally experienced the toxic effects of mercury poisoning.

It was through Freya Koss that Victoria learned about a holistic dentist within an hour of her home.

Chapter 11

The worst is yet to come

Victoria's mouth was examined on October 27, 2004 by Dr. James M. Heltzel, DMD, a Las Vegas, Nevada dentist whose business card proclaimed "advanced, nontoxic dentistry."

"He listened to me. He was one of the few doctors or dentists that acknowledged that I could have a compatibility problem." Dr. Heltzel was a member of the American Academy of Biological Dentistry, Holistic Dental Association, and International Academy of Oral Medicine and Toxicology.

Following the consult, the dentist referred Victoria to the Nevada Clinic in Las Vegas to check for compatibility of dental materials with her body.

According to published brochures at the time, the Nevada Clinic practiced complimentary medicine and all the doctors were fully qualified and licensed to practice homeopathic medicine.

- Complimentary medicine is a range of non-mainstream medical treatments generally addressing the causes of diseases rather than their symptoms and also taking steps in the prevention of disease.
- Homeopathy, or homeopathic medicine, is a medical philosophy and practice based on the idea that the body has the ability to heal itself.

Victoria would be seeing doctors whose philosophy for diagnosis and treatment is based upon the whole body concept, often referred to as "holistic."

During a three-year period Victoria's tooth #19 was crowned three different times. Armed with a Meridian Stress Assessment, Dr. Heltzel replaced the crown for the third time. There was no compatibility testing for the first two crowns. This time, Dr. Heltzel used a composite that was said to be completely compatible with Victoria's body. "It also fit very well."

Not long after this procedure, the dentist replaced Victoria's nine remaining amalgam fillings with composite materials that posed no threat to her health, based on test results.

It wasn't a bit too soon. Her gums were showing signs of discoloration. The discoloration happened so gradually that it never alarmed her. "You think stuff like that is normal, as it happens to you." Once the mercury was removed, her gums began turning pink again.

There was one noticeable exception. The gum over her upper right front tooth (#8) remained discolored with a bluish/grayish tint.

Unfortunately, after the amalgam filling was replaced in tooth #14, the tooth became abscessed, and the pain became nearly unbearable, so the dentist prescribed the antibiotic clindamycin.

Within a few days, the antibiotic triggered extreme pain on the left side of Victoria's stomach.

"I remembered reading about the side effects, and you could get pseudo membranous colitis. She experienced severe pain in the left abdomen, severe diarrhea, and lost 20 pounds in a few days. "I'm not sure which pain was the worst."

Victoria began considering a root canal on the recommendation of Dr. Heltzel.

During the course of the email correspondence with Freya Koss, who worked with Consumers for Dental Choice, Victoria mentioned that she was scheduled for a root canal procedure on tooth #14. At this time, the two had been corresponding by email for several months.

Koss then asked for a phone number and immediately called Victoria to plead the case against root canal-treated teeth. "She begged me not to get that root canal under any circumstance."

"Oh, if only I had listened."

"But, I didn't listen. I was vain. I didn't comprehend what a root canal could do to a person's health. I guess I was ignorant." Victoria had not resolved in her own mind one nagging question. "Why would a dentist do something like that to you if it's harmful?

The answer would become clear in time.

However, Victoria was unaware of a 10-page 'white paper' published in 2004 by Premier Research Labs (prlabs.com). The paper contained a recommended reading list of more than 30 tooth-related articles plus a tooth-organ chart showing the relationship of the teeth to organs and other body areas.

The 'white paper' was truly an expose about making the right dental choice. It pointed out how root canal toxins can slowly leak and eventually depress the immune system which can then pave the way for cancer and other degenerative diseases.

"Many root canal fillings and sterilizing techniques are harmful in and of themselves," the article stated, "such as the placement of gutta percha (which may contain mercury, lead, [cadmium] and barium, all of which can slowly leach into the body via the tooth), silver point (made of pure silver which also leaches into the body, producing symptoms similar to mercury poisoning) and [formocresol] used as a sterilizing agent (a powerful carcinogen)."

(Silver point is a soft metal sometimes used to seal the canal of the root.)

Victoria needed to know the information in the following paragraph, but she was unaware.

"Researchers have proven that most root canal fillings, such as gutta percha, cannot adequately fill the millions of microscopic tiny tubules inside the root canal tooth. With many spaces left in these tubules, bacteria can multiply and create toxic by-products which slowly poison your system over time." In a molar, there can be up to five miles of tubules.

It was the personal testimony of a cancer survivor who had spent many years teaching courses on human health at the university level that finally allowed Victoria to connect the last of many dots in the root canal mystery, a series of dots that stretched back to her mid-teens.

Vaughn Jelliffe's powerful story involving her own infected root canal teeth was published in 2010 but Victoria didn't read the book, *Cancer and Chronic Disease: Healing With Body Resonance* (vaughnjelliffe.com), until 2012.

Diagnosed with leukemia, Jelliffe started searching for a possible infection in her body. "Sometimes the universe gives us what we're asking for, lays it right on our path," she said.

Here's Vaughn Jelliffe's story, quoted directly from her book:

"I went in for a regular checkup with my local dentist, the one who had referred me to the specialist on root canals. Over the years I had loaned this woman books on health, because I always think that everyone is interested in what fascinates me. However, few people are really interested in reading these books and my dentist, being one of the disinterested, never read any of them.

"On that particular day she had been left a book by another patient. 'You know I'll never read it.' We both laughed because it was such a true statement. She offered the book to me.

"It was called *Root Canal Cover-up* by Dr. George Meinig, DDS. Although I had considered root canals as a problem from my reading of [Hulda] Clark, somehow I didn't pay enough attention. After all, I wanted to save my teeth.

"In Meinig's book, he explained that teeth with root canals are dead spaces within the body. The nerve has been removed so the teeth do not hurt. There is no blood supply and no servicing from the lymph system. They are literally rotting, that is, they are filling up with anaerobic bacteria. This type of bacteria does not need oxygen to grow.

"Antibiotics cannot touch the infection for two reasons. First, because the space is a sealed infection site and second because antibiotics have no access route into dead tissue. Once a tooth is badly infected, the anaerobic bacteria start to spread out through the tiny drainage canals of the teeth into the surrounding tissue. They attack the jawbone and from there the bacteria hitchhike to other weakened parts of the body through the blood stream.

"In principle, teeth with root canals are a poor idea because everything in the body needs to be serviced by the blood supply, by oxygen, and by the lymphatic system. A root canal tooth creates a dead, embalmed space within the body and establishes a pocket where anaerobic infection can thrive. It was as if a light bulb went on in my head! I suddenly knew that my root canals were hidden sites of infection. My body was producing extra white blood cells to fight this infection.

"I shudder now when I hear about people getting root canals because I know that they are likely going to end up with infection. Eventually all of these teeth can become infected. Once an infection

99

has settled in, the immune system becomes heavily burdened and illness is not far behind.

"The next part of my journey was trying to find someone who would pull my beautiful teeth with root canals. They looked lovely on an x-ray, but it is difficult to see bone infection on an x-ray. No local dentist could see any problem with them. And, of course, it's against all dental standards to pull functional teeth.

"Luckily, I had heard about a dentist in another town who refused to do mercury fillings. I thought he might be open to my request for extractions. After I presented him with my dilemma he told me he couldn't do it because he might lose his license. He said, 'It's against all standards of care under the dental association. I could be sued.'

"After hearing my appeal, he remembered reading about a clause that allowed someone with a terminal illness to make a special request and in certain circumstances to have their request granted. 'Tell me what to write so we can protect you legally and I'll do it. I want these teeth pulled.' Together we crafted a release form that would protect him from these concerns and he removed my three infected teeth.

"Right before the dentist performed these extractions, he reviewed the x-ray which had been done prior to my root canal saga two years earlier and compared it with his own recent x-ray of my mouth. He said. 'This can't be the same person. In the first set of x-rays, there's a lovely strong jawbone. In the second set of x-rays, there's no indication of bone at all.'

"When he pulled the teeth, he called out to his assistant to come and witness something extraordinary. 'Have a look,' he said, 'there's no bone. I can look right up into her sinuses.'

"Immediately after my teeth were removed my white blood cell count dropped substantially."

Twenty years after her diagnosis with cancer Vaughn Jelliffe is still living a healthy and productive life. She is working on a second book.

Although Victoria had been warned about the dangers of a root canal, she set the red flags aside and finally agreed to see an endodontist in Las Vegas, Michael Squitieri, on the recommendation of Dr. Heltzel. Dr. Squitieri did a root canal procedure on tooth #14 on December 20, 2004.

At one time, Dr. Heltzel personally did root canal procedures in his office, according to his staff. By the time he saw Victoria, however, he apparently had stopped doing root canals. One staffer told Victoria that Dr. Heltzel wasn't "sure" about the effects of a root canal-treated tooth.

In one of Dr. Heltzel's promotional tracts, he describes his passion for learning: "Exploring new dental advances isn't just a way to satisfy my patients. I also do it because I love to teach and I love to learn."

Victoria obtained documents in Dr. Squitieri's office, including a brochure labeled, "Saving Teeth Through Endodontic Therapy." One paragraph heading in the brochure struck a nerve: How long will my tooth last?

A two-sentence answer was provided in the brochure: Although the pulp is removed, your tooth remains alive, nourished by surrounding tissues. With regular brushing and flossing, proper diet and periodic dental checkups your tooth may last a lifetime.

A tooth with no nerve and no blood supply is alive? That defies logic. Such a tooth is actually dead. And dead is dead! Victoria's root canal education was only beginning, but the brochure's claim may have momentarily alleviated her fears, although there was still confusion in her mind.

Between information gleaned from books and Freya Koss, something was wrong with this picture.

The brochure was presenting a claim. The facts, however, would turn out to be very different. There is no such thing as a good root canal.

The good, the bad, and the ugly of root canals weren't really on Victoria's radar, however. She was in terrible pain, and willing to accept any relief.

Contrary to popular opinion, a root canal is not always a perfect solution for pain. In hindsight, Victoria would be the first person to admit that she should have had the tooth extracted.

At home, she was "dealing with the devil himself," in her words. In the midst of this turmoil, the idea of having to deal with a missing tooth seemed to be more than she could handle. Life was stress, stress, and more stress. Would it ever stop?

Most Americans tend to associate the dates of historic events with significant events in their own lives. For example, it's hard to find an American over aged 60 who does not remember where they were on November 23, 1963, when John F. Kennedy was assassinated in Dallas.

Likewise, most adults distinctly remember the night that Princess Diana, the Princess of Wales, was killed in a Paris car crash on August 31, 1997. She shares the same birth date as Victoria, July 1.

It was to be expected that Victoria would associate the root canal procedure on her first molar in the upper left of her mouth with a historic event. Two days after the root canal procedure, the Indian Ocean Earthquake occurred on December 22, 2004. It was the third largest earthquake ever recorded on a seismograph, and it triggered a tsunami that killed some 250,000 people in 14 countries.

Victoria's mouth pain was gone but her heart was hurting, for herself and the people in Asia.

At one point, she explained, the abscessed tooth was "so painful, I couldn't think about anything but the pain. Suddenly the severe pain was gone after the root canal. I was elated." However, over the next few months, sinus infections and earaches were occurring with greater frequency and pain was slowly creeping up on her again.

Even when confronted by Victoria, her medical doctor and her dentist would not concede even a remote possibility that her root canal tooth was infected, and was the trigger for her pain – a pain that wasn't there before the root canal.

Finally, in desperation to end this trauma, Victoria wrote a letter to Dr. Heltzel dated July 20, 2005. She stated: "My tooth #14, the one I had the root canal, is still hurting and it is getting a lot worse as time goes on. I have found some information on root canals and I would appreciate it, if you could find time to read it in your busy schedule before I come for my next appointment."

Victoria advised Dr. Heltzel that she would need to take into consideration the condition of her stomach. "After taking the clindamycin and developing pseudo membranous colitis, my digestive tract has never been the same."

In the last paragraph of her letter to Dr. Heltzel, Victoria said she wanted to "be sure whatever decision is made regarding my tooth #14, it will be the best thing for my health and well being."

At the time, Victoria was uneasy about root canals, and she definitely had no clue that the tooth meridians for the stomach and the breast are one and the same.

While reading an email from Chet Day, she was exposed to excerpts from the book, *Root Canal Cover-Up*, by Dr. George E. Meinig, DDS, FACD. Day operates one of the internet's oldest natural health websites (chetday.com) as well as a natural health company he started in 1993. He offers free newsletters and an archive of thousands of health articles.

Dr. Meinig received his Doctor of Dental Surgery from the University of Michigan. His research, first published in 1993, completely contradicted the brochure Victoria had read. She was now being told that a root canal tooth is not alive. It's a dead bone in the mouth, with no nerve connection and no blood supply.

She headed to the nearest book store. Within two weeks, Victoria had read every last word in Meinig's book which explains the dangers of a root canal-treated tooth.

Victoria was already familiar with the American dental researcher, Weston Price, who worked along side a team of 60 of the nation's leading scientists and published his work in 1923.

Price's research data was documented in two volumes, *Dental Infections, Oral and Systemic* and *Dental Infections and the Degenerative Diseases,* totaling 1,174 pages. Dr. Meinig said Price's 25-year research project was "revered by both the dental and medical professions."

It was learned that bacteria and their toxins can escape from teeth and travel in the bloodstream to tissues and organs in other parts of the body, a process known as the focal infection theory.

So, what happened to the research? "As in so many disputes about medical discoveries," wrote Meinig, "even though the majority of leading doctors believed in the focal infection theory, these leading scientists were overridden and silenced."

"The cover-up of his outstanding research has kept the world from knowing about the staggering number of medical diseases that actually take place because of dental infections," Meinig concluded.

In her follow-up dental visit to Dr. Heltzel on July 26, 2005, Victoria was told that everything was fine. "That's when the nurse told me, he used to do root canals but he doesn't do them any more."

Infections under root canal teeth are not always apparent in a dental x-ray.

Victoria began having constant earaches and sinus infections. She had not had an earache since childhood.

With a copy of *Root Canal Cover-Up* in her hands, she went to Dr. Pejman Bady in Pahrump, Nevada, who wrote a script for a head CT scan on August 29, 2005 at Desert Radiologists in Las Vegas which revealed nothing. He, too, brushed off the idea of a connection between a root canal and Victoria's pain.

An obvious oral infection continued to be ignored and Victoria became more concerned about her two root canal-treated teeth. Four more years would pass before she would discover a technology that revealed her root canal infection where dental x-rays and a CT scan showed nothing.

The article from Chet Day also enlightened Victoria about the Price-Pottenger Nutrition Foundation, which is the custodian of Dr. Price's research memorabilia. Dr. Price's nutrition research followed his 25 years of root canal studies.

"I was in severe pain until the root canal was done," Victoria insisted. So, why did she endure the pain and wait so long to rid her body of a root canal tooth?

Her answer sheds light on an often overlooked element of good dental care in modern America. She was concerned but didn't comprehend the possible health threat posed by the root canal tooth. More significantly, nobody believed her. Nobody helped her. She was on her own by default.

Furthermore, no one was willing to confirm that a root canal tooth actually posed a serious health threat. Even her holistic dentists were ignoring the dangers. Why? Were they uninformed? Or were they afraid?

There was one other element in Victoria's decision-making process, the same element faced by most women. She was an attractive woman. It was about her looks. "I was too vain!" she was quick to say. "Who wants a hole in their mouth where a tooth used to be?"

Eventually, a pattern emerged. Victoria was allergic to metals, some more than others. She didn't yet understand that her heavy metal sensitivity was life-threatening. And she didn't understand that an infected root canal tooth can be life-threatening. She was a walking time bomb.

She was allergic to:
- Metal in earrings.
- Metal in dentist's file left in the root canal tooth.
- Metal in watch.
- Metal in IUD (birth control device).
- Metal in braces.
- Metal in retainer.
- Metal in dental crown.
- Fake gold flakes in plastic retainer.
- Metal in toothpaste tube.
- Metal in amalgam fillings.

Unfortunately, this pattern of metal sensitivity had not been connected to her diagnosed breast cancer. Once recognized, the metal sensitivity issue, with no medical cooperation, would become life-threatening.

As they say in the South, 'You ain't seen nothin' yet, honey.' The worst is yet to come.

The root canal-treated tooth that was part of the trigger for Victoria's breast cancer diagnosis (tooth #8) was done by a family dentist in 1968 when she was 15 years old. The connection between an anaerobic infection in the jawbone and cancer and many degenerative diseases had been studied very little, much less proven. And definitely not accepted.

Chapter 12

What do you mean by needle?

Christmas Day 2007 was strange in several ways. Victoria's usual jolly Christmas spirit was missing. She couldn't shake the fear triggered by the lump. Sometime during the day, though, she remembered something that might be important.

Seven months earlier – May 18, 2007 – Victoria had a Meridian Stress Assessment, the second one done for her by Dr. Margaret Colgate, PhD, CHES (certified health education specialist) in Asheville, North Carolina, an independent practitioner. The computerized assessment offers a functional health evaluation of how the stress in a person's life is affecting their body – organs, glands, tissue, and systems.

"She told me in regard to my right front root canal (tooth #8) if I ever have a problem with my right breast to have this root canal checked. My dentist, Dr. Matthew Young, recommended I go to her." At the same time, Victoria became aware of some swelling under her right arm. She could feel the swelling, but it didn't hurt.

Victoria made an appointment about a week after Christmas with Great Smokies Medical Center, which advertised its alternative medical services in Asheville, North Carolina. She had been there on several occasions to pick up supplements recommended by Dr. Colgate, and had even taken her mother there for a checkup several months earlier.

A day before her medical center appointment, she had her teeth cleaned. "I told them I wouldn't have x-rays because I had a lump in my breast. My dentist, Dr. Young, also knew I had a root canal in my right front tooth."

On January 10, 2008, Dr. Pamela Shuler, CFNP (certified family nurse practitioner), examined Victoria's lump "and scheduled me to come back for more testing." The next day Victoria had an ultrasound at Mountain Ultrasound Imaging, and then returned to Great Smokies, where blood was collected for lab work and she had her first breast thermography.

It's fair to say that Victoria had heard of breast thermography but in name only; she knew nothing about it. She didn't know how thermal imaging worked, or how the results would be reported, and she didn't even know if it hurt. "I was even kind of scared because I didn't have knowledge of it. I understood it wouldn't cause me any harm."

Less than three weeks after finding the lump in her right breast, Victoria was listening to the CD "Keeping Hope Alive," the story of Rene Caisse, who used the healing power of herbs in a product called Essiac tea (her name Caisse spelled backwards) during the 1920s to strengthen the body's defenses, even to the point of curing cancer.

As a nurse, Caisse devoted herself for the next several decades to treat thousands of seriously ill patients with this herbal tonic, achieving remarkable results.

In 1958, she met Dr. Charles Brusch, and together they improved the formula which was passed on to radio broadcaster Elaine Alexander, who developed and marketed the herbal tonic under the name Flor-Essence. It has become one of the most widely used herbal tonics.

Alexander was forced to market the product as a "gentle detox tonic" rather than a cancer cure to avoid government condemnation and persecution.

Victoria began drinking the herbal tonic almost immediately.

On January 16, 2008, Dr. Shuler's office at Great Smokies called Victoria "and they scared me to death. They wanted to see me immediately. I had to be there at 11 a.m. I rushed and was so nervous getting ready and then on the drive to Asheville they called and told me I could come later. I told them, 'No, I had rushed to get ready and was almost there.'"

Victoria was stunned at the report. According to Dr. Shuler, "My analysis of breast thermology came in at TH-4 which establishes a 65-85% risk of malignant disease." The report indicated "abnormal metabolic and/or vascular processes" that define a thermology criterion and establish a probable risk.

To calm her anxiety, Dr. Shuler told Victoria that the imaging on two previous patients with a TH-4 report turned out to be non-malignant.

Victoria's thermography was evaluated by Therma-Scan™ Reference Laboratory, LLC, and Dr. Shuler reviewed the report with Victoria. The last sentence in the summary stated: Comparative thermology restudy is urged in 90-120 days.

In other words, a first-time thermal imaging study has limitations because there is no comparative data, and that's why the report suggested that Victoria have a follow-up thermal scan in three or four months. Dr. Shuler never suggested having the follow-up imaging. Instead, she immediately referred Victoria to Hope Women's Cancer Center in Asheville for more testing.

Victoria was not interested in a toxic treatment plan, but that's exactly what she got offered.

Victoria was starting to taste the 'fear factor' that is associated with Western medicine's diagnosis and treatment of cancer. It would only get worse.

From Victoria's journal on January 21, 2008: "Christine from Great Smokies called and said my creatine kinase enzyme (a marker in blood tests) was 504 and it shouldn't be above 165. She made it sound like it could be the muscle in my heart and I could have a heart attack. She wanted me to immediately drive over there. She scared me to death."

At the time, Victoria was attempting to move into her new house. The home site is 45 minutes from Asheville. A crew of workers was there – TV people, alarm men, and electricians.

"I was beyond exhausted from moving and this whole tumor ordeal," she remembered. "I thought I can't drive over there right this minute with all this going on." And she didn't go.

Later, when she had time to do some research on the internet, she discovered that the elevated enzyme number could be caused by a shot. "My mother had given me a B-12 injection the day before I had taken the blood test. Why didn't they ask me that? Do I look like I am going to have a heart attack? They had a complete blood panel study of me. This was really uncalled for."

On January 23, 2008, nearly four weeks after finding the lump in her right breast, Victoria showed up at the Hope Women's Cancer Center. The building was near a commercial shopping area that Victoria had frequented since 1999. Previous shopping trips were pleasurable. Today's trip would prove to be a torturous three-hour ordeal.

"The waiting area reminded me of the Ritz Carlton in Palm Springs with its rich color schemes, expensive decorating and plush chairs covered in high-end fabrics."

The women who occupied the waiting area were a stark contrast to the décor. Most of the women were pale, frail and hairless. "It was their eyes that got me. It was as if the life was already out of them."

Victoria was only a few minutes away from the start of an epic, twisted series of events that would literally change her life forever, and not for the better.

Dr. David Hetzel, the oncologist, is married and has four daughters. He "insisted" that she have a mammogram.

According to the cancer center's website, Dr. Hetzel has a special interest in clinical research for women's cancers. He is a Primary Investigator for the Gynecology Oncology Group, as well as the American College of Surgeons Oncology Group. Both organizations perform surgical and chemotherapy clinical trials for women's cancers.

A baseline mammogram done 16 years earlier was the only mammogram Victoria ever had prior to 2008. "They insinuated if I didn't have the mammogram, they wouldn't help me." Reluctantly, Victoria agreed, a decision that she would soon regret. "But when you're scared to death, you're likely to do anything. Desperation makes for poor choices."

The mammogram was done almost immediately upon arrival. Then Victoria waited. An entry made that day in her journal emphasized the waiting: "We just waited, waited, waited."

Victoria was lying on the exam table as Dr. Hetzel looked at the mammogram image on a light box in his office and said he saw some calcifications. "But he really couldn't tell me anything from the mammogram," she recalled.

At this point, he had not examined Victoria's breasts. "He was going to release me until I asked about the lump I felt in my breast."

"He came over to examine me then. He said, 'Oh, there's a lump in your breast? It could be cancer.'"

Victoria would live to regret asking Dr. Hetzel about the lump. But that's why she was there. Over the next couple of years, several different doctors looked at the January 2008 mammogram and each expressed different thoughts about what it showed. One radiologist said flatly that because of the density of Victoria's breasts, the mammogram was totally inadequate for a diagnosis, which is the case for most young women with dense breasts.

How will I know if I have cancer or not? Victoria asked.

"The only way we'll really know if you have cancer is to have a biopsy," Dr. Hetzel replied. In fact, subsequent events associated with Victoria's biopsy delayed publication of this book by more than three years.

Victoria had not yet read *Cancer Research Secrets,* by Keith Scott-Mumby, MD, PhD (alternative-doctor.com). The author quotes Dr. Donald Kelley, DDS: "The only accepted legal medical diagnosis of cancer is by biopsy. This is not 100% accurate, for there are false positives as well as false negative biopsies. We, that is, you and I, are not permitted to make a diagnosis of cancer. Nor are we permitted by law to use any system of diagnosis except biopsy for cancer diagnosis. The Medical Establishment tightly controls the diagnosis of cancer."

Victoria's previous dealings with the medical community were few and far between. Although she was health-conscious, and she wanted to 'know' if she had cancer, she was ill-informed about a biopsy procedure, much less its dangers.

The procedure was described as a "needle biopsy." In her mind, Victoria envisioned a needle, much like a sewing needle or one used to remove a splinter, or the needle she used to give herself B-12 shots.

The word "needle" was used for a reason. Victoria would have offered an objection had she heard the words, "harpoon gun." Frankly, she would have stood up and walked out. "I would not have tolerated being misled by the size of the so-called needle. It

110

was something much larger than the needles in my vocabulary or my imagination."

Giving a woman the impression that the biopsy probe is a "needle" is, in essence, like a dentist describing mercury fillings as silver amalgam. It's not truthful. Silver is a very small part of a "silver amalgam filling." It's more than half mercury.

Carefully chosen words can convey a false meaning, and thereby easily disguise something dangerous, even when the words are legally allowed because they have become Standard of Care.

Victoria was taken to a cubicle with a curtain reminiscent of a spa and told to remove her top. She was allowed to leave on her black jeans. She was asked to put on a plush white cloth robe, again suggestive of a health spa.

There was a serene feeling in the air, said Victoria. Women were quietly tip-toeing around the waiting area wearing these plush white robes, as if they were about to have a full-body massage. The visual presentation, although programmed to create a peaceful atmosphere, in no way blocked out the undercurrent of fear.

"You felt like you were at a spa until they take you in for the vacuum core biopsy." It was all about presentation or strategy, said Victoria. The Greeks used a massive wooden horse to trick the Trojans into dropping their guard. "To me, the cancer center's appealing surroundings accomplished the same thing. What a drama."

There was a brief waiting period, and she was escorted to the room where she would have the biopsy. She found herself lying on her back on an exam table. She was aware several people were in the room. No one had said anything that would contradict the mental image she had formed. "I'm still thinking I'm getting a needle. How hard can this be, and then I will know if I have cancer?"

"The doctor said he can tell me if I have cancer. I won't have to go home and wonder about it."

She was in the presence of several nurses, technicians and the doctor for at least five minutes before the biopsy. During this time, she received local anesthesia in the breast.

- She was not given any details about the procedure, other than a "needle biopsy."
- She would have asked questions if she thought it was any more complicated than a simple needle.
- She was not asked to sign a consent form to have something foreign placed in her breast.
- She was not advised that something foreign could be left in her breast accidentally, metal, plastic, or both.
- She was not given any information that the procedure could pose a risk to her health.
- She was not told that women already are suffering from severe pain, infection, rashes, and other health issues as the direct result of a biopsy.
- She was not told that women all over the country are having complications as the result of a stereotactic breast biopsy.
- She was not told about documented cases of equipment malfunction.
- She was not told that the FDA has hundreds of documented cases in its database describing pieces of plastic or metal breaking off in the breast during a biopsy procedure.
- She was not told that many women have objects left in their breast and they still don't know about it.
- She was not told that imaging a piece of plastic that could accidentally sheer off in a woman's breast during the procedure is difficult if not impossible to locate with typical imaging techniques used by doctors.

Victoria heard the words "needle" and "biopsy." She was given no other description, explanation, or disclaimer. "There was a complete lack of informed consent. Had I been told even one of these facts, I would have flatly refused the biopsy and ran out the door wearing the white robe."

The biopsy dictation notes were made on a four-page form where some information was fill-in-the blanks, but most of the dictation involved the use of check-off boxes. For example, the location was a clock measurement where the number "2" was written for 2 o'clock on the breast, and a check was made by "subareolar" (beneath areolar of the nipple).

Victoria's copy of the dictation form shows a check in the box by the following statement: "The procedure was discussed with the patient and she was given the opportunity to ask questions. Her consent for the procedure was obtained and she was placed on the … ultrasound table in the supine position" (lying down with face up as opposed to prone position which is face down).

Three or four times, Victoria asked a question and emphasized the word "needle" and got the same response each time. "It's just a needle." Was she required to ask 10 times? Would someone finally have told her the truth had she done so?

Also on the dictation form, a box with this statement was checked: "The skin was prepped with (Betadine, Chlorprep), 1% Xylocaine was injected and a small stab incision was made."

The next sentence in that paragraph states: "The probe was moved into the breast and ultrasound images were taken to insure proper needle positioning."

The word "stab" is not a misprint. That's the actual word used in the dictation report. It's the actual violent sensation that Victoria experienced. She was stabbed, and she wasn't prepared for it – physically or mentally.

It wasn't until June 2010 – 29 months later – that Victoria was able to obtain a copy of the biopsy dictation report. It was not included in the medical reports that she had previously requested from the Hope Cancer Center. Only when another doctor requested Victoria's records did she get a copy of the biopsy dictation report. While reading the narrative for the first time, she spotted the phrase, "small stab incision was made."

Mention is also made about surgical markers in two paragraphs of the biopsy dictation form. However, the website of The Breast Center at Hope does not say one word about the possible placement of a clip or marker or the use of wires in a woman's breast during a stereotactic biopsy procedure. Yet, the use of such material is considered Standard of Care in the breast biopsy business.

The website does describe the technique as a "minimally invasive procedure that is useful for small lumps and micro-calcifications that cannot be felt, but are detected on the mammogram. This method involves combining the mammogram and computer technology to localize the area and draw out cells for analysis."

The site also describes the procedure for a stereotactic biopsy, but Victoria had not read it:

"To perform the procedure, you will lie face down on a table with a cutout for your breast," the website states. In Victoria's case, she was lying on her back, not face down.

"The breast is compressed into a small mammography machine and several images are taken. The computer program along with the films taken, guide the physician to the exact biopsy location. Using local anesthesia, a very small incision is made and a special probe is inserted through the incision. A vacuum is attached to the probe and the probe is rotated 360 degrees, and tissue samples are taken at various locations."

Victoria had not been asked to read the website information nor was she given any written material that described the procedure. More importantly, no one had used the word "probe" or "stereotactic" in her presence. The carefully chosen word was always "needle."

The website goes on to state: "Following the biopsy, a small sterile strip and an ice pack is applied to the incision."

The least informed person in the room was the patient who was about to have the procedure. Even after the procedure, Victoria was the least informed person in the room.

The procedure she was about to have was much more involved than the insertion of a simple sterilized needle. By definition, it was a stereotactic ultrasound-guided core biopsy. It did not require use of the mammogram images.

"All along, I thought we were dealing with a regular needle, like when you get a shot," she said.

Instead, she heard the sound of a motor. In her mind, Victoria imagined a vacuum cleaner. In some way unknown to her, the biopsy device was connected to a rhythmic sucking sound. Already traumatized, she could see the machine but didn't have a clue about its role in the procedure.

Then she felt an instrument the size of an ice pick being forcefully pressed into her breast. She instantly felt violated. She was stabbed!

She knew it was too late to stop it. The damage was done. "You can't believe they did that to you. Blood is all over you. You didn't even know that was going to happen to you."

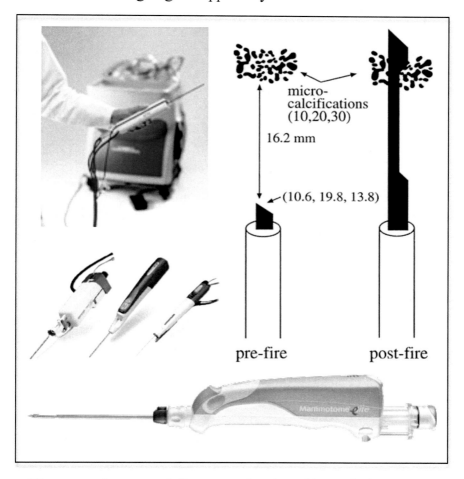

These are pictures and diagrams of various biopsy devices referred to in the cancer industry as "needles."

"I looked down and there was blood all over. I felt like I'd been raped because I felt it was such a violation of my body from what I was told. I was so angry I wanted to scream at the doctor."

After the procedure, Victoria was given instructions on "what to expect after a biopsy."

Victoria's cousin Denise was in the waiting room on January 23, 2008, when Victoria walked down a hall and met her. It had been about 45 minutes since the biopsy procedure. Victoria was wrapped in an Ace™ bandage and fully dressed.

Denise is two years older than Victoria. Her mother – Victoria's favorite aunt – had dealt with three kinds of cancer over a 10-year period. "My cousin watched her mom (my Aunt Matt) endure the torture of the chemo and radiation." Aunt Matt died in 2001 of heart complications related to the toxic treatments.

Denise was an only child and she and Victoria played together frequently, and Victoria was often invited to go on summer vacation with her cousin.

Victoria was shell-shocked. On eye contact, Denise knew something was terribly wrong. "What happened to you?" she asked Victoria. "You can't believe what they did to me when they told me it was going to be a simple needle. I feel like I was just raped."

During the three hours that Victoria was at the Hope Women's Cancer Center trying to make sense of all the drama, an elderly lady in the waiting area walked around with a sweet smile and a pleasant greeting. She carried a tray of pastries, and announced in a cheerful voice: "It's Chemo Day. Would anyone like a donut?"

"Even then I knew that sugar fed cancer," Victoria remembers. "Denise was mad that this lady was turning chemo, the same dangerous drugs that killed her mom, into something so cheerful."

On the Hope Cancer Center's office notes for this day, Dr. Hetzel had written: "Overall appearance is excellent." That only described Victoria's general health and outward appearance. In her heart, it was a different story.

Before leaving the Hope Women's Cancer Center, Victoria was given a one-page postoperative instruction document that warned against heavy lifting for three days, and no swimming or soaking in a tub for one week.

What a difference an accurate pre-biopsy instruction document could have made for Victoria. She needed to read a document that spoke the truth and revealed reality. Substituting a stabbing in reference to a needle is not reality. Regardless of what it's called in a doctor's office, it's outright deceit. The three most important words that Victoria should have been told in order for her to have informed consent were hidden in the biopsy dictation report – 'probe' and 'stab incision.'

Alone at home that evening, Victoria cowered like a rape victim. Having made the choice to keep the lump in her breast from her family, she had no one to talk to. She was ill prepared for the violent nature of the stereotactic biopsy a few hours earlier. "It hurt so badly." Both the noise and the bleeding scared her. She was traumatized. "I cried and cried. I was lied to."

The following day the Hope Women's Cancer Center called and asked Victoria to return for an ultrasound on her left breast, not the right breast where the biopsy was done the day before. This started a new round of trauma for Victoria. The phone call itself scared her. Her body reacted with physiological responses – muscle tension, stomach cramping and nausea, and heart palpitations.

The day before, it had taken only one hour for Victoria to become disillusioned with the Hope Cancer Center's practices – the hour immediately before, during and after her fateful right breast biopsy.

Regarding the request for her to return for an ultrasound, "I told them I had an ultrasound done at Mountain Ultrasound Imaging two weeks earlier of both breasts and didn't need another one. They insisted I did." In response, Victoria called and authorized the transfer of her January 11 ultrasound images to the Hope Cancer Center.

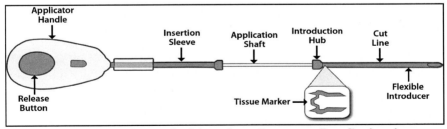

Caption published in Journal of American Roentgen Ray Society in an October 2000 issue describes one tissue marker delivery system (MicroMark; Ethicon Endo-Surgery). Marker is inserted at conclusion of stereotactic biopsy. "Flexible introducer does not fit inside 13-gauge cannula used in coaxial sonographically guided core needle biopsy. Instead, flexible introducer must be cut at site indicated to permit clip with its inner applier shaft to pass into cannula."

Chapter 13

When is zero something?

About a week after the biopsy, the doctor's office informed Victoria by phone that she had a 'stage zero precancerous condition.' In retrospect, the wording was awkward and misleading, she says. Victoria had every reason to be elated. "It's a stage zero precancerous condition; I'll do what I have to do so it won't turn into cancer."

Ironically, at this point, a non-invasive, radiation-free thermogram that is FDA-cleared and cost $150, appeared to have provided as much information as a mammogram, ultrasound, and a biopsy combined.

"Adding to my confusion, I didn't understand why the girl in the office insisted over the phone that I return for another doctor's appointment."

The medical terminology had been confusing for a "left brain" academic who was accustomed to dealing with numbers. "When did zero mean something rather than nothing?" she wondered.

"I'm thinking everything is fine." Only one person in Victoria's family was told about the biopsy, her cousin Denise, who had accompanied Victoria a week earlier to the Hope Women's Cancer Center and was there when the biopsy was done.

Denise even offered to be with Victoria during her return visit on January 31, 2008. Victoria told her it wasn't necessary. "I didn't even understand why we needed a return appointment. I had a stage zero precancerous condition. I didn't need to waste her time too, and I didn't want her reliving the horror of her mom's treatments in the hospital such as the chemotherapy done at Hope Cancer Center."

"I called my cousin and told her I don't have cancer. Little did I know what was in store for me."

A study in *The Scientist* exposing fraudulent breast cancer research was not published until September 16, 2008, eight months after Victoria's biopsy. The magazine reported that almost all of the research done on breast cancer cells for the last 25 years is bogus.

Dr. Robert J. Rowen, MD, explained what happened in his Second Opinion Healing Volume (secondopinionnewsletter.com). Lab research on tumors often used a consistent single standard cell line, wrote Dr. Rowen. "Cancer cells are immortal. They will forever divide. So researchers can ship them from lab to lab for research."

Breast cancer researchers used cells from this one line for years, Dr. Rowen explained. "Unfortunately, the cell line they were using wasn't breast cancer! It was melanoma cells."

Dr. Rowen is emphatic when he says this revelation is "devastating to those researchers who say science is infallible. This news means that the 650 studies (or more) done on this cell line are invalid. They have nothing to do with breast cancer."

Dr. Rowen reached a conclusion: "Medical dogma insists that we should practice evidence-based medicine. That's how Big Pharma gets it edge. They can afford the studies. But now we know that 'evidence' is easily flawed."

Dr. Rowen says the best evidence is a doctor's clinical experience. If this is true, and I believe that it is, why are doctors handcuffed by the AMA guidelines and Standard of Care? If an alternative to surgery, radiation, and chemo will work with 'no harm' to the patient, why not at least explain this to cancer patients as an option?

This is not how it works, however.

"While patients are encouraged to think that the health-care system is competent and wise, it's actually more like the Wild West," wrote Marty Makary, MD, in the September 24, 2012 issue of *Newsweek.*

The quote was taken from the surgeon's book, a *New York Times* bestseller, *Unaccountable: What Hospitals Won't Tell You and How Transparency Can Revolutionize Health Care.*

Victoria felt like she'd been in an old-fashion shootout and had taken a lead bullet in the right breast during her biopsy. Intuitively, she knew nobody had properly prepared her for the procedure or the pain that followed, and she could sense that something was wrong in her breast.

The headline and subhead on Makary's five-page expose stated: Hospitals can kill you. Bad doctors. Prescription errors, surgical slips.

Medical mistakes injure or kill hundreds of thousands of Americans every year. Why patients are kept in the dark.

Consider four key claims that merited bold-face type in the magazine:

- At nearly one third of hospitals, fewer than 50% of employees said they'd feel safe there as patients.
- One recent study at a Milwaukee hospital found that 29% of heart-echo interpretations were incorrect.
- Forced to make outcomes public, New York's Erie County Medical Center cut its heart-bypass mortality rate from 18% to 1.7%.
- The number of U.S. patients killed annually by medical errors is equivalent to four jumbo jets crashing each week.

A promotional description for the book states: "Accountability in healthcare would expose dangerous doctors, reward good performance, and force positive change nationally, using the power of the free market."

Dr. Makary told the story about listening to the wishes of an elderly woman when he was a medical student. The woman died after a procedure she didn't need and didn't want. At a morning staff meeting, when McKary attempted to convey her wishes to forgo both a biopsy and treatment, he was "shredded up, down, and sideways."

Are doctors aware of their own dismal track record? The answer to that question has been taboo in the world of medicine, at least until January 2012 when the silence was shattered by Ken Murray, professor of family medicine at the University of Southern California.

He made headlines worldwide after publishing an essay in the online magazine Zocalo Public Square, which argues that most practicing doctors would not put themselves through 'life-saving' interventions that are big on promises, but small on success, and involve great pain and distress.

"Medics' skepticism about the worth of their own 'life-saving' interventions has long been suspected," according to Dr. Martin Scurr, writing in the *Daily Mail*, a British tabloid newspaper. "Like most doctors," he said, "I understand that much of the care we offer patients who have serious, life-threatening illnesses is ultimately futile."

"Worse," he added, "it can involve many months of grueling treatments that might possibly extend the length of one's life, but do nothing for its quality."

In one poll, Dr. Scurr reported, "around half of the German specialists admitted that they would not undergo the operations they recommended to their patients."

"The drive for the doctors to do a biopsy was like a train no one could stop," he said. Funny he should say that. Victoria sent me an email in October 2009: "I have dealt with this lump since December 2007 and it has been an exhausting ride. I for sure do not want to get back on the cancer train."

Was this to become a prophetic statement?

As a grade-schooler, Victoria lived about 10 miles north of the small town of Saluda, North Carolina, and one of the most famous three-mile stretches of railroad track in the United States, the Saluda Grade, between Saluda and Melrose.

That's correct; the climb up the mountain was steeper than any railroad line going through the Rocky Mountains, or anywhere else in America – over a 5% grade at its steepest point.

It was the steepest, scariest, and most daunting standard-gauge mainline railway trackage in the country. Famous in the late 1800s and 1900s for the many wrecks caused by runaway trains, the line was mothballed in 2001 primarily because of shifting coal traffic on the Norfolk-Southern Railroad, but the ballast, ties, rail, switches, and signals remain in place.

The biopsy of Victoria's right breast wrecked her life, produced more havoc and created more pain in her body, mind, and soul than any runaway train that has ever gone down the Saluda Grade.

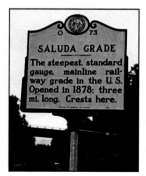

Historical railroad marker in Saluda, North Carolina.

Chapter 14

Which bad treatment do you want?

Two days after being informed she had a stage zero precancerous condition, Victoria's high spirits tumbled to the ground on January 31, 2008, when she met the doctor again. "This had to be one of the most shocking days of my life."

"I've got good news and bad news," said Dr. Hetzel. "Which do you want first?" Victoria was sitting on the end of an exam table and she opted for the bad news first.

Dr. Hetzel was standing in front of her. His next statement will forever be etched in Victoria's mind. "You have DCIS." This is the acronym for Ductal Carcinoma In Situ. Victoria found herself thinking, "What?"

"The tumor is behind the nipple and your breasts are small. We'd need to take your nipple and we'd need to do radiation too," she was told.

"Radiation is also a 'perfect carcinogen,' which can both initiate and promote tumor formation," according to acclaimed science writer Ralph Moss in his free newsletter dated July 18, 2003, from Cancer Decisions (cancerdecisions.com). "For that reason," said Moss, "I would not be so quick to make adjunctive radiation part of the standard protocol for this precancerous condition."

But doctors are quick to recommend radiation. Why? Could it possibly be about money?

The U.S. dollar isn't what it used to be. However, 10 years ago, the American Cancer Society estimated there would be more than 47,000 cases of DCIS in 2003 alone, and that translates to spending more than $331 million just for the radiation portion of breast cancer treatment.

"I'm thinking, how can you turn stage zero precancer into, 'I'm losing my breast.' I didn't believe it."

It was days later when Victoria actually obtained copies of her medical reports. The biopsy report described the tissue sampling as follows:

The breast biopsy tissue consisted of nine cores, measuring in aggregate an area defined as 4.0 cm x 2.0 cm x 0.3 cm (or about 1.6 inches x eight-tenths inch x one-tenth inch).

According to the report from Pathologists' Medical Laboratory in Asheville, the "greatest extent of ductal carcinoma in situ in any given core as measured on a glass slide is 5 mm." That's about two-tenths inch.

The report adds: "No definite invasive carcinoma is identified." The lab report also states that the area "is inflamed."

The ultrasound images taken during the biopsy reported the palpable lump as measuring 1.7 cm x 1.1 cm x 1.3 cm.

Victoria was quite familiar with this lump. She had felt it, rubbed it, pinched it, agonized over it, and slept with it. Not once did she consider it to be larger than a small marble, perhaps a half inch in diameter.

Dr. Hetzel began describing the medical remedy – surgically remove the right breast. He used four sentences that put Victoria into a state of shock.

"We need to at least take part of your breast," he began.

This declaration was followed by a stern warning. "It's big," he said, "and it's behind your nipple. We should just take the entire breast, do a complete mastectomy." In the same breath, the doctor added, "I have a good friend that's a plastic surgeon … we can make an appointment for you."

The implication was unmistakable. It was a "Dolly Parton moment," Victoria thought. "He's offering me larger breasts, but they won't be my breasts." Victoria is a loyal Dolly Parton fan and relates to her because the singer is both beautiful and smart.

"I was shocked to hear his offer; 'I could get both breasts any size I wanted.'" Victoria was insulted as well that the doctor would 'assume' that she had a problem with small breasts. As an adult, she had always been a petite woman, averaging 115 pounds on a 5'7" frame, who wore a size 34-A bra.

Aside from selecting the breasts size of her choice, Victoria learned that insurance companies are mandated by law to pay for the reconstructive surgery to make both breasts the same size following a mastectomy, regardless of the amount of breast reduction or enlargement.

Among the medical records that Victoria retrieved from Hope Cancer Center is a one-page biopsy follow-up dictation by Dr. Hetzel dated January 31, 2008. "We discussed her seeing Dr. Conway (plastic surgeon) for evaluation and recommendations regarding this process."

Dr. Hetzel added: "Patient was reassured about this and we again reviewed the options for the right breast. Central mastectomy with resection of the nipple would be required if she does not want a mastectomy along with radiation therapy." Either way – resection or complete mastectomy – Dr. Hetzel was requiring radiation.

Victoria wanted a cure, not a band-aid taped over a symptom. How many options was Victoria offered? Count them. She was offered three options, but only two of them related to treating her diagnosed breast cancer. The third option was all about cosmetic surgery.

1. Central mastectomy with resection of the nipple, plus radiation therapy.
2. Radical mastectomy, plus radiation therapy.
3. Reconstruction on both breasts, any size Victoria wanted, thanks to her insurance company and the law. This option is offered allegedly to address physical and emotional issues faced by women who accept a mastectomy as their method of treatment.

For some women cosmetic surgery will be required and could make them feel better about themselves. But doctors are routinely pushing the cosmetic surgery procedures in order to 'sell' their toxic treatments, and they give women no other options.

Dr. Hetzel again insisted that he must have another ultrasound of her left breast. Victoria did not understand. "Is he after money or what?" she wondered. He had the images of both breasts from Mountain Ultrasound Imaging taken on January 11. The doctor's insistence was confusing, but Victoria was tired of fighting him over an ultrasound image, so she agreed to have another one. "He said he had to have his own image of my left breast."

Before leaving the Hope Women's Cancer Center, Victoria was given a packet of material that consisted of nearly 30 pages of information about DCIS, a half dozen pages with information about support groups and meeting places, and a 68-page booklet entitled, "A Guide to Breast Health Care."

One document – putting DCIS into perspective – even admitted that not too many years ago, the incidence of DCIS was rare. Today, about 20% to 25% of newly diagnosed breast cancer cases are DCIS. "In fact, as the use of mammography has increased, so have the findings of DCIS, and today, at least a third of cancers detected by mammography prove to be DCIS."

This statement is particularly alarming in view of overwhelming research proving that DCIS is a stage zero precancerous condition.

On September 28, 2012, the News Orleans *Times-Picayune* published a story in the daily's Living Section by columnist Sheila Stroup with the headline, "New Orleans is a mecca for breast reconstruction."

"If an insurance company pays for a mastectomy," the article stated, it must also cover breast reconstruction surgery. "That was a law passed in 1998."

Stroup reported that a doctor's clients must be told about the coverage by insurance companies. "And, in Louisiana, we have a statute that says doctors must inform women of all their breast cancer treatment alternatives, including reconstruction," she wrote.

Victoria was offered two treatment alternatives, and both involved a form of radical surgery followed by an unknown quantity of radiation poisoning. She had no interest in submitting herself to such damaging treatments. However, it's fairly obvious that Dr. Hetzel offered Victoria two 'approved' conventional medical options. He may have met the letter of the law in North Carolina in doing so, but his two recommendations did not provide Victoria with real options.

The medical options were quite matter-of-fact: You can do this bad treatment or this bad treatment. Which bad treatment do you want?

Think about Victoria's dilemma in terms of politics. There are two main political parties in the United States. On many issues,

125

politically speaking, Americans are split down the middle. It appears to be that way in medicine, too. When it comes to unconventional cancer treatments, there probably will always be a clash between the forces of freedom of choice and consumer protection (status quo that leaves the pharmaceutically educated doctors in complete control). But there's one big difference.

When a person dies during or after treatment by a medical doctor who was using surgery, chemo, radiation, and pharmaceutical drugs, there is no consequence for the medical doctor. Their treatment was Standard of Care, even though it didn't work.

On the other hand, alternative doctors who treat people with cancer and the patients get well and live have actually gone to prison because they helped save the lives of their patients. Cal Streeter is one of the best known examples.

Dr. Streeter, an osteopathic physician, spent 18 months in a federal prison in 2003-2004 for getting cancer patients well by using a combination of nutritional and conventional potions.

Consumer advocate Tim Bolen, who publishes the Bolen Report (bolenreport.com), wrote in 2006 that Dr. Streeter was "punished for being alternative." He primarily treated cancer patients "by revitalizing the body's immune system." Streeter told the world about the bogus attack on him in his book, *A Doctor Goes to Prison*. His second book is about immune health and cancer prevention. To inquire about both books, send an email (hes1220@gmail.com).

At least 30 states have passed laws pertaining specifically to cancer. Unfortunately, most of these laws protect America's Cancer Industry.

Victoria and every other American should be able to elect to have surgery, if that's their choice. The patient should also be able to elect not to have surgery, if that's their choice. That's Dr. Streeter's position. Such a position should not be a crime. The real crime is the concerted effort to eliminate any freedom of choice.

"I am appalled at the brutality involved in the diagnostics, surgery, radiation, and chemotherapy associated with conventional cancer therapy, without any promise or hope of survival," Dr. Streeter said.

Alternative therapies may be clouded in mystery because of the aggressive efforts to silence advocates like Cal Streeter, but the therapies are not a secret. You will find amazing stories of personal cancer cures in hundreds of newspapers, magazines, periodicals, websites, DVD's, and especially books.

For example, in 2008 Jeanetta Alford produced a one-hour DVD, "A Cancer Survivor by God's Grace." Her documentary details the natural therapies she used to recover from breast and colon cancer.

Alford's personal story is described on the back cover of the DVD: "After being told she might not live even 10 years, Jeanetta asked God for wisdom and guidance. As you watch her story unfold you will see that God truly opened every door of opportunity for Jeanetta to return to wellness."

In essence, Alford cured her cancer by using God's natural laws and a program of detoxification, nutrition, stress management, and correcting oral pathology. She did not succumb to the "you're going to die immediately" mentality.

During Alford's presentation, she mentions the book, *Alternative Medicine, The Definitive Guide,* edited by Larry Trivieri, Jr. and John W. Anderson, copyrighted 2002 with introduction by Burton Goldberg. Many professionals consider this book, available at most large bookstores, to be the 'Bible' of alternative medicine.

It presents treatment plans by more than 400 physicians, discusses 50 alternative therapies, and includes information on more than 200 health issues.

I'm not sure enough Americans will step up and demand access to non-traditional cancer treatments to turn the tide in my lifetime, but individuals possess a lot more power as a group than they often realize. For example, the judge in Dr. Cal Streeter's trial received 3,000 letters with testimonies and support for the doctor from his patients. These are people who had their freedom of choice taken from them by a health system that is out of control.

Victoria was offered two radical and toxic options. Is this all traditional medicine can offer after billions and billions of dollars have been spent on breast cancer research?

Is this something to be proud of? Does anyone find this unbelievable? Where did all the money go? And for what?

A full-page ad in the October 2012 issue of *SELF*, a women's magazine, shows an attractive woman, from the eyes to the waist, with her arms crossed over her bare breasts. The message states: "Courage. Believe in a world without breast cancer. Know we're here until it's true."

The sponsor of the Breast Cancer Awareness Campaign ad is The Estee Lauder Companies, "devoted to defeating breast cancer through education and medical research."

Early detection, diagnosis, and cure of breast cancer are already here. Women just don't know about it.

A woman with diagnosed breast cancer should flee from any doctor that can't intelligently discuss other options for a cure, aside from slash, burn, and poison.

Chapter 15

Castrate him, then fire him

There is no shortage of readily available information on the topic of having a mastectomy, but you will have to search for it. Doctors don't typically tell women about the 'reality' they should expect, nor will they provide any realistic assessment about what a woman should anticipate before or after the radical surgery, either written or orally.

Yet, doesn't it make sense that a woman who is about to lose a part of her femininity should be fully briefed on the actual surgical procedures and, more importantly, the difficulty she will face during recovery? Some of the woman's challenges will be in uncharted territory.

One of many websites on the subject of mastectomies describes "10 Insider Tips" where "all clinical content" on the site is physician-reviewed. I'm not sure exactly what physicians are reviewing, but the "tips" on this site are worth reading several times. They should be a red flag for every woman to investigate the radical surgical procedure before having surgery.

"Even if you ask your doctor, he's not going to tell you the truth," said Victoria. "Maybe he or she doesn't even know the truth, unless it happened to them. Besides, how could a male doctor really understand what a woman will face when she loses her breast?

The 'insider tips' sent chills down my back when I first read them. Why is there no outrage from women who were never offered options other than having their breast surgically removed? If a woman could keep her breast and be cancer-free, isn't that an option to consider?

Well, there's a problem with that logic. The question itself is too logical. How can a woman remain logical when the oncologist is telling her she's going to die unless she gives up her breast? In other words, the breast 'must' be surgically removed if the woman is to live, or so she is told.

Tip #1 says go shopping for button-down-the-front shirts. The last thing you want to try to do with incisions, drains, bandages, and sore shoulders is pull a turtleneck over your head, the site says. The truth is that most women, following a mastectomy, can't raise or maneuver their arm well enough to put on any kind of pull-over garment. Drains and bandages make little difference. The woman's arm is basically immobile.

Why do women choose the mastectomy option? Is it fear? Is it the lack of information? In all fairness, some women may have such advanced cancer that surgery is the only option. That is not true for most women, however. They have other options. It's a crime they are not told.

Tip #2 says to expect to write your name on the breast that's being cut off.

Doctors want to make absolutely sure they're removing the correct breast. Doctors and their insurance carriers are keenly aware of malpractice laws. If the doctor is so incompetent that he or she does not know which breast is about to be surgically removed, are you really comfortable with this situation? Are you comfortable with this doctor?

Tip #3 warns to get used to areas of the chest that will be numb or tingly. It's almost inevitable for a surgeon to cut or damage nerves in your chest area. Keep a journal. I'll wager that no doctor will tell you beforehand that you will end up with numb or tingly areas on your chest wall. In fact, doctors don't even think of your chest wall as part of this equation. After all, they're just cutting off a 'breast,' so they say. Ask any woman with a mastectomy; the muscles, nerves, feelings and mobility in the chest wall are never the same again. There's a total disconnect between the two sides of the body. They don't function in unity as they did prior to surgery.

Tip #4 warns to expect up to four drains dangling from your chest/midsection after surgery. Removing the drain is akin to having a tooth pulled without anesthesia. Did the doctor explain this beforehand? It's a terribly painful process. Actually, a doctor typically ignores the pain aspect. Women who have only one drain should count their lucky stars, and feel sorry for women who have four.

The tips get more graphic. Tip #5 warns that a mastectomy can be visibly shocking after surgery, and the procedure is not for the faint of heart. Exposed muscle and fat may be visible. When the results of the breast surgery are seen for the first time, most women will remember this as one of the worst days of their life. Their body image as they knew it is over.

Tip #6 offers a time line – the longer you're in surgery under a general anesthetic, the longer the recovery. This tip is absolutely true. No editorial comment is required.

Tip #7 addresses the possibility that a positive (for cancer) sentinel node will require further surgery, leaving a "fairly major, looping scar in your armpit." Depend on it. The doctor will almost always have an excuse for removing your lymph nodes. In reality, your body needs its lymph nodes. Get used to the pain, inflammation, and swelling under your arm and in your chest area. The nodes are there for a reason.

Tips #8 and #9 warn about the danger of a sudden stop while in a vehicle (ripping open incisions) and the necessity of having physical therapy "to restore your shoulder mobility." Without therapy, you will never regain mobility in your arm and chest area. Even with therapy, it's a toss up. Your arm movement will never be the same, regardless of therapy.

Tip #10 seems to encourage a woman to finally get the size and shape of breasts that she always wanted. Why do doctors always imply that a woman's breasts are inadequate? A mastectomy removes sensual feelings in that breast area forever. Is that what you really want?

If a group insurance policy or HMO is covering your mastectomy, they legally have to pay for reconstruction and cosmetic surgery on the other breast to make them match. It's part of the federal Women's Health and Cancer Rights Act of 1998.

Under the law, coverage must be offered for reconstructive surgery in a manner determined in consultation with the attending physician and the patient. Coverage includes reconstruction of the breast on which the mastectomy was performed, surgery and reconstruction of the other breast to produce a symmetrical appearance, and prosthesis and treatment of physical complications at all stages of the mastectomy, including lymphedemas.

Considering all these warnings, it's hard to imagine any woman being excited about her forthcoming mastectomy. Yet, many women engage the process of having this radical surgery without ever asking a single question. Some women defer the decision entirely to their spouse. Some women have blind faith in the doctor and accept what they are told as the only way to stay alive. Other women don't like the doctor's plan but they are lacking knowledge of other options.

On some subjects, many of us know just enough to be dangerous. Yet we live in the Information Age, and all of us can access data with the click of a mouse. So why are most of us so uninformed about alternative cancer treatments?

Examine the typical day in an active woman's life. You'll quickly recognize the answer. Most women are busy – consumed with challenges like family and work – and they have precious little time to find answers on their own. And if they find an alternative treatment they want to consider, their health insurance typically will not pay for it.

Alternative treatments don't rise to the level of Standard of Care, and they usually don't have the millions of dollars of funding necessary to produce a viable application to the FDA for formal government approval.

Besides, there's nothing rational about how insurance companies view alternative treatments. The insurance company might spend $350,000 on a surgical and chemotherapy treatment plan for a breast cancer patient and refuse to pay $12,000 for a safe and effective breast cryoablation. To me, that's totally irrational. But that's the power of the cancer industry.

With breast issues, doctors too often leave women feeling pressured to act immediately.

Personally, I'm outraged because most women do not know about radio-frequency and cryoablation techniques, much less one of the dozens and dozens of other natural cures for breast cancer where a woman keeps her breast. The latest breast cancer treatments include safe and effective medicines that can be applied transdermally, and they're virtually unknown to contemporary oncologists. Imagine rubbing something on the breast to cure cancer.

Pressured. This is precisely what happened to Victoria. She was pressured and the doctor never told her about other options. She was scared, and fear leads to bad choices. Pressure is what most women face, and most women are not prepared for it.

"I didn't know the underlying reasoning for his (Dr. Hetzel's) comments at that time," said Victoria. Nevertheless, having been told that a mastectomy was her only option, the next thing she heard from the oncologist was that she also needed radiation. "I thought to myself, that causes cancer. I wouldn't have radiation."

Victoria did not realize that the oncologist was following a tightly written script where he offered a biopsy to "know" if she had cancer, and he offered surgical and radiation options, as well as breast reconstruction in both breasts after surgery. But that was it. Other women might be offered chemotherapy rather than radiation, and some women will be offered both.

And Victoria did not know that the biopsy results could be wrong. Biopsies are not 100% accurate.

"I'll never forget that day. I'm sitting there on the end of the exam table, and I'm in shock. I'm thinking, 'My God, what are you saying to me ... I'm going to have my breast removed and radiation.'"

"That is like some of the worst news you could ever hear in your life," thought Victoria. "That dreaded, fearful diagnosis, I had just gotten it. I couldn't believe it."

Furthermore, the doctor wanted to order another ultrasound on her left breast. "I told him, 'I've had the left breast done (ultrasound). I sent you the results.' But he insisted. He had to do the left breast also."

Victoria's mind raced. She remembers thinking, "There's one thing you've learned in life, Victoria, and that is, take some deep breaths, and you need to think about this, this is serious." It was as though she was in a twilight zone and everything was moving in slow motion.

As she sat at the end of the examination table, fully clothed, with her feet dangling in the air inches above solid footing, apprehension swelled up inside her. "I didn't trust this doctor. I didn't get a good feel from him. I didn't get a good feel from the office." The office space was undergoing remodeling and "even the waiting room was decorated like a 5-Star Hotel."

Victoria wondered: "How do I know that my breast being removed is not the new addition?"

"He's like the sales person at the cancer center," she thought. "It was like a cancer palace, only the women sitting in the beautiful building had no hair. I gazed into their eyes. It was as if their souls were missing. Eerie."

As her mind raced, Victoria found an inner strength. "I won't let this jerk see me cry," she thought.

Then and there she put her foot down, both physically and mentally. Standing upright again, and in full control of her faculties, she ordered the nurse not to make an appointment for reconstruction surgery.

Once the doctor knew that Victoria firmly intended to think about his diagnosis and the only remedy he offered, "He took his finger and he looked at me in the eye and he said, 'You better not wait longer than four months. You'd better not.'"

Again, Victoria's mind focused on her family's health history. "Everyone in my family is extremely healthy and I never had fear of getting breast cancer. I was in shock that he said I did. After I was diagnosed that is when the big fear set in. What was required of me to live, according to these doctors? It scared me so badly."

Victoria was alone. In the privacy of her car, she began sobbing. Only one friend and her cousin knew that she was at the doctor's office to learn more about a "precancerous" condition in her right breast. Throughout most of her ordeal, she has kept it this way, primarily because it is her body and she neither wanted nor was willing to tolerate pressure from her mother, siblings, or friends to "do what the doctor says."

Victoria still couldn't believe what she was being told to do, and she saw no good purpose in upsetting her family. Keeping her cancer diagnosis private was important to Victoria in more ways than one. While she did not want to alarm her family, she did not want overbearing pressure from them either.

About five years later, on February 16, 2013, Victoria listened to a recorded message provided by the Church of Spiritual Living in Palm Desert, California. In a real way, the message was a vindication of her decision.

A woman described the decision-making process for her own life "and I know where I want to go with it, and my intuition says this is the path to take, and then I hear an opinion from a friend or family member and allow their opinion to override my gut instinct, my intuition, my choice."

Others can provide insight and information to help us make a decision, the speaker explained, "but we always know what is best for us, we always know the direction to take. When you get right down to it, we know best, we know the decision that will take us to where we want to be."

"It's time for us to stand on our power, time for us to know, indeed, we know it all," she said. "We've got that infinite intelligence. We certainly can trust it 100%. So when you're going through your day, trust your knowledge."

Victoria drove out of the parking lot at Hope Cancer Center, and by mid-afternoon returned to Great Smokies and cried to Dr. Shuler. "I was in shock about what Dr. Hetzel had just told me. I told Dr. Shuler how much I disliked that place. I felt like I was at The Stepford Wives. Nothing about Hope Cancer Center seemed real – the building was decorated beautifully, the furniture was expensive, the housecleaning was immaculate, and wearing a plushy, white robe made me feel like I was at a spa in Palm Springs."

(Stemming from a novel by the same name, "Stepford Wives" is often a label associated with women who have beautiful homes, clothes and cars, yet they are abused and don't know it. The Hope Cancer Center looked great, but lacked the substance for healing that Victoria was searching for.)

Dr. Shuler acknowledged that other patients had expressed the same concerns, and then recommended another cancer specialist, but Victoria declined to make an appointment. "After I checked their website," she said, "I knew it was going to be the same song and dance as the Hope Cancer Center and I didn't want to be scared to death again."

At Great Smokies, Victoria confronted the alternative facility that had initially referred her to the Hope Cancer Center.

"You people are supposed to be what I would consider alternative, or trying to help people in a different way than the normal medical establishment," she said.

She asked one practitioner. "Why would you send me to a place like that for a biopsy? I felt safe coming to you first, and thinking that you would send me to a place that I would relate to. I did not relate to that place at all. That is not my type of consciousness."

"Pressure and fear should never be part of the equation when you have health issues," says Victoria. "That alone can make you sick."

Dr. Shuler wanted Victoria to have a blood test for cancer that cost $2,800 from Remissions Lab. Why? To see if intravenous Vitamin C treatments would help her diagnosed cancer. Before Great Smokies would administer the Vitamin C protocol, they required the patient to have this particular blood test.

Before she starts writing in her daily journal each morning, Victoria reaches for her calendar on the bedside nightstand. It's a different type of calendar. In fact, it has a name – "365 Meditations and Reflections for Women Who Do Too Much Calendar."

She tears off the next page and reads a challenging thought for the day. Some examples:

Saturday, December 31, 2011: Doing too much is a "normal" state for women. We can always do more than we think we can do. Our secret task is not to become depleted in the process. When we accomplish that, anything is possible and everything falls into place.

But of all the calendar quotes, the one that pierced Victoria's heart and took her back to that dreadful day when Dr. Hetzel suggested a mastectomy was the reading on Sunday, December 20, 2009. It was titled, "What we do for beauty."

A friend of mine in her sixties, who had some "fibrous material" in her breasts, called me in a panic.

"What's wrong?" I asked.

136

"My doctor told me I should just have both of my breasts cut off," she said.

"Why?" I asked.

"He said that they are of no use to me or my husband anymore and I should just have them removed," she said between sobs. "What should I do?"

I snapped back: "Suggest castration for him and then fire him."

On February 6, 2008, Victoria heard from Dr. Shuler at eight o'clock in the morning. "She told me she had discussed my condition with Dr. John Wilson and Dr. Eileen Wright (at Great Smokies) and I should have the surgery. She said I needed to have it cut out."

"After I told Dr. Shuler I declined the blood test, she would not even allow me to have intravenous vitamin C at Great Smokies."

It was Dr. Linus Pauling, known as the father of vitamin C and twice a Nobel Prize recipient, who advocated the use of intravenous Vitamin C and was largely ridiculed for making these declarations, but today, large doses of vitamin C are used by many practitioners for cancer patients as part of nutritional therapies.

Why? Because they believe Pauling was right and that vitamin C is indispensable to the body in its fight to regain health from cancer.

Dr. Shuler's message seemed to be reinforced by Paul, an employee of Remission Labs, who related that his mother had died of breast cancer and had tried to heal herself naturally and nothing worked. He told Victoria she needed to have her breast removed "and not fool around." He also told her "they had better treatment in Germany and he would help me find a place I should go."

Paul told Victoria that she "should definitely have the blood test to see if I had cancer in the rest of my body."

On February 7, 2008, Victoria realized that she was physically and emotionally exhausted. She rejected the expensive blood test.

"My spirit needed a break from all this. I felt so overwhelmed at this point, all this had scared me to death. I was very disappointed with Great Smokies. They claim to be an alternative type of medical establishment. That was a far cry from what I got from them. This is when I decided to treat myself, which I did until mid-2008."

"When this first happened I would sit at my computer and research and research for hours. It was very time consuming to do all that." This is when she ordered a DVD from Co-Dependent Pictures, Inc. called iCureCancer.com (website is the same name) produced and directed by Ian Jacklin, a documentary filmmaker, who shares the stories of medical doctors, alternative healers and patients who have cured themselves.

Meanwhile, she ordered a "zapper" from Hulda Clark, a small battery-powered generator that produced specific frequencies that were found to kill cancer cells or inhibit abnormal cell growth. Then she sat down and penned a note to Dr. Shuler. "The best thing I'm doing for myself is remaining calm, praying, and not making my decisions with a desperate attitude."

Victoria ordered a 'tumor and cancer driver' for the zapper. "I can't say scientifically if it did anything or not."

On February 12, 2008, she watched a German-produced documentary about the emotional trauma of cancer. And she let her mind wander off track for a moment as she thought about refusing the radical surgery, "but I don't want to die either. Am I gambling with my own life?"

Then there was the reality check. "It's really a gamble to do the doctor's treatment. How could radiation be healthy? There is a way you can cure yourself."

Even with a positive attitude, Victoria declares: "There's nothing that compares to being told you have cancer."

Ironically, she received a letter from The Breast Center at Hope, an affiliate of Hope Women's Cancer Center dated February 12, 2008, that implies Victoria did not have cancer. The letter stated: "You had a mammogram at our facility and after reviewing your mammogram, our radiologist recommended a biopsy to evaluate for the possibility of abnormality." Possibility?

The second irony is that Victoria had the biopsy at the Hope Cancer Center 20 days before the letter was mailed reminding her to "make an appointment" to have her biopsy. Already disillusioned with the biopsy procedure, Victoria was taken back by an obvious form letter which left the appearance of sloppy business practices or an organized effort to run a cancer treatment center like a business. Whoops, isn't that what it's all about?

There's nothing wrong with cancer treatment centers operating as businesses. Americans simply need to recognize this fact. The cancer industry is not the Salvation Army or the Red Cross. It's a for-profit business venture!

The money is in the medicine, not the cure.

By the second week in February 2008, Victoria was reading the book, *The Cure for All Diseases,* by Hulda Clark, PhD, ND. The cover of Clark's book mentions research findings showing "all diseases have simple explanations and cures once their true cause is known."

By this time, Victoria had forgotten about the expensive blood test, but they didn't forget at Great Smokies. On February 21, 2008, "Christine [employee of Great Smokies] called and pressed me to take the blood test."

"Even after I told them I needed time to think, they're still calling." Medicine is big business.

This is a microcosm of what's happening all over America, in city after city. It's not just about cancer either. There's a kidney dialysis center in small towns all over America, or at least there's one nearby. Big cities have dozens of them.

The cancer business is second in size to its big brother, petrochemicals, according to Patrick Rattigan, ND, whose lengthy expose, the Cancer Business, was published on the website, theforbiddenknowledge.com. "In the 20 years from 1970 to 1990, in the USA alone," he reported, "the cancer business was worth an estimated one trillion dollars."

I'm not certain anyone knows how much the cancer industry was worth in the past 20 years – 1990-2010. By comparison with the one trillion dollars from 1970-1990, however, the national debt in June 2013 was $16.9 trillion.

What do these numbers tell us? Simple answer. By any standard, cancer is big, big business.

Chapter 16

Don't speak too soon

As Victoria thinks back to that dreadful day – sitting alone with Dr. Hetzel on January 31, 2008 – she admits there was "a part of me that just didn't believe it."

What if? Life is full of them.

What if her intuition had taken over? The outcome of her breast health struggle and her life might have been very different.

What if the famous poem by Rudyard Kipling had suddenly come to her mind, and she remembered the first two sentences?

- If you can keep your head when all about you are losing theirs.
- If you can trust yourself when all men doubt you.

Victoria was listening to a cancer doctor describe his fix for her problem. "To make it healthy, he wanted to cut off my breast and give me radiation. Nothing about that sounded healthy to me."

"How did a stage zero precancerous diagnosis call for this radical treatment?" Quizzing herself silently, she thought: "There has to be a better way. Is that all you can offer?"

Victoria had never had cancer before. No one in her immediate family was a victim of cancer. Although her mother had squeamos cell on a leg, she wasn't a victim. She cured herself with a natural treatment. Victoria had no reason to know anything about alternative cancer therapies. What she was being offered by a medical doctor defied common sense.

She went for months without being told of options. The oncologist offered only one solution – the medical monopoly's favorite trilogy – cut, burn, and poison (radical surgery, radiation, and chemotherapy). The trilogy was packaged with fear and intimidation, carefully administered by a licensed medical doctor who was following the "standard of care" that his profession demands.

Victoria began researching DCIS, starting with a 504-page report by Ralph W. Moss, PhD, entitled, "The Moss Report on Ductal Carcinoma In Situ (DCIS)." The Table of Contents alone is six pages. The cost of the report, which Victoria downloaded and printed at an office supply, was $300.

Moss is a science writer who was independently investigating alternative cancer treatments. He is a former assistant director of public affairs at Memorial Sloan-Kettering Cancer Center, and author of the award-winning PBS documentary "The Cancer War."

In an open letter from Moss to the reader on Page 9, he stated in the second paragraph: "First, I firmly believe that there are scientifically valid cancer treatments that exists outside conventional Western medicine."

Moss deals with mainstream approaches to cancer, and he also presents dozens of alternative treatment approaches – a total of 118 in this one report.

"Ultimately, after intelligently assessing your options, you need to make treatment decisions," Moss says in his open letter. "All my life I have promoted rational choices, yet in the end your choice may involve a leap of faith. Knowing which treatment to move towards requires using your intuition, as well as factual information."

Victoria's intuition gave her confidence that there had to be treatment options she simply had never heard about. She was still searching for a cause. How could her healthy lifestyle result in a breast cancer diagnosis?

She knew nothing about research in Switzerland where Dr. Thomas Rau, who operates the Paracelsus Clinic, found that 98% of his breast cancer patients had a disturbance on the stomach meridian. She was ignorant about meridians and certainly didn't know that a woman's breast belongs to the stomach meridian.

"I was trying to educate myself and do the right things. I just didn't know about the connection between cancer and your teeth yet. I didn't even know about the Paracelsus study."

By late February 2008, Victoria was reading the book *Outsmart Your Cancer*, by Tonya Pearce.

Then she attended a seminar presented by Dr. Theodore Rozema: "Are You Tired of Being Sick?"

Victoria learned about Dr. Rozema's Biogenesis Wellness Center in a rather peculiar manner. Rozema was listed in the Moss

Report as a clinic that practiced "outside the box" medicine. In fact, Moss noted that many of these clinics are "accused of failing to practice according to 'prevailing community standards.'"

"Some noteworthy practitioners have been prosecuted, sued or have even lost their license for little more than being different," said Moss.

Victoria was viewing MapQuest on her home computer looking at directions to Dr. Rozema's office when her mother called and said, "Victoria, there's a seminar advertised in the paper put on by Dr. Rozema. I think you'd like to go." And they did. "That was a sign to me. I said, 'Okay God, I need to get there.'" Her mother was fully aware of Victoria's healthy lifestyle and eating habits and her hunger for knowledge."

Dr. Rozema told a simple story about himself with three main points:

1. The pharmaceutical companies loved him. He was writing scripts for drugs, left and right.
2. The hospitals loved him. He was admitting patients, left and right.
3. Then he looked at his patients and their outcomes. "This isn't working."

His presentation had a profound impact on Victoria. She knew Dr. Rozema would be a doctor that she could relate to. His treatments avoided toxic procedures. And Dr. Rozema had publicly admitted the pharmaceutical drugs he once relied on weren't working.

Well, pharmaceutical drugs are working, but in a very harmful way. Pharmaceutical drugs are impacting accidental overdoses in the U.S. and are now the Number 1 cause of accidental deaths, surpassing car crashes. Dr. Sanjay Gupta, CNN's Emmy award winning chief medical correspondent, reported accidental overdoses as the biggest man-made epidemic in the United States.

The number of pain prescriptions increased 600% from 1997-2007, according to the U.S. Centers for Disease Control and Prevention.

Dr. Gupta, on assignment in Washington state, also related the story of a teenager who died after taking too much narcotic medication after a dental procedure, a story told to him by Dr. Gary Franklin, medical director for Washington state's Department of Labor and Industries.

Hundreds of health practitioners are following Dr. Rozema's example of avoiding toxic drugs, detoxing, and nourishing the body with wholesome foods. Two of these practitioners are Dr. Rich Anderson, honorary ND, NMD, and author of the book, *Cleanse & Purify Thyself,* the definitive guide to internal cleansing (AriseAndShine.com), and his associate, Toni Toney, author of the book, *EcoDiet* (ToniToney.com).

Several years ago I met Dr. Anderson and Toni, who is an environmental activist, researcher, and organic food advocate, and we had an opportunity to chat about the oral pathology connection with diseases. Victoria purchased Dr. Anderson's book when she met him in January 2013.

"If an angel came and gave a formula that would cure almost any disease, it would be against the law to claim its effectiveness," Anderson wrote in his first chapter.

The statement is true, and that's sad. The way medicine is now practiced in the United States, the American Medical Association and the Food and Drug Administration must be the final authority on truth, whether they're right or wrong.

We do live in a country that guarantees freedom of speech, said Anderson, and anyone "is welcome to use a system of healing that has been proven to work, but they won't profit much monetarily. The health profession makes money on sick people, not from well people."

"If we were to make everyone well with a system that works, we certainly wouldn't perpetuate our incomes," Dr. Anderson stated. "After all, there would be little use for this book, a really effective healing program, or even the entire health system. Just how sincerely do we want to heal?"

Dr. Anderson builds a powerful case for attitude and determination as important factors in anyone's wellness efforts. "Evidence clearly states that no matter what the disease, as long as a person has the right mental attitude – an absolute determination to find the solution and the willingness to do whatever is necessary to achieve good health – he will bring into his world that which he desires; he will succeed."

Dr. Anderson's probing questions represent a synopsis of Victoria's philosophy. She had created an attitude that she would find the truth, and nothing would deter her. It was the medical doctors who pledged to Do No Harm that put up the most stumbling blocks as she sought the truth.

"Too many times, we have heard the story of the doctor delivering the death sentence, called a prognosis, upon his unwise and gullible victim and then that person dies an unnecessary and often horrible early death. Was that person's life shortened because of cancer? Or was it shortened because he believed the doctor?" asked Anderson.

"Yet, thousands of bright individuals, after having a similar sentence handed to them, realize that what the doctor was really saying was this: 'If you follow my program, you will die about such and such time.'"

Says Dr. Anderson, the wise individual politely replies: "Thank you, doctor, but I want to get well and will therefore find a program that works." And the wise individual continues to look until he finds a way, like tens of thousands before him.

Victoria's future came down to a split-second decision. Dr. Hetzel had not examined her breast and seemed ready to release her after reviewing her mammogram which showed nothing he was concerned about. But Victoria asked about the small lump in her breast. What if she had kept her mouth shut and left the office?

What if she had realized the true extent of the personal stresses she was dealing with and how they can affect a person's health? She was overwhelmed with stress.

What if she had known that an infected root canal tooth or a jawbone infection could be causing the lump? She was dealing with both oral issues.

What if she had been told to get her mouth fixed first and follow some simple but natural and effective protocols and then determine if the lump disappeared? A group of integrative doctors should have suggested this, and definitely not directed her to a cancer clinic first.

What if she could have delayed the overpowering urge to "know immediately" if the lump was cancer? Had she remained calm, Victoria could have avoided the rush to judgment.

What if she had waited 90 days and had a second thermal breast study, and then evaluated her lump and her health status? This was actually the recommendation of the medical doctor specialist who evaluated her thermal images for Great Smokies.

What if the doctor and nurses at the Hope Cancer Center had told her the truth about the size of the biopsy needle and what they intended to do? Victoria would have refused the biopsy and left immediately.

Victoria should have said, "I need to think about this after I calm down. I want to make a rational and educated decision." But that's not what happened.

Chapter 17

Some cancers can go away

It was February 29, 2008 – Leap Year – when Victoria experienced a strange pain that would come to haunt her valiant effort to save her breast. It was nearly five weeks after the biopsy. "Mother hugged me really tight," she said. "There was a sharp, needle-like pain in my breast. I never had that pain before the biopsy. It happened again when I was tightly hugged by an uncle."

She had no clue that she might have something else in her breast, and it wasn't a tumor behind the nipple.

By March 3, 2008, she was watching DVD's about healing foods and wrote in her journal that "the lump was going down."

"Where can I turn?" Victoria asked herself. "If I go back to a regular oncologist, they're going to tell me the same thing." She started her personal research campaign, determined to learn everything there was to know about natural treatments for cancer.

She started with diet. One of her first purchases was a heavy-duty food blender. She added every organic fruit and vegetable that she believed would help her situation. She cut out sugar. "I watched everything that I ate." Victoria introduced more exercise to her daily regimen and continued drinking Essiac tea.

From February until June 2008, she was working on recovery by herself. "And it was actually getting better," she says. "It wasn't as large or sore."

On March 5, 2008, she started reading the book, *The Science of Being Well,* by Wallace D. Wattles – timeless wisdom and a practical program for vibrant health from the forgotten 1910 classic that could improve not only your health but everything else in your life. It's available as a free ebook on the internet (scienceofbeingwell.net) with new material and editing by Dr. Alexandra Gayek, ND.

A week later she was watching a video on food healing by Dr. Lorraine Day, an internationally acclaimed orthopedic trauma surgeon and best selling author who reversed an advanced chest cancer tumor by rebuilding her immune system using natural therapies, so her body could heal itself (drday.com).

Victoria added a new daily recipe to her regimen – a Cancer Crusher smoothie published in a Qigong recipe book "Smoothie Formulas," that offers food-healing wisdom. She was already making smoothies with her three-horsepower blender.

On March 17, 2008, she wrote in her diary: "The lump feels two-thirds smaller."

Although the lump was feeling much smaller, her breast continued to hurt. While doing Qigong on March 24, 2008, the pain became much worse.

Victoria was first exposed to this form of Chinese medicine in February 2007 where she learned actual exercise techniques and food healing – focused on smoothies – at a three-day conference in Asheville sponsored by Supreme Science Qigong Center (qigong.com).

Qigong basically is the manipulation of Qi energy. Over 4,000 years ago Chinese medicine said, "Blood is the mother of Qi." The Old Testament book of Leviticus 17:11 says, "For the life of the flesh is in the blood."

She was so impressed with what Qigong did for her own health that Victoria got her teaching certificate in March 2007.

Maybe the Qigong, which requires a lot of arm and chest movement, was irritating the biopsy site, Victoria thought. So she stopped doing Qigong, but two months after the biopsy, she reached in an upper kitchen cabinet to put away a glass, "and it made my breast hurt really badly all day long, even worse than before."

This biopsy should have been healed by now. Why was her breast not healing?

Victoria's ongoing research began focusing on why her breast was so sore following the biopsy. One of the subject phrases she started researching was "normal pain after biopsy."

What is normal biopsy pain? Victoria was experiencing intense, sharp, stabbing, burning pain. "This isn't normal," she thought. "Is it infection?"

In fact, it was most noticeable when doing either The Cloud Hands in Qigong or Downward Dog, a movement she learned in her

Yoga class. She felt a sharp pain in her right breast in the exact area of the biopsy with either movement. "There was something wrong in there."

On March 31, 2008, Victoria did two things: she stopped Qigong and she stopped drinking coffee.

On April 4, 2008, she was second-guessing herself again. Her journal entry for the day: "This breast is really wearing on my state of mind. What a gamble. I thought today, I believe I can get myself better. If I'm wrong, I die."

"Why isn't there a one-stop source for the kind of help I want?" she wondered.

Stopping her physical activities had definitely allowed her body to begin healing again. In mid-April she resumed her Qigong. But on April 17, 2008, she was doing yard work and pulled a water hose across the lawn. There was a sharp, piercing pain. She still did not know that a foreign object could be in her breast.

It happened again on April 29, 2008, while she was riding a bus at Epcot Center in Florida and she raised her arm to grab an overhead handle. On the trip with family members, she had to do without her smoothies and she noticed her stress level was much higher, and the breast was "much sorer and harder."

Why the hardness? she wondered.

By mid-May, Victoria was watching the DVD, *Crazy, Sexy Cancer* (CrazySexyCancer.com). Kris Carr was a 31-year-old actress/photographer who cured her incurable cancer and found a happy life. Her website describes her adventure by saying "healing is about truly living rather than fighting."

It's an attitude that Victoria claimed. "It's about rising to the challenge of life and turning lemons into champagne," Carr's website stated.

On May 27, 2008, Victoria went to a chiropractor, the same one her mother uses. "I did not tell him about my breast condition. Now I know how stupid that was." For the adjustment, she was on her stomach and the chiropractor was pushing on her back, and then he did an abrupt movement, more like hitting her. "The impact was on my upper back, directly behind my right breast."

"It hurt like hell," she said. She wasn't expecting it. During an adjustment a couple of weeks before, the chiropractor had not used that level of force at that location. He was skilled and Victoria recognized the benefit of her previous chiropractic adjustments.

She was in an awkward situation. She couldn't say anything because she didn't want her mother knowing she had any health issue. The adjustment would have been fine – he had done it numerous times before – but the problem was the breast biopsy done four months earlier.

When she got home, she discovered blood on her blouse – two drops of bright red blood on a white top. The blood came from the nipple. "Then it started hurting a lot worse after that."

There was one critical benefit that Victoria missed getting from this chiropractor; he did not use thermal imaging. There are an increasing number of chiropractors across America who utilize thermal imaging in their practices. One of them is Dr. Adam Fedorow in Goshen, Indiana, who is encouraging every one of his patients to take advantage of Digital Infrared Thermal Imaging.

Dr. Fedorow speaks to the "opportunity" that the chiropractic profession "holds in the palm of their hand, or should I say on the tip of their tongue!" Chiropractors see large numbers of patients. "How many of these people may have long-term systemic diseases that we are unaware of?" he asked. "Or how many of us simply have not taken the time to ask simple little questions here and there to see into the health or disease of the individual patient?"

How is your dental health?

That's the "simple little question" that Dr. Fedorow wants chiropractors to begin asking. The question is a "powerful probe into the view of the overall health of an individual."

"Follow me if you will," says the chiropractor. "If a patient presents with right shoulder blade area pain, we would probably treat this patient with an upper thoracic and lower cervical adjustment. Some would even do some physiotherapy in this region. Several weeks of treatment go by and the patient is no better, still with a lot of pain. Do we persist with upper thoracic and lower cervical adjustments or do we begin to look elsewhere?"

Here's where thermal imaging technology on site in a chiropractor's office can pay huge dividends.

"With some differential diagnosing and a referral to an MD we find that this patient has been suffering with a gallbladder issue all along. The gallbladder will refer pain to the right shoulder blade area. Much is the same with the dental connection."

Dr. Fedorow explains how he is using thermal imaging in his practice as it relates to oral pathology.

"Infected teeth, periodontal disease, cavitations, and mercury will wreak havoc on the overall health of a human being. This connection is very easy to grasp with the evidence based scientific data presented to us. Much the same with our nerves, we understand that an impingement in the spinal column wreaks havoc on any cell or organ in our body.

"This concept is mirrored with dental infection and long term systemic disease throughout our body. We understand that if we release the impingement on the nerve we allow the nervous system to function at its fullest potential, which in turn allows the cell or organ to operate at its optimal potential. If we rid the body of dental infection then in turn the body can operate at its fullest potential."

Dr. Fedorow witnessed several success stories with his own patients and quickly understood what a massive benefit scanning faces for oral pathology could provide to anyone that was facing any long term systemic disease.

"The power is in the tongue," he said. "Go ahead and start asking the question: How is your dental health? You never know whose life you are going to change! I have added this little question to my repertoire of questions in my office and it has literally saved lives."

After the chiropractor's adjustment and the discovery of blood on her blouse, Victoria did not have a good day. In fact, "It was depressing." Her journal entry stated: "I feel like I should plan for my death." The lump was definitely larger. Gardening over the next few days caused her breast to hurt even more. "I was feeling very good until that blood."

"I decided I needed to find a doctor that would help me, my way."

As she continued to research 'normal biopsy pain,' she made an appointment with Dr. Theodore Rozema in Landrum, South Carolina, the medical doctor turned integrative physician she had heard speak in Hendersonville. "He's the kind of doctor that would help me," she thought.

Several days before seeing Dr. Rozema, Victoria found a question about pain from a biopsy posted on an interactive breast cancer website. It was the same question she was asking herself.

From the website: "I had pain afterwards but then was fine, but now 20 days later, I am having intense, sharp, stabbing, burning pain – totally not related to my cycle nor is it normal for me. Could they have aggravated that cyst? Is this normal? I'm assuming it's normal to have pain from a biopsy but it's delayed and I guess I'm worried about infection or something. There is no redness and I have had infections before so outward appearance looks nice and normal but I know that pain is not normal, or is it? I just want to know why my breast is killing me."

On June 10, 2008, Dr. Rozema gave Victoria a thorough physical exam. As part of the exam, Victoria had answered numerous written questions.

She was asked to describe in her own words her most persistent medical problem with symptoms. Here's what she wrote:

"I felt a lump in my breast December 25, 2007. I had a breast core biopsy January 23, 2008. Before the biopsy I had slight soreness. After the biopsy I had a great deal more soreness that lasted for a few months. On May 27, I had a chiropractic adjustment and my nipple had a slight bloody discharge and my right breast has been sore ever since."

"You're probably one of the healthiest people I ever see come through my door," Victoria was told. "All your systems are in excellent condition. It's just amazing how healthy that you are," Victoria remembered him saying.

For the first time, Victoria heard the magic words that had eluded her. Someone with extensive medical experience said, "We will try different avenues."

Testing for toxic metals in her body revealed that Victoria had lead and mercury "off the charts." She also had big-time oxidative stress.

Her South Carolina doctor tested her hormones, thyroid and adrenal glands. "After the testing I was taking DHEA and pregnenolone (hormones), Iodoral which is a high-potency iodine (thyroid), and cortisol (adrenal glands). I took the cortisol for a couple of months, but it was making my stomach hurt so badly I couldn't take it any longer." An intravenous vitamin C program was begun.

At a July 8 follow-up visit, Dr. Rozema gave Victoria a cassette tape containing his notes. This is the edited and condensed transcript:

- Blood pressure is fine. Blood laboratory says wonderful things about you. You don't have diabetes. You don't have gout. Kidney is clearing waste from blood stream very effectively. Kidneys are working great. The salt, potassium, calcium, phosphorous are all normal. Electrolytes are all in balance. The proteins in your blood stream are in balance.
- Every one of your liver function tests is perfect. Iron is good.
- Your cholesterol is only 192. Your triglycerides are 54, perfect. Your bad cholesterols are 93, perfect. The good guys are so high that the risk of heart disease from the cholesterol system is less than half that of the average person your age. Wow!
- All the measurements we do on your thyroid hormone are perfect. Your red cells, white cells type and size are perfect.
- Now this is interesting that the country that has less cancer than any other country is Japan and the country in the world that has the highest intake of iodine by their citizens is Japan. It has been found that if all the cells of your body have enough iodine, it protects against breast cancer and female cancers.
- We may adjust some of your vitamins, minerals and nutrients.
- We did a hair mineral analysis and this is kind of interesting, tin showed up high in the hair. Lots of aluminum. Tremendous amount of antimony. Your lead is really high, 20 times higher than it should be. Nickel and mercury are high.
- Why is this important? We know lead and mercury are contributors to cancer. So over time we want to get those out.

- Our gut is our lifeline to the planet; 85% of our immune system is in the digestive tract.
- When you get up in the morning you are not making enough cortisol. Your adrenal glands are tired. They are not doing the refreshment during the nighttime. So I am writing you a prescription to go to the drug store and buy some hydrocortisone which is exactly the same compound that your body makes.
- Your DHEA levels are low, and your 17 hydroxy progesterone levels are low. You're low in the raw materials, these all come from the adrenal glands.
- You are not gluten sensitive.
- Just looking over your condition at this moment you're in a heck of a better condition than most people who show up in my office.

Dr. Rozema had Victoria list her diet in detail for a 10-day period "and we discussed in detail what I could do for improvement." She was provided with guidelines to have a near perfect meal. "He told me I was doing good with my diet."

Under Dr. Rozema's guidance, Victoria had 40 intravenous vitamin C treatments and 19 EDTA treatments to rid the body of heavy metals, which the doctor said were overworking her immune system. In the process, her body was too busy fighting off heavy metal toxicity and ignoring other vital functions. Toxic metals act like a 'straight jacket' on the immune system.

Dr. Rozema is no stranger to modern developments in chelation. He and Bruce Halstead, MD, are the co-authors of the book, *The Scientific Basis of EDTA Chelation Therapy,* copyrighted in 1997. Chelation can be described as the binding action of certain chemical substances to a metal ion.

Dr. Rozema helped write protocols for the National Institute of Health.

"I was very careful to eat a very healthy diet and took all the supplements the doctor recommended. I also tried to exercise and eliminate as much stress as possible. I don't think anyone could have devoted themselves to getting healthy or tried as hard as I did to make it happen. I also did lots of research and reading to try and help myself."

The first vitamin C treatment was July 8, 2008.

Compared to her previous medical care, there was a totally different atmosphere in Dr. Rozema's office. Instead of women with pale and drawn faces and no hair and no eyebrows, Victoria noticed that nearly all the patients had a smile on their face and a sense of hope. "What a contrast with the cancer center in Asheville."

"For the first time I took a sigh of relief. A calmness came over me. I felt much better. I really appreciated the way I was treated and he did not try to scare me to death. He realized that fear can depress a person's immune system, and the immune system is needed to maintain good health."

Victoria was not one to run to the doctor's office every time she had a cold or sniffle, whether in childhood or as an adult. "I was just always very healthy."

"Having good health is what's always on my mind," she reflected. "I've never been around too many people with bad health. I was in total shock when they told me I had cancer."

An examination three months later revealed that the breast lump was decreasing in size and Dr. Rozema told Victoria it had not attached to the chest wall.

In November 2008, Victoria read an article in a Hendersonville, North Carolina newspaper that claimed most cancers will go away on their own. "I never went for what Dr. Hetzel told me, or my breast would already have been removed."

The headline in the *Times-News* read: "Study suggests some cancers may go away."

According to the report, this was the reaction of Dr. Barnett Kramer, director of the Office of Disease Prevention at the National Institutes of Health: "People who are familiar with the broad range of behaviors of a variety of cancers know spontaneous regression is possible. But what is shocking is that it can occur so frequently."

Dr. Laura Esserman, professor of surgery and radiology at the University of California, San Francisco, was quoted as seeing a real opportunity to figure out why some cancers go away.

"I am a breast cancer surgeon; I run a breast cancer program," she said. "I treat women every day, and I promise you it's a problem. Every time you tell a person they have cancer, their whole life runs before their eyes."

Dr. Esserman added: "What if I could say, 'It's not a real cancer, it will go away, don't worry about it.' That's such a different message. Imagine how you would feel."

"At the Hope Cancer Center, I was not given any hope to keep my breast," said Victoria. But she found hope anyway.

Something else happened in November 2008 that would prove to be pivotal in Victoria's battle with diagnosed breast cancer. In the chelation room of her South Carolina doctor's office one morning, she saw a man walk in with a book and start talking to another man about the connection between oral pathology and cancer.

She already had a hint of suspicion that a root canal tooth was somehow involved, but she didn't know there was a book about teeth and the cancer connection.

Victoria's IV vitamin C treatments took place in a large, tile-floored room at Dr. Rozema's. About 20 comfortable recliners were strategically placed so patients could get their treatments and still carry on casual conversations with each other. Most patients were like-minded and were eager to exchange information about alternative therapies and lifestyle.

As she sat attached to a clear medical-grade plastic tube that was dripping vitamin C into her left arm, she could make out the larger letters on the book cover (*Am I Dead?*). She could also see the words at the top of the book's cover (*Cancer cured ... the coming storm*).

As words from the man's conversation drifted over to her chair, she could tell he was talking about a place "up there in North Carolina in the mountains, and they've got a cure for breast cancer. I'm thinking to myself, 'I've got to hear this.'"

The man had brought full-color thermal scans of his whole body. Victoria could see the colorful images. She had seen her breast images taken January 14, 2008 at Great Smokies, but she had never seen full-body images.

The conversation she overheard was food for thought.

Chapter 18

Power of suggestion

Throughout her ordeal, Victoria never gave up hope. Often she was disappointed. Frequently she was frustrated. Although her stamina ebbed and flowed, she basically remained in a state of exhaustion. It was the process that was exhausting, however, not her health issue. "I still felt great."

Once in a while, she was angry. But she always kept a sense of humor. "Is this a movie I have just described?" she would ask herself. Then she'd answer her own question. "No, unfortunately, it has been my life."

Well, it was Christmas season again – one full year after she discovered the lump in her right breast.

On December 30, 2008, Victoria made the 25-minute drive from her rural home to the Biogenesis Wellness Center in Landrum, South Carolina for her last intravenous vitamin C therapy for the year. The winter had not been too severe by western North Carolina standards. On this day, the mountain weather was unseasonably warm, and the temperature in South Carolina was upper 60s. Traffic on the scenic Interstate 26 was tolerable.

Her journal entry states: "I got up at 5 a.m. Hopefully, this is the last time I will be going for the vitamin C treatment. I said goodbye to everything in my mind. I did enjoy getting to sit there for four hours and chatting with everyone."

It was one of the few times that Victoria would ever be found sitting still.

The next day she woke up before dawn, "so grateful I still had my breast. I looked up and wished upon a star."

Although the lump was shrinking, Dr. Rozema wanted Victoria to have a mammogram because he wasn't familiar with any reliable alternatives, even though he had been practicing integrative medicine. "He wanted me to have another test done to see how we were doing," although the doctor could feel the lump shrinking, and said so.

She, of course, emphatically declined the mammogram but agreed to have thermal imaging. If Victoria had learned anything by now, the dangers of mammograms were at the top of her list.

On January 5, 2009, she went to Asheville Integrative for a non-invasive thermal breast study. This analysis was being done nearly one year after her biopsy in January 2008. It was her second thermal imaging. The two tests could not be compared, however, because a different camera technology was used in each one.

Her medical report was written by Bryan Cotton, MD, who was one of 16 doctors reading and reporting on the thermal scans for a medical group, Electronic Medical Interpretation.

"There are significant thermal asymmetries seen in the breasts. There are vascular feeds from the upper and lower sternum to an area of hyperthermia at one-o'clock in the upper inner quadrant of the right breast. This is very suspicious and neovascularity is highly likely," the report stated. "This may correlate with the DCIS found by needle biopsy."

"The slight areas of hyperthermia in the upper quadrants of the left breast do not appear suspicious but should be monitored for change," the report also said.

Under a section labeled 'Discussion,' the report stated: "The thermal findings in the left breast are considered within normal limits. The thermal findings in the right breast are consistent with a malignancy until proven otherwise."

The outcome of Victoria's thermography session was not what she was expecting.

As her grueling journey stretched into months, and then years, Victoria began to wonder about all the tests she and her insurance company were paying for. "If the diagnostic testing is so good, why should I taint the results? Why shouldn't I make the doctors, radiologists and pathologists work without the benefit of the power of suggestion?" she wondered.

In fact, there's a lot of science behind her premise. An article on an internet website written by Stan Reents (athleteinme.com) directly asserted, "Don't underestimate the power of suggestion."

"The mind is very powerful," Reents stated, "but it can be easily misled." Even physicians are susceptible, he said.

He cited a research project where people were recruited to participate in an analysis of a drug used to improve sleep. The subjects were told some would receive the drug and others would be given a placebo. At the end of the study, many subjects reported sleeping better, and some wanted to continue taking the medication.

There was a catch, however. Both groups received a placebo and no one was given an active drug. The difference was the power of suggestion.

Each time Victoria agreed to a new test and reported her previous medical history, she almost guaranteed the test results would be the same.

At the end of her journey, Victoria concluded that revealing her diagnosis prior to each additional test was a big mistake. "If I had it to do over again, I would let them figure it out for themselves. That's what you're being tested for."

On January 12, 2009, a week after the images were taken at Asheville Integrative Medicine, the thermographer, Ginger Scalone, called and challenged her patient: "If you don't get surgery, Victoria, you're going to end up with chemo and radiation later."

"Ginger said she had never seen anyone heal themselves. She scared me to death. My nerves really got shot. I was expecting a good report."

No doubt, Scalone wanted very much to help, but delivering this news by phone, at best, would be considered poor judgment. At 8:30 in the morning, Victoria was just starting her day and was upbeat and focused. Within seconds, her world was upside down again, and she was in a state of shock.

It was Scalone that recommended Dr. Suzanne Hoekstra at Parkridge Hospital in Hendersonville, North Carolina. Many of Scalone's clients reported that Dr. Hoekstra was compassionate and had an easy way about her, Victoria was told.

Chapter 19

Cancer center ambush

One estimate places the number of root canal procedures done annually in the United States at 30 million.

Dr. Thomas Rau, who runs the Paracelsus Clinic in Switzerland, reported that 98 out of 100 breast cancer patients treated at his clinic had one or more root canal teeth on the same meridian as the patient's breast tumor.

Victoria did not know either statistic, and she definitely did not know about the established connection between infected root canal teeth and breast cancer, probably because this information about root canals was revealed in a 1925 study by Dr. Weston Price and 60 prominent researchers, but the study was suppressed by the American Dental Association.

The ADA's dental school indoctrination is so thorough that some graduating dentists receive their degrees without ever hearing about or reading the writings of Dr. Price.

Imagine, for 88 years, a proven connection between a jawbone infection and cancer was known by the organization that controls dentistry in the USA!

"For me, I would have considered my dentist, Dr. Matthew Young, to be the logical person to tell me about a possible connection between my right front root canal tooth and a lump in my right breast," said Victoria. "The lump was noted on my patient chart because I was refusing dental x-rays."

The next place that Victoria expected people to point her in the right direction, she says, was at Great Smokies.

Dr. John Wilson at Great Smokies Medical Center was given the book, *Am I Dead? ...or do I just feel like it*, by a Tennessee dentist who was the doctor's patient.

The center's website states: "Founded in 1979, Great Smokies Medical Center of Asheville is the oldest integrative medical practice in NC. The Center provides comprehensive outpatient healthcare services and utilizes both mainstream and alternative

159

healthcare options to address obstacles to health and enhance the body's innate ability to heal."

It was Great Smokies that recommended Hope Cancer Center and actually made her appointment. In hindsight, Victoria considered her experience with The Hope Cancer Center "terrible." More bluntly, she says she was "ambushed." She was expecting information about options. She was not expecting the only options to be surgery and radiation. She felt cheated.

Although Victoria's story is basically being told sequentially in real time, and uses the real names of doctors, dentists, medical and cancer clinics, as well as other health practitioners, the reader should not construe that the practice of ignoring certain alternative treatment options for cancer is limited to North Carolina.

It's a national crisis. There's a lot of talk about alternative technologies, but most doctors who are willing to utilize these new strategies are still afraid of their state's medical boards and the catch-phrase, Standard of Care.

The Standard of Care is used to determine when a doctor can be held responsible for malpractice in all medical and dental fields.

Generally speaking though, the Standard of Care is based on what other doctors with similar knowledge and licensing do in similar circumstances, or it can be based on what is determined by a state licensing board. Conveniently, the Standard of Care is not very standardized.

The Standard of Care can vary not only from state to state, but from local region to local region. A doctor practicing in an urban area may have access to different methodology than a doctor practicing in a rural area. These geographic differences are taken into consideration when determining the Standard of Care.

In the case of a doctor, there can be alternative forms of medicine which some doctors perform and others do not. A doctor must be able to defend the procedures he uses and must be able to prove that other doctors would treat a patient similarly under similar circumstances. The jury in a malpractice case will ultimately decide whether the doctor's treatment was reasonable and appropriate based on evidence provided by both sides regarding the local Standard of Care.

Sorry, there is no easy and understandable definition for Standard of Care.

- One website (TheFreeDictionary.com) says it's a written statement describing the rules, actions, or conditions that direct patient care.
- A medical definition describes a diagnostic and treatment process that a clinician should follow for a certain type of patient illness or clinical circumstance.
- The 2009 Journal of Clinical Oncology says there is no medical definition for Standard of Care although the term is firmly established in law and is defined as "the caution that a reasonable person in similar circumstances would exercise in providing care to a patient."

Victoria's life was hanging in the balance, and doctors at every turn were refusing to step outside their confusing "Standard of Care box" to help her.

The teaching methodology in medical and dental schools is partly to blame. After all, money talks, and the medical schools are controlled by money – big money from Big Pharma. An equal portion of blame falls on the licensing and regulatory arms of the medical and dental boards in each state. And another equal portion of fault is found with American citizens who so willingly allowed this take-over to happen.

Where is the outrage?

I wish I could report that Big Pharma's sole interest is in protecting the public, but I can't say that. It wouldn't be true.

Several years ago, Dr. Raymond Hartman, a private consultant and researcher, gave me a copy of his 'white paper' that was intended to educate readers about cancer prevention "by maintaining a healthy immune system." He dedicated his research to the late Dr. Philip Binzel, MD, who was convinced that most doctors in this country are dedicated individuals but they are "tumor-oriented" or "lump and bump" doctors as a result of their medical school training and they have no concept of how nutrition or even natural therapies relate to preventing or curing cancer.

Victoria is not angry in the sense of being mad at individual doctors as much as she is mad at a medical system that makes good practitioners fearful of stepping outside their safe comfort zone. Don't get the wrong impression; there are some medical doctors whose actions – or lack of action – make her blood boil. They are not off the hook.

Victoria lived in North Carolina, and by dictate of geography, most of the doctors that examined her were under the authority of the North Carolina Medical Board.

To illustrate the problem, for example, the North Carolina Medical Board has been granted seemingly unlimited power by the state legislature. This power is wielded legitimately in some cases to police bad doctors and investigate complaints, but it's more likely to be used to stomp out competition to mainstream medical doctors by regulating, intimidating, and ultimately terrorizing those who want to incorporate alternative therapies.

In the spring of 2011, health advocates across America suddenly focused on North Carolina, where citizens were seemingly unaware of NC Senate Bill 31, a vaguely worded bill that sought to turn healers into felons by criminalizing alternative medicine.

The legislation was literally cruising through state government without a single dissenting voice being offered by state senators or representatives.

Opponents determined that its vague generalizations could criminalize a wide range of health related fields from herbal practitioners to nutritional counselors.

There was real concern the government would use the legislation to reign in all forms of medicine that are outside the current control of the North Carolina Medical Society and its licensing and enforcement arm, the North Carolina Medical Board.

One of the most vocal voices of opposition was Mike Adams, editor of an internet-based health information newsletter (NaturalNews.com), who has established himself as an independent online guru on the subject of natural health.

"The only thing that stands between a person and their own perfect health is information," stated his website (HealthRanger.com). "Empowered with the right information, anyone can improve their health, reduce their dependence on prescription drugs, enhance their quality of life and expand their mental awareness and creativity."

Bill Irwin, the man who wrote the Prologue for this book, believes in information. The blind thru-hiker conquered the Appalachian Trail with commitment, perseverance, the will to survive, and information. He conquered cancer the same way. Many people who face a cancer diagnosis have all the ingredients to win, except the right information.

It was Adams who gets credit for leading the backlash to the threatening legislation in North Carolina.

"As virtually the entire North Carolina legislature now knows, NaturalNews readers have been loudly condemning the lawmakers there over the recent 'stealth bill' SB 31 which introduced new language that would transform homeopaths, naturopaths, herbalists, and midwives into criminal felons," Adams wrote on April 6, 2011.

If the bill had stood as proposed, it would have made MD's, ND's, and chiropractors legal in the state; everyone else in the healing and wellness industry would have been illegal.

Monopoly medicine is itself a crime against humanity, wrote Adams.

He says the world is "insane" today. Physicians who offer "only poisonous medicine and the psychiatric drugging of innocent children are given the monopoly 'right' to treat disease, while the holistic healing arts practitioners who actually know how to help people heal are being criminalized as felons."

Within hours of the outcry on the internet, health and wellness practitioners in North Carolina were messaging their legislators. The senate bill's language was finally changed. But for how long?

Said Adams, "If North Carolina lawmakers had any sense whatsoever, they would be working on laws to legalize health freedom in the state, not criminalize those who practice it."

The 12 members of the NC Medical Board are appointed by the Governor: eight licensed physicians, one licensed physician assistant (PA) or approved nurse practitioner (NP), and three members of the public with no ties to health care.

Adams called for stripping the NC Medical Board "of its monopoly" and declared that North Carolina's population would choose holistic medicine if given a free market choice over the kind of medicine they are being forced to accept.

"Enemies of health freedom are enemies of America," Adams said.

"Let the state lawmakers of every state in America be warned: The health freedom movement will no longer tolerate being criminalized for bringing our healing gifts to the world. We will stand unified against your poisons, your corruption and your monopolistic racketeering on behalf of the pharmaceutical industry," he said.

One of the groups that claim to be expanding the horizons of traditional Western medicine is the American College for Advancement in Medicine (ACAM). Their website (acamnet.org) says, "Integrative medicine combines conventional care with alternative medicine."

While not shunning Western medicine, ACAM physicians, according to their website, "incorporate appropriate and proven alternative treatment options," including allopathic, osteopathic, regenerative, holistic, naturopathic, and functional medicine.

At least 'some' ACAM physicians recognize that the mouth is not an isolated component of human anatomy.

If you enter the words "oral health connection" into the website's search feature, up pops a PDF file, "The Unseen Connection to Cardiovascular Health – Your Mouth." The document is a presentation by Dr. Michael Margolis, a biological dentist in Mesa, Arizona, who is also a DIM (doctor of integrative medicine).

Dr. Margolis lectures on the effects of a patient's oral cavity and its impact on the rest of the patient's body.

On the subject of the debilitating effects of mercury on humans (silver amalgam fillings), Margolis employs ancient history to prove his point. He tells how, 2,500 years ago, the Greeks utilized liquid mercury as a murder weapon. They poured it into the victim's ear, where it paralyzed the brain and caused immediate death.

About four years ago, I received a phone call from Dr. Roger Billica, who was NASA's Chief of Medical Operations at the

Johnson Space Center in Houston, Texas from 1990-2001, where he supervised the clinical space medicine programs for America's astronauts and the International Space Station.

He had just finished reading my book (*Am I Dead?... or do I just feel like it*) and was calling to thank me for writing it. He told me that he was practicing integrative medicine and there were some 1,500 physicians just like him scattered over 30 countries who were members of ACAM.

Dr. Billica graduated from the University of North Carolina at Chapel Hill School of Medicine and served in the U.S. Air Force. He entered private practice in Fort Collins, Colorado following his NASA career and became a member of ACAM.

Dr. Billica said ACAM was focused on "whole-body wellness." However, one of his comments shocked me. He declared, "And we know we must have the dental connection." Was he referring to the ACAM organization or was he using "we" in the editorial sense that he knew this? I wasn't sure.

In hindsight, I should not have been shocked. NASA knows a lot more about the connection between oral pathology and cancer and degenerative diseases than they're letting on publicly. Twelve years ago, in April 2000, NASA put together a select committee and held a Space Dentistry conference. The subject: Astronaut care for exploration missions during travel beyond Earth orbit.

The NASA committee was interested in learning about recent dental developments and whether dental disease or dental trauma, or both, are likely to emerge on long space missions.

Dr. Billica encouraged ACAM to place renewed emphasis on the oral pathology connection and he copied me with emails to their Irvine, California corporate headquarters, but the not-for-profit never initiated any communication to discuss the oral pathology connection to cancer and many degenerative diseases. And I received no response from requests made to ACAM to have a meeting.

ACAM claims to be the voice of integrative medicine. "Our goals are to improve physician skills, knowledge and diagnostic procedures as they relate to integrative medicine; to support integrative medicine research; and to provide education on current standard of care as well as additional approaches to patient care."

Yet, their online store does not offer a single book on the subject of oral pathology. Not one!

ACAM claims to enable "members of the public to connect with physicians who take an integrative approach to patient care and empowers individuals with information about integrative medicine treatment options."

I have breaking news for the headquarters staff. Doctors who are members of ACAM are not empowering anybody if they fail to include the oral pathology connection. Dr. Billica gets it. Dr. Margolis gets it.

At cancer clinics in Europe, the first doctor a patient sees is a dentist. In the book, *Am I Dead? … or do I just feel like it,* the emphatic statement is made, "Your dentist is your most important doctor."

Victoria asked herself, "Why didn't Great Smokies ask about my teeth? They charged me a ton of cash – $2,404.23 – for every lab test imaginable. Based on the lab results, they prescribed their expensive supplements, which I did use at first. But nobody inquired about my mouth."

"I don't know why these two places (Great Smokies and Dr. Young) would not tell me about the book. It would have saved me lots of anguish, a ton of money, and more than four years of my life."

Victoria wanted to scream. "It's a book, for crying out loud! I wasn't expecting them to put themselves in harm's way with the medical or dental boards. I would not expect them to jeopardize their practice, if that's what they were afraid of. But it's a 350-page book. Let me form my own opinion. It's my life. I should be able to live it the way I want, with all options on the table."

Chapter 20

This hat trick is quite slick

There's an old adage about giving someone who is misbehaving enough rope and they'll hang themselves. Is this where the North Carolina State Medical Board is headed? Will state legislators and private citizens eventually get enough of the heavy-handed tactics that make it so difficult in North Carolina to get help with alternative technologies?

Health freedoms and the individual's right to choose their own path of health and wellness are arbitrarily being controlled and slowly and steadily taken away all over the country, but no place do residents appear to be more threatened than in North Carolina.

Is your state next? Why is this important to this story?

Victoria had to cross the state line into South Carolina to find an integrative medical doctor who felt safe enough in his own practice to help her the way she wanted to be helped.

She had to cross the state line into Tennessee to find a dentist who felt safe enough in his own practice to help her the way she wanted to be helped.

Many integrative doctors, alternative practitioners, and dentists are so busy looking over their shoulders that it affects the outcome of their treatment. The patient gets cheated.

This is wrong!

In general, medical doctors are not interested in thermal imaging. In North Carolina, the medical board is trying to manipulate and restrict the use of non-invasive thermal imaging technology.

The way the board is pulling off this hat trick is quite slick. Give credit where it's due.

So far, other states are not attempting to restrict an individual's choice to choose thermal imaging. It seems to only be happening in North Carolina and Canada. If the medical board had its way, the only health practitioners in North Carolina would be MD's, ND's, and chiropractors. That would shut out many legitimate wellness practitioners and deny residents access to many technologies other than traditional medicine.

Even before the ruckus over SB 31 in the North Carolina legislature, thermal imaging centers in the state were under scrutiny, including Proven Health Management in Clyde, North Carolina.

Some people believe that receiving a letter from the state medical board is a right of passage. I received my letter, sent certified mail and dated January 14, 2010, in my capacity as a researcher and certified thermographer. "It has come to the attention of the North Carolina Medical Board that you are performing diagnostic breast scans and sending those scans to out of state individuals for interpretation, including evaluation and possible diagnoses."

Try to follow this thinking because the example is insanely funny.

Here are the facts:

False Accusation #1 – Proven Health did use thermal imaging equipment to capture breasts as well as full-body images taken by certified thermographers, but Proven Health never diagnosed anything. This fact was clearly stated in all literature, and it was stated multiple times. Clients were also required to sign a disclaimer that acknowledged this fact, and their signature had to be witnessed.

False Accusation #2 – Proven Health did not send scans to out of state individuals for interpretation, including evaluation and possible diagnoses. Scans were electronically sent to a medical group, Electronic Medical Interpretation (EMI), which evaluated images but did not diagnose.

The state medical board also stated: If the out of state individual doing the interpreting is a physician who does not possess a North Carolina license, then that physician is practicing medicine without a license. This constitutes a felony pursuant to NC General Statute 90-18.

Fact – Proven Health had no way of knowing where the electronic images went via the internet. And Proven Health did not know where the individual doctors who work for EMI resided and were licensed. Proven Health was told they were licensed medical doctors who had special training in understanding thermal imaging. Those are facts.

Here's the absurdity of the entire drama.

A licensed medical doctor with an unblemished record in either neighboring Tennessee or South Carolina could receive one of the electronically transmitted scans and the physician could evaluate the scan and return their written report to EMI, which in turn transmits the report to Proven Health electronically (to be mailed to the client), and, according to the North Carolina Medical Board, the doctor who evaluated the scan is guilty of practicing medicine without a license – a North Carolina license, of course.

The 'doctor' has committed a felony. Keep in mind that the doctor who reads the scans has no way of knowing where the client lives, either, or even the state or country where the thermal images were done.

However, in the above example, if the individual in neighboring Tennessee or South Carolina evaluates the scans and is not a physician, the 'individual' would only be guilty of a Class 1 misdemeanor.

Why would a medical doctor be guilty of a felony and a person who is not a doctor would only be guilty of a misdemeanor? Do you see the absurdity of this comedy?

In reality, the medical board's position had nothing to do with protecting state residents. It had everything to do with power and control. And, if the medical board's leash is not drastically shortened by the state legislature in coming years, the board will continue to push for vague and generalized laws that will enable them to limit or shut down every alternative practice in the state.

Among natural health practitioners, North Carolina is now considered to be the most dangerous state in the nation in which to own or operate any type of alternative health care options. As the North Carolina Medical Board's power grows, state residents will see their health freedoms continue to be eroded. That's the tragedy! It struck Victoria in a hard way. She was forced to go out-of-state to continue monitoring her body with non-toxic thermal imaging technology. She took her business to South Carolina.

169

In its 'Personal and Confidential' letter, the medical board stated: "The Board demands that you cease and desist aiding and abetting the unlicensed practice of medicine immediately." The certified letter was signed by David Henderson, executive director of the medical board. The letter was copied to Michael Bonfoey, district attorney in Haywood County. So much for personal and confidential.

Here's the translation of this drama.

Every potential client at a thermal imaging center in North Carolina should arrive for imaging with a script, a doctor's order for the thermal image. And only doctors licensed in North Carolina should evaluate the electronic images.

Otherwise, the screening center will be aiding and abetting the unlicensed practice of medicine.

Here's the problem.

Very few medical doctors (those licensed by a state medical board in any state) understand thermal imaging which is contrary to what they learned in the pharmaceutical-controlled medical schools. Furthermore, most clients who choose thermal imaging do so because they do not routinely see medical doctors. The clients choose alternative options. Their choice is being taken away by a contemptuous 12-member state government- appointed and endorsed board.

What are the motives?

According to author Linda Johnston, MD, many professions historically have used laws, licensing, legislation, unions, and guilds to protect their own economic interests. Medical boards, including the one in North Carolina, hide behind the catch-phrase Standard of Care.

In other words, it doesn't matter if a treatment or alternative practice actually works for a patient; what matters is whether at least 51% of the state's medical doctors use or support the treatment or practice.

Stated another way, a medical doctor in North Carolina can legally treat thousands of patients using drugs or procedures that do not work and produce no favorable results for the patients because more than half of the state's doctors use the same ineffective protocol. The doctor still gets paid, even if the patient dies. Why would they change their Standard of Care? They're not going to.

Few North Carolina residents are even aware that the state's medical board does not receive funding from state or local governments. One hundred percent of the board's operating revenue comes from fees paid by its licensees, including license application and annual renewal fees.

Victoria knows all this, but she was forced to become a professional medical researcher in search of finding a way to avoid harmful treatments and save her own quality of life. Most state residents, however, neither have the incentive, time, money, or expertise to do this.

Furthermore, the state medical board is an independent agency that regulates the practice of medicine and surgery "on behalf of the state of North Carolina," according to the board's website. Medical board employees are not on the state payroll and do not qualify for state benefits or retirement.

So, why then would the state medical board need a powerful lobbying position? Obviously, state legislators are relieved to have "medical doctors" policing their own ranks, and that makes it much easier for the medical board to push through legislation that's favorable to their determined march for absolute control of healthcare in North Carolina.

What's happening in your state?

Chapter 21

You'll die if you don't do this

With the prominent exception of her encounter with Dr. Theodore Rozema, it seemed everywhere Victoria turned she found health practitioners toying with her fears. You'll die if you don't do this. You'll die if you don't do that.

It was the beginning of a new round of stress. "I think that stress really harmed me," Victoria insisted. "After the early-morning phone call from Ginger Scalone at Asheville Integrative Medicine on January 12, 2009, I could feel the lump getting larger again. When she told me she had never seen anyone heal themselves, she created all the fear, all over again."

The thermographer asked no questions about Victoria's oral history either.

In mid-December 2008, Victoria saw a commercial on television. She was tuned to the ABC affiliate in Asheville, WLOS Channel 13. The commercial was touting a breast cancer cure without surgery, radiation, or chemotherapy.

"The girl in the commercial still had her hair."

Although she saw the brief commercial only once, the visual jogged Victoria's memory of the man with the book at Biogenesis Wellness Center in Landrum, one month earlier. She remembered the colorful thermal images, the title, and she had seen the words "breast cancer cured" on the back cover.

At the time, Victoria had every reason to believe she was already on the road to full recovery, and she didn't need this service. "Dr. Rozema was a very competent doctor and I agreed with his treatment protocols. He did no harm. I didn't yet comprehend the oral pathology connection." The actual complications of her biopsy were yet to be known.

She finally ordered the book, *Am I Dead? ... or do I just feel like it. Cancer cured ... the coming storm.* In 45 chapters, the book connects the dots between the author's heart attacks with anaerobic infections in the jawbone. It also explains how thermal imaging was

172

being used to show the connection between oral pathology and cancer.

It was Saturday, January 17, 2009, a good day for reading, and Victoria had already started the first chapter. The temperature outside was hovering just above freezing. Victoria didn't want to leave home even though her mother was insisting she come next door for dinner.

"I read for hours. I couldn't put it down. That is the only thing that makes sense to me," she thought. "It is my mouth. That is the trigger for my breast lump. It is my right breast, root canal on the right side, wisdom teeth extracted on the right side only. And I've always been so healthy." (Victoria did not have wisdom teeth on the left side.)

Predictably, breast cancer survivor Suzanne Somers wrote on page 218 of her book, *KNOCKOUT*, that she had root canals on her right side and was diagnosed with right breast cancer.

But root canal-treated teeth aren't the only culprits in the mouth. In her book, *Heavenly Answers for Earthly Challenges*, Joyce Brown tells her own true story about a near-death experience that she eventually connected to a badly infected tooth.

While suffering from rheumatoid arthritis and other health issues including internal bleeding from her sinuses, Brown confessed that she was unaware that "such a simple thing as a tooth could cause or contribute to so much damage to health."

Brown had to sign waivers to get a dentist to extract what appeared to be a perfectly healthy tooth. One dentist took an x-ray and declared, "Joyce, just as I thought, there is nothing wrong with this tooth." But the gold crown with silver amalgam packing material underneath was actually the source of a deadly infection. When shown the extracted tooth cut in half, her ear, nose and throat specialist declared that the roots had been embedded in the sinuses and were "dissolved" by the infection.

"Within two or three weeks the intense pain from my arthritis was almost completely gone. I began recovering miraculously in many ways and my rheumatoid arthritis went into remission," wrote Brown.

Meanwhile, it wasn't snowing in the mountains which normally would have kept Victoria indoors, but she found herself "book bound" and indoors anyway. In addition to being engrossed in *Am I Dead?... or do I just feel like it,* she was reading *Cancer, Step Outside the Box* by Ty M. Bollinger (CancerStepOutsideTheBox.com). Both books were released in 2007.

Bollinger is a CPA, health freedom advocate, cancer researcher, and a former competitive body builder. He has appeared several times on the syndicated radio program Coast to Coast AM (CoastToCoastAM.com). On one of those shows, he said there's "ample evidence that the war on cancer is a fraud," and "multinational pharmaceutical companies are running the show."

By late December 2008, Victoria's primary physician felt there was a 40% improvement in the size of her lump; much of the size reduction was being attributed to the weekly intravenous vitamin C treatments and the intravenous chelation for toxic heavy metals. Dr. Theodore Rozema shared with Victoria how he cured his mother's breast cancer naturally when other doctors wanted to do a mastectomy. Victoria was all ears.

There's ample scientific evidence suggesting that ascorbic acid in bowel tolerance doses is able to block many allergic reactions. In hindsight, Victoria believes the vitamin C (80 grams per week on average) was doing exactly that for the adverse reaction in her breast.

Victoria was still 18 months away from solving the puzzle of the mysterious breast reactions she had been experiencing since the biopsy in January 2008.

Meanwhile, she made an appointment in early January 2009 for an evaluation at North Carolina Institute of Technology (NCIT), a private research and educational organization operated in a large three-story home on private property in rural Madison County, North Carolina, located about an hour west of Asheville, where Robert H. Dowling, D.Sc., was using thermal imaging technology to visually establish a firm connection between oral pathology and breast cancer.

Although Victoria had seen the cover of the book in late 2008 at Dr. Rozema's office, the apparent success of her treatments with Dr. Rozema caused her to file a mental note but not make a purchase at that time. When she saw the short TV commercial in December 2008 on the Asheville station and again saw the cover of the book in the commercial, her interest was aroused.

In the commercial, she heard a young woman telling how her breast cancer was cured without surgery, radiation, and chemotherapy. It was a similar story to one she had heard a patient of Dr. Rozema telling several months earlier.

"The lady in the commercial had beautiful hair and wasn't wearing a 'chemo wrap' to hide her baldness. She looked happy and really healthy," Victoria thought. "There has to be something to this, or these people would get sued. It must be true or they couldn't put it on TV."

Her prior thermal experience was limited to breast scans only, which were done at Great Smokies Medical Center and Asheville Integrative Medicine. Neither place took images of her face for the purpose of evaluating potential oral pathology. In fact, oral pathology was totally ignored by both medical facilities.

One of these breast studies done January 5, 2009, alarmed the thermographer and the thermographer alarmed Victoria.

"In my mind, I never wanted to think that I had cancer. I always considered it a precancerous condition because I had researched DCIS." As a result, in the preliminary interview at NCIT, when asked if she had cancer, Victoria answered no.

However, once Victoria came to grips with the word games she was being treated to by doctors, nurses, oncologists, and even thermographers, she was able to acknowledge that she did have a breast condition and it wasn't going away on its own. She is quick to say that she was dealing with information she had at the time, and some critical information about her breast biopsy was missing. "It was like I was dealing with a loaded deck, but I didn't know what the deck was."

"Once I read *Am I Dead? ...or do I just feel like it,* I had enlightenment. I didn't have to do any of that terrible stuff that Dr.

David Hetzel at the Hope Cancer Center had told me. Now I had found a way to keep my health, my breast, and my dignity."

Victoria was now learning about a technique for a cancer cure known as thermal ablation, a procedure that can destroy cancer cells by utilizing extreme heat or freezing. At the time, radio frequency ablation (heat) was more common. RF ablation is not the same as radiation therapy.

Cryoablation is a technique that uses compressed gases to freeze a tumor.

Both radio frequency and cryoablation procedures require the placement of needles (probes) into a tumor. The probes become the delivery system for the gases that create an ice ball or the radio frequencies that generate extreme heat.

Yes, her good-faith efforts with nutrition, exercise, stress management, and nutritional supplementation had paid valuable dividends. Perhaps she had realized the most dividends from the intravenous vitamin C therapy and the chelation of heavy metal toxins, including high levels of mercury that had leached into her body over time from her 'silver' amalgam fillings which were removed five years earlier. Simply removing 'silver amalgam fillings' loaded with mercury does not remove mercury that has accumulated in the body.

Testing showed that Victoria also had high levels of lead, which compromises the immune system.

Victoria had two things going for her. The mercury in her teeth was properly and safely removed by a holistic, mercury-free dentist, and her primary physician had directed her through the process of detoxing heavy metals, including mercury and lead.

She was doing almost everything right.

On the horizon was another challenge. Victoria could not win this war unless she won the next battle.

Victoria had toxic teeth, but didn't realize it yet. "I thought I was doing so good. I even had braces and had all my mercury fillings removed. My teeth were white and straight. I thought I was sitting pretty. I was getting a clean bill of health from my dentist." Victoria was yet to learn that the toxic attacks from anaerobic infections (bacteria that are sealed up and living without oxygen) in the jawbone will always win out.

Thermal images taken at Asheville Integrative Medicine on January 5, 2009, confirmed that Victoria was experiencing a new level of inflammation in her right breast, although Dr. Rozema, at the same time, was confirming a rather large reduction in the size of the lump. Even Victoria could feel the lump was getting smaller, and her energy level was high. "I felt great. Nothing is making sense, but the thermographer did scare me." The last thing Victoria needed was more stress.

Reasons other than cancer can trigger an inflamed breast. For one thing, inflammation can be caused by an infection and the inflammation will be visible in thermal imaging. And inflammation could also be seen in a thermal image if a foreign object was in a woman's breast and it had triggered an allergic reaction.

Victoria was now seriously considering an ablation because it was the only treatment she had heard about that she would even consider, and the only diagnosis she had been given was cancer.

Victoria was much closer than medical doctors to solving the mystery, but she wasn't there yet. Did she have an infection? If so, it had to be a hideous one. Was she having an adverse reaction? If so, what could possibly be causing it?

"I hadn't been in the hospital for an illness since 1964 when I had a bad case of the flu. Being sick is foreign to me. I felt like between the choices I had – lose my breast, or ablation – the ablation would be a cake walk."

"Although Dr. Rozema was telling me the lump was getting smaller, thermographers were obviously alarmed at the extensive area of inflammation in my breast scan."

"With the information I was being given and the reactions I was having, I was beginning to believe if I didn't take drastic measures I was going to die. It seemed like I wasn't winning. I was experiencing a radiating pain going up from my breast and down from my breast. It was a battle I fought day and night. I didn't feel in my soul I had to lose my breast," said Victoria. "We have put a man on the moon. After all these years you still have to disfigure a woman that has diagnosed breast cancer?"

Of course, at this point in early 2009, Victoria had no clue about what was really going on in her breast.

What exactly does Victoria mean by "diagnosed" breast cancer? It's simple. Not every breast issue that is diagnosed as cancer is actually cancer. Stage zero DCIS is only one example. That was her diagnosis: stage zero precancerous condition.

"I had never heard of ablation, until I read the book, *Am I Dead?... or do I just feel like it.* I think that is the case for a lot of women that have breast cancer."

Oncologists and pharmaceutical companies have their standard talking points when asked about ablation. It's not approved, it's experimental, another 10 years of research is needed, insurance companies say it's investigational, and so forth. The real reason is about power, control, and money. Remember, the money is in the medicine, not the cure.

Even the most expensive cryoablation procedure cost but a fraction of the tab for radical surgery accompanied by chemo or radiation.

There's very little follow-up required following an out-patient ablation. Most women are in and out of the hospital in the same day. They leave the facility with their breasts, hair, dignity, and a minimum of discomfort.

Victoria made her appointment for full-body thermography at the imaging center, associated at the time with NCIT, in Clyde, North Carolina. Carrying her secret alone on her shoulders was taking its toll. "I told Mother I was going to Clyde about my root canal tooth. I was tired of lying."

Allowing for the proper cool-down period, Victoria's full-body imaging took about an hour. It was 100% safe and painless – nothing like a mammogram. The thermal images along with a narrative about her symptoms were emailed to Electronic Medical Interpretation (EMI), a medical group whose doctors specialize in reading thermography.

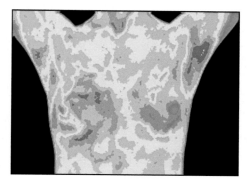

Thermal imaging revealed Victoria's internal adverse reaction in January 2009, but no rash was visible on the outside of the breast. Red and orange shades are hotter than yellow and green colors. White is the hottest and blue is the coolest.

This time Victoria was having full-body imaging. Only a half-dozen images of the breasts were taken previously at the Asheville centers. Full-body imaging included scans of the head – face, both head profiles, back of the head, and neck – plus the breasts, back, abdomen, and upper and lower extremities. The findings were back in a couple of days.

Dr. Darren Wright's report stated: "Focal hyperthermia at the corners of the mouth may relate to focal oral or dental inflammation. Hyperthermia overlies the region of the thyroid and may relate to underlying dysfunction."

Sinus, TMJ, and carotid artery dysfunction were ruled out in Dr. Wright's report.

Neither Great Smokies Medical Center on January 14, 2008, or Asheville Integrative Medicine a year later on January 5, 2009, imaged Victoria's face. Had they done so, based on Dr. Wright's thermal report, Victoria may have been alerted to an oral pathology issue that was critical to her health. She was already seeing a Hendersonville dentist who was aware of a root canal issue in her upper right front tooth and the dentist was aware she had a lump in her right breast. "I alerted him to the lump because I did not want to be exposed to any radiation from the dental x-rays."

Furthermore, had Great Smokies imaged Victoria's face in January 2008, she may have been alerted to an oral pathology issue that would have taken her on an entirely different treatment approach.

179

Medical personnel at Great Smokies failed to consider the oral pathology possibilities that Victoria was facing. What was the excuse?

On her patient health history intake form on January 10, 2008, Victoria clearly stated that she had a copy of Dr. Meg Colgate's Meridian Stress Assessments for February and May 2007. On the Energetic Assessment of Dental Issues chart, Dr. Meg had written "monitor" by her right front root canal tooth #8 "and she told me it was stressed."

In her own handwriting on an internal office form, Dr. Pam Shuler wrote "copy Dr. Meg's reports for chart." Dr. Colgate previously worked at Great Smokies and had a professional relationship with Dr. Shuler and Great Smokies.

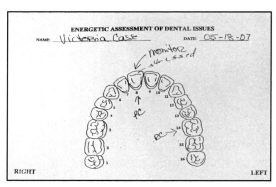

Dr. Meg Colgate's handwritten report.

There's no excuse why medical personnel at any medical facility are ignoring the oral pathology connections with diseases, except it's a matter of choice. A person's oral health can no longer be separated from that person's general health if genuine full-body wellness is the goal. The mouth is not separate from the body.

Victoria's stressed root canal tooth was begging for attention, but medical professionals were ignoring the obvious.

- Victoria's dentist, Dr. Matthew Young, referred her in January 2007 to Dr. Meg Colgate for the assessment that originally identified her stressed upper right front tooth (#8).
- Dr. Pam Shuler at Great Smokies knew about the stressed root canal tooth in January 2008.

- Asheville Integrative was not told about the stressed tooth but had the opportunity to find it using thermography, but did not image her face.
- Under the section labeled Breast, the January 23, 2009, report from Dr. Wright stated: "No significant thermal changes are noted as compared to 1/5/2009." The report also noted that "localized spread of disease cannot currently be excluded."

Had an expert in thermal imaging interpretation been able to evaluate Victoria's thermal face scan in 2007, she would have had an additional diagnostic tool that could have resulted in the extraction of her infected root canal tooth in the upper right front (#8). It is not unreasonable to speculate that the lump in her right breast could easily have gone away on its own – no biopsy and no cryoablation required. After all, a lump in the same place in the right breast had gone away on its own in 1993.

Finding a book that explained the trigger for breast cancer and how to get it fixed was a milestone for Victoria. However, she would face one other challenge that had nothing to do with infections in her jawbone or even a diagnosed breast condition.

Victoria was about to experience a challenge that would test her wits and rival her diagnosed cancer treatment regimen. This challenge would come to be described as a millstone, a weight that would stress every aspect of her being and bring her to the brink of self-destruction.

She had to fight her insurance company, Blue Cross and Blue Shield. Every step of the way, it was like pulling teeth.

She banged head first into what seemed like a graduate-level college course in "insurance economics." In other words, even a Philadelphia lawyer would have a hard time understanding it, and would have become completely exasperated with the endless red tape, delays, and excuses. But she persisted. She was up to the fight. What about all the sick people who aren't?

Most women will be a candidate for cryoablation; however, issues like a tumor's size, exact location, proximity to the skin's surface, and proximity to major arteries can sometimes preclude a woman from using this technology.

Victoria's lump was still somewhat pliable (typically, the larger a tumor grows, the harder it gets). The interventional radiologist that was evaluating Victoria's records determined that a CT PET scan with intravenous contrast was necessary before he could reach any conclusion because her breast tissue was dense. The mammogram taken at Hope Cancer Center was practically worthless because of her dense breast tissue.

Women with dense breasts have more glandular tissue than fat in their breasts, and the condition is actually somewhat common in young women. Mammographic imaging of women with dense breast tissue frequently provides inaccurate information.

Chapter 22

Once diagnosed, forever diagnosed

Several years ago, when this book was still in its infancy, I asked Victoria: If you could change one decision in the past, what would it be? Without hesitation, she said, "I would not have been conned into having the so called 'needle' biopsy."

Little did we know that the monthly magazine *Real Simple*, whose mission is to simplify women's lives, would ask the identical question of its readers for its Fifth Annual Life Lessons Essay Contest. The winner is Adrienne Starr, 37, of Falls Church, Virginia.

Starr voluntarily gave up a promising singing career – a major stress event in her life – before being diagnosed with breast cancer and discovering that chemotherapy and hormone treatments "had robbed me of my once effortless high notes, leaving me with a stunted range," she wrote in the magazine's April 2013 issue.

Her doctor warned that she'd lose her long hair, a quarter of her breast, and possibly her fertility. "What I didn't think to ask was whether I would lose my voice," she said.

As Victoria's continuous battle to save her breast from diagnosed cancer heated up, much of her energy was being drained by a war with her insurance provider. By the end of 2008, she had already paid more than $20,000 out-of-pocket to her South Carolina doctor, and her insurance company, Blue Cross and Blue Shield of North Carolina, had only reimbursed about $1,000. Keeping her breast and maintaining her excellent health were getting to be a costly and time-consuming adventure.

Each treatment for heavy metal removal was $120; insurance was paying $25. Each vitamin C treatment was $130; insurance was paying $30.

Victoria did not know until a few weeks after her biopsy how much her insurance company was billed for her biopsy and mammogram. Her explanation of benefits revealed a total $2,620. However, if Victoria had known the cost up front and been faced with paying these fees out-of-pocket, she might have been more hesitant about agreeing to the two medical procedures – biopsy and mammogram. Hesitation could have prevented much heartbreak. In hindsight, she would have been better off; her life as she knew it would not have been destroyed.

While she was already opposed to mammograms, she was not knowledgeable about biopsies – few women are – and the explanation given to her about a needle biopsy fell far short of reality. Today, she is 'adamantly' opposed to biopsies. At that moment in time, though, she was scared and convinced by her oncologist that it was the only way she would know if she had cancer, and to her thinking, a "needle" seemed easy at the time.

She now knows better.

Her insurance also paid for two ultrasounds, procedures that are safe, free of side effects, and have no pain. "Any woman who says a mammogram is not painful is delusional," she says.

Victoria paid another $2,404 out-of-pocket for blood work done at an alternative medical facility which doesn't file insurance; the insurance company declined to pay "because that's not their approved way of doing it."

Many medical centers, including most alternative facilities, do not accept insurance because of the time and paperwork hassle. Dr. Rozema's wife, Frances, told Victoria that their wellness center stopped filing insurance because it required an entire staff and it was taking time away from patient care.

Eventually, her insurance company was paying minimally, but the work required for Victoria to file the claims with the correct diagnostic and procedure codes was becoming overwhelming.

The claim forms themselves surely must be written to discourage anybody from filing. They are that ridiculous and complicated. To make matters worse, every time Victoria spoke to a different claims representative, they had a different perspective on her claim.

For example, on one claim form, Victoria was given the choice of using a "procedure code" or "Description of Services/Supplies." She chose the latter, description of services, because "I thought it would be more detailed."

Her claim was rejected by Marcia Lashley. Why? The claim representative demanded that Victoria report the "procedure codes."

Lashley wrote a handwritten two-page note telling Victoria how she needed to change her claim request. Said Lashley, "each procedure code must be listed separately, with the diagnosis code and charge for that code on one line. Do not total."

If you've ever wondered why filing insurance is so complicated, consider this. In describing BCBS's accounting function, Lashley stated: "Data entry does not go to the receipt to find information."

Victoria pointed out that the claim form gave the choice of reporting "procedure codes or description of service." That form is "outdated and you must use the procedure code," Lashley told Victoria in a phone call. The identical form was still on BCBS's current website more than three years later. How many other customers have had their claim rejected because of this foolishness? How many other customers were too sick to keep filing?

Victoria could manage an entire accounting office and data processing center for a major developer but could not properly complete the insurance claims, according to the insurance clerks. "If this lady had worked for me, I would have fired her."

Victoria wants all women to know, the diagnostic code for breast cancer is 174.9 because it "took me a long time to figure that out, and nobody helped me. Even though I do not believe DCIS is cancer, I had to play the game and use their code."

Victoria was very aware of the ongoing negative effects of the insurance drama as the challenges of dealing with red tape traumatized her body and shot her stress level into orbit. Her care was contingent upon adequate personal finances to pay for the cure she wanted – and it wasn't radical surgery, chemo, or radiation.

She was scheduled for a breast ablation on April 30, 2009 that had been pre-approved for insurance payment, but the interventional radiologist required a CT PET with intravenous contrast before he could confirm that the procedure was appropriate for Victoria's breast issue. This is not a cheap test. It typically costs from $3,000 to $5,000. She tried for more than a month to get her insurance company to pay for it. They wouldn't pay for a CT unless she agreed to have a mammogram.

Fortunately, Victoria located an imaging center in Dayton, Ohio, about 150 miles south of Toledo on Interstate 75 that would do the imaging for $900 cash. She drove to Ohio. Although she was only in the CT scanner for 18 minutes, a lot of preparation was required.

Victoria was given a few special instructions. "The whole day before the CT PET, you cannot exercise. No fats, dairy, fish, or chicken. I was hungry all day. It was hard to be on the road and eat like this."

The images were taken on April 16, 2009 and were overnighted to Dr. Allan Kaufman, an interventional radiologist at Toledo Hospital in Toledo, Ohio. For several years, Kaufman had been a pioneer in using radio-frequency ablations and was beginning to use the cryoablation technique in 2009. He was using these techniques for several organs as well as breasts. He was doing a great service for women.

A CT PET combines two different imaging techniques.

The CT uses x-rays and a computer to make images of sections of the body. It shows organs, bones, and tissues in greater detail than regular x-rays. The intravenous contrast is an enhancing agent to help produce a clearer image.

A PET scan uses different colors to show varying levels of cell activity. When the CT image is laid over the PET image, doctors can pinpoint the exact location of abnormal cell activity (detect cancer, for example).

Since the PET scan shows areas of increased metabolic activity, the diagnostic technique creates a problem that often goes unnoticed: an infection is also an area of increased metabolic activity. The PET scan cannot reliably tell the difference between infection and cancer, or allergic reaction and cancer. The same is true for infrared thermal imaging.

From the moment she had her second thermogram in January 2009, thermal imaging reflected an unusually large area of inflammation over the right breast. Victoria would come to learn that inflammation does not always equate to cancer.

Here's why this is important in Victoria's case. She had an infection and an adverse reaction taking place in the breast and did not know it. The second hint of this inflammatory process came when her integrative medical doctor did a breast culture on a nipple discharge in December 2009 and discovered a bacterial infection (staphylococcus), and a radiology report from an MRI in January 2010 found an inflammatory condition "most compatible" with an active infection.

As it was, after the CT PET in Dayton, the radiologist wrote that the increased hyper metabolic activity "would correspond to the patient's known breast cancer."

Did she really have cancer? Had she not informed the radiologist that did the CT PET that she was diagnosed with stage zero precancerous DCIS, would his report have indicated cancer, or an infection? Secondly, here's a question that's even more pertinent: What if Victoria had known about the infection and reported to the radiologist that she had an infection and she said nothing about DCIS? What would the radiologist have reported?

Thirdly, examine the radiologist's level of potential liability. Having been told that his patient had diagnosed DCIS, wasn't he obligated to reach that same conclusion? I'm not saying that no radiologist will buck the power of suggestion, but they better have their loins girded if they do. If he had concluded the imaging showed infection and Victoria died of cancer, he would have been in big trouble.

There's plenty of published evidence that even a sophisticated CT scan can be wrong. Take the diagnosis of sinusitis, for example. Too many ENT's (ear, nose, and throat doctors) consider the CT scan the gold standard for identifying sinus infections. As a result, one specialist could tell a patient their scan "doesn't look bad" and there's nothing wrong with their sinuses, while another ENT would trust the same patient's history and symptoms and make the opposite diagnosis.

Sophisticated technology had already missed an important diagnosis in Victoria's life. Suffering with an earache and pain of killer proportions on the left side of her face, a CT head scan more than three years earlier missed a serious jawbone infection at a root canal tooth (#14).

Chapter 23

Screw the policyholder

"If you live long enough, your health insurer will screw you." That was a headline several years ago in The Huffington Post.

Victoria's unjustified battle with her insurance company, Blue Cross and Blue Shield of North Carolina, was in full swing. "They always came up with some game why they wouldn't pay. It was almost impossible to deal with them. They'd always find something they said I hadn't done. It was one thing after the other. Nothing was easy with the insurance company because I had to file a lot of the claims myself."

On July 27, 2009, three months after Victoria's ablation, Pat Van Slambrouck, RN, who works in the Precertification Department at the Toledo Hospital, sent a letter to Victoria confirming that on April 22, 2009, the Precertification Department had contacted BCBS at "1-888-206-4697 and per Cameron no pre-cert required for outpatient Breast Cryoablation using CPT code 19105." The letter was needed as evidence in Victoria's appeal to the insurance company which reneged on its earlier approval.

In reality, BCBS did not pay for the "surgical" component of the ablation procedure ($1,850) and never notified Victoria or her medical team until the procedure was over. Victoria made the discovery when she received her explanation of benefits from BCBS. That's a document that says: This is not a bill.

BCBS did pay $14,546 towards the total bill of $16,396. Meanwhile, one of Victoria's friends was recovering from breast surgery and reconstruction. The same insurance company in a different state happily paid out $150,000 for her surgery; she didn't file a single form. Since the friend had agreed to 'conventional' treatment, her doctor's office and hospital staff submitted all the paperwork and got paid promptly. On the other hand, Victoria struggled for weeks to meet their requirements. "When I jumped one hurdle, they came up with another one."

They say all is fair in love and war. The friend's paid benefits were $150,000 for mutilation and a nearly three-month recuperation period while out of work. Victoria cost the insurance company a little over $14,000. Is this the 'new math' we keep hearing about?

If you accept the conventional wisdom and do slash, burn, and poison, your insurance company appears eager to pay out large sums of money. If a woman wants to have a minor and minimally invasive procedure like an ablation that allows her to keep her breast, she's on her own financially. She might get paid for the hospital stay, but not likely for the procedure.

Even before the ablation, BCBS was refusing to pay for the CT PET. Her medical doctor, Theodore Rozema, was on the phone one day screaming at a BCBS doctor as Rozema argued on Victoria's behalf – Victoria was not having a mammogram.

According to Dr. Rozema's wife, who explained the give and take between the two doctors over the phone to Victoria, the insurance company doctor was insisting on a mammogram plus a staging CT; otherwise, the CT PET would not even be considered for payment.

The insurance company doctor was bluntly pushing Victoria's treatment to chemo and radiation, instead of ablation. "My doctor recommended that I have the ablation and Dr. Rozema had already written me a script for the CT PET with contrast."

It's noteworthy to remember that Dr. Rozema had been treating Victoria's breast for nine months and was completely familiar with her case.

More out-of-pocket expenditures were on the way. She still needed the CT PET with IV contrast. On February 13, 2013, I was listening to consumer advocate Clark Howard on WDBO in Orlando when he warned listeners of his syndicated talk show to get five quotes before consenting to pay for a medical procedure out of pocket.

Howard told the story of a 62-year-old female who needed a hip replacement and she got quotes from five comparable hospitals, ranging from a low of $11,000 to a high of $126,000 for the identical procedure.

Finding an imaging center that would schedule Victoria for the appropriate CT PET scan as an out-patient who was paying cash proved to be a lifesaver for her, but the search wasn't easy. She

189

could not swing the $5,000 that one imaging center wanted to collect in North Carolina, but she could handle the $900 cash being charged by an imaging center in Dayton, Ohio.

Unfortunately, Victoria had to drive to Ohio to get the imaging, return to North Carolina, and drive back again two weeks later for the ablation. Even with all the driving, lodging, and food, it was a cost-effective maneuver.

Victoria was not yet fully aware of what was really happening in her breast. She was experiencing weird reactions. There were moments of burning sensations, and sharp shooting pains, and it was occurring in different places. And she could feel something in her breast. "It feels like a knife point jabbing me. I thought, 'If this is cancer, it's eating me up.'"

Meanwhile, Victoria's friend, who was diagnosed with DCIS by biopsy, also carried Blue Cross Blue Shield in Connecticut, and her policy paid $150,000 for the mastectomy of the diagnosed cancer-infected breast plus surgical reconstruction of both breasts.

Furthermore, Victoria's friend was originally scheduled to miss only 10 weeks of work, but an infection extended that time period, costing her thousands in out-of-pocket expenses and missed income.

On September 16, 2009, BCBS explained their denial of ablation coverage in a four-page letter signed by Nicole McKoy, Appeals Analyst I, Member Rights and Appeals, Network Support. Victoria's case had been reviewed, according to McKoy, by a Blue Cross and Blue Shield of North Carolina Plan Medical Director.

"BCBSNC will not provide coverage for cryosurgical ablation as a treatment of benign or malignant breast tumors or pancreatic cancer because it is considered investigational. BCBSNC does not cover investigational services," McKoy wrote.

Victoria was now desperate to find answers to her insurance dilemma. She called Adam Searing at the North Carolina Justice Center and was referred to Ellen Wolfley with the Consumer Protection/Antitrust Division of the North Carolina Attorney General's office. It was Wolfley who revealed the state statute regarding clinical trials.

What do clinical trials have to do with Victoria?

North Carolina General Statute 58-3-255 states that clinical trials are to be covered by insurance policies and cryoablation procedures were being studied in clinical trials in 2009, according to the website cancer.gov/clinicaltrials/ACOSOG-Z1072. In fact, the trials were already in Phase II, having started in September 2008.

And Victoria had an ablation more than four months earlier and was paying out-of-pocket.

This means that Victoria's chosen treatment therapy should be covered by her insurance company, according to law. Why didn't the insurance company tell her? Instead, they forced her to do the research on her own, and then fight to get them to reconsider. It was another time-consuming and stressful process that literally was harming her health.

Was the insurance company trying to avoid paying a legitimate claim?

"Health insurers routinely weasel out of, or delay for months – even years – making payments for valid medical and hospital claims," according to Peter Ognibene, who wrote an article posted in September 2009 at the website, huffingtonpost.com.

Ognibene maintained that many people who work for health insurers quickly learn that the surest way to get ahead "is to screw as many policyholders as they can." He described documents obtained by the House Committee on Energy and Commerce, for example, "that Blue Cross of California awarded a perfect evaluation score to an employee whose efforts to rescind the insurance of thousands of policyholders saved the company nearly $10 million that would otherwise have paid their doctor and hospital bills."

There is a bit of irony in Victoria's CT PET imaging episode. BCBS did, in fact, end up paying for the CT PET with contrast, but it was a full year later. All Victoria asked was to have the $900 cash imaging fee reimbursed to her by BCBS. She didn't ask for mileage, lodging, food, or lost time. When she finally received a reimbursement, it was in the amount of $4,050 – the amount the imaging center normally charges when a client does not pay cash.

All was not lost, however. Victoria ended up making 27 cents an hour for her invested time.

"I earned it," Victoria declares. "I worked a year for it. But what would happen if someone did not have the same skills or endurance? I could have been an attorney after I got my CT PET paid for."

After what Victoria has been through, she could also be a breast cancer consultant and educator. She has earned that distinction as well.

The Wall Street Journal published an in-depth article entitled "Citizen Scientists" in December 2011 written by Amy Dockser Marcus. The sub-head read, "Ordinary people are taking control of their health data, making their DNA public and running their own experiments. Their big question: Why should science be limited to professionals?"

While the article dealt specifically with studies using DNA, the basic principle is the same. Why should breast cancer research and education be confined to professionals?

Perhaps we should refine the question: Why do cancer victims have to do more and more of their own research to find acceptable treatment plans? The answer is not complicated. Critical information is being suppressed. If it were not for 'alternative' media, alternative treatment options would be totally suppressed.

Citizen scientists have one thing in common, the *WSJ* article reports. They believe that too much science happens behind closed doors.

In an article in the March 2013 issue of *O*, the monthly Oprah magazine, the celebrity tells how doctors are eagerly embracing the newly discovered DNA links to more than 2,500 diseases. There's a problem, however. "Many doctors have little to no formal training in genetics, and that lack can lead to devastating mistakes."

In one case, the magazine reported, a doctor's misunderstanding of a test resulted in one woman, age 41, having an unnecessary hysterectomy while a misinterpreted genetic test for breast cancer led to a 47-year-old woman having a second mastectomy "she likely didn't need."

Starting immediately after her biopsy, Victoria was pressured into thinking her diagnosed breast cancer was getting out of hand. But it wasn't. In reality, she had plenty of time to do her research and make informed decisions. She was warned that she should not delay treatment more than four months. Her ablation was 16 months later.

In every cancer diagnosis, a person's best plan of action is to take a deep breath, calm down, and learn about your options.

There is a saying attributed to Buddha that Victoria feels is appropriate for every woman who is diagnosed with breast cancer: "Believe nothing, no matter where you read it, or who said it, even if I have said it, unless it agrees with your own reason and your own common sense."

"I paid all this money out (monthly premiums)," said Victoria, "and they won't even pay for a CT PET, and you're arguing and fighting with them, and even my doctor in South Carolina had a big argument on the phone with them, saying 'This is what my patient chooses to have done.'"

But the argument fell on deaf ears. The insurance company had a list of approved treatments, and a treatment for 'saving' Victoria's breasts was not on the list.

Not on your life. Remember, the money is in the medicine, not the cure.

It's a vicious circle. Pharmaceutical companies invest heavily in medical schools so doctors are trained to write prescriptions. Doctors invest heavily in pharmaceutical stocks. Many Americans invest in the stock market also. If their portfolio contains pharmaceutical stocks and they advocate alternative treatments, they end up cutting their own throat.

Nevertheless, Victoria tried to get help in her battle with the insurance company. "You see all the work that I did," she said as she spread out hundreds of pages of letters and notes and journal entries. "It was day after day, working on it, working on it, just exhausting me, but nothing helped."

To make matters worse, Victoria could find little support or encouragement in her quest to find a natural solution that would cure her diagnosed cancer and save her breast.

Question: Did you ever find any medical doctors willing to tell you that there might be options other than radical surgery, chemo and radiation?

Answer: "No one but my doctor in South Carolina gave me any hope of saving my breast."

Question: In hindsight, what information did you need most?

Answer: "If somebody had said, 'There is a place that can help you the way you want to be helped which is not mutilating or poisoning my body.'"

According to Victoria, that's why her first visit to see Dr. Rozema was so significant in her quest for healing. He plainly said, "If you do not wish to have that treatment (surgery), we will try to go in there and get at the source of what's causing your cancer." She added, "I felt safe when I went to him, but he didn't offer a cancer cure. In fact he even told me ... 'I do not treat cancer.'"

Victoria shot back: "Well, that's fine because I don't have cancer." It was June 2008 and she still did not "own" cancer, to use her words. Her retort was easy because she had thoroughly researched DCIS.

Question to Victoria: At what point did you find a reason to have some hope?

Answer: "The book (*Am I Dead? ... or do I just feel like it. Cancer cured ... the coming storm*). I read that book almost in one day. The only other book that's had an effect on me like that was *Gone With The Wind*. I'm a southern girl, I could relate to Scarlet." (Margaret Mitchell's 1936 romance novel was transformed into the 1939 Academy Award-winning film by the same name, starring Clark Gable and Vivien Leigh. It premiered at the Loew's Grand Theater in Atlanta, Georgia.)

"I just couldn't put that book down *(Am I Dead?)*. I thought, this looks like an answer, and it's making sense and I'm very intuitive and it's working well with my intuition. I knew this book would be the answer I was looking for."

Remember that Victoria had already experienced her father's death and she and her mother were certain that his passing was the direct result of an abscessed tooth on the left side of his mouth.

194

There was one concept in the book that Victoria was already familiar with. A doctor who had checked her bio-meridians (the body's energy pathways) had once forewarned her, "If you ever have a problem with your right breast, you have that [right front] root canal checked."

Like her diagnosed breast cancer, the root canal tooth was on the right. In fact, all the oral pathology relating to her right breast was on the right. And thermal imaging proved it.

"The book confirmed the source of the lump in my breast," she stated. "I'm so healthy. What did go wrong? If you're this healthy, something had to cause it."

A Texas research scientist and inventor, Bob Jones examined nearly 38,000 patient records before submitting an application to the U.S. Food and Drug Administration in 1992 for FDA approval of the Cavitat machine that he invented. It's a non-invasive diagnostic device, based on bone sonography imaging that can detect differences in bone porosity that can reveal hidden jawbone infections.

For Victoria, Jones had uncovered one critical bit of information that impacted her ability to recover from a breast lump. In his massive study, the scientist found that 94% of root canal-treated teeth had positive pathology.

Chapter 24

Natural treatments versus mastectomy

In late April 2009, Victoria was only a few days away from entering the hospital for a breast ablation, her chosen option over a mastectomy (the radical surgery that would cut off her breast). It sounds incredible, but she was not dreading her out-of-state treatment. "I felt blessed because I would not have to be mutilated to save my life like I was being told by an oncologist."

On April 24, Victoria sent me an email advising of her appointment on Thursday morning, April 30, with Dr. Allan Kaufman. "To put icing on the cake my insurance is paying. Michelle (Dr. Kaufman's assistant) was very nice this morning [on the phone] and even gave me hotel information. I feel so much more relaxed."

Does this sound like a typical female response to a cancer diagnosis and treatment plan that typically involves surgery, and chemo or radiation, or all three? I don't think so.

Most women who are preparing for breast surgery are dealing with fear, anger, and sadness, not to mention emotional repercussions, and what she will see each time she looks in a mirror. Single women have to consider the reaction of men they may date, and married women must consider the reaction of their spouses. In reality, either situation could become a deal breaker in a relationship.

Victoria devoted the next two days to preparations before driving to Ohio. On April 27, her email stated: "I am going tomorrow for my vitamin C in South Carolina to keep my immune system as strong as possible until I have my ablation. I am going to take a walk at 6 p.m. to clear my mind when it is a little cooler."

Two days before her ablation, Victoria did last-minute laundry and watered her garden. "I am excited to get my life back. I know I have more things such as my teeth to do, but this is a great step. I have been working on reducing this lump since January 2008 and I am ready to hit it with the big guns. I think the process of dealing with the lump was getting the best of me."

Why is it that women continue to turn to radical surgery, chemotherapy and radiation for a breast cancer diagnosis when viable alternatives are available?

That question was posed by JB Bardot in an article posted October 8, 2012 on the website, NaturalNews.com.

"It arises from habit, fear, and a belief that there is no other way. Close-mindedness on the part of the medical profession combined with the hard sell of Big Pharma contributes to women remaining uninformed about the latest in breast cancer alternatives, leading many down the path of bad medicine."

What if ABC's Good Morning America host Robin Roberts, 52, had chosen a treatment approach other than partial mastectomy, chemotherapy drugs and radiation therapy when she was diagnosed with breast cancer in 2007? Would she have developed a pre-leukemia condition?

Is it worth the trade-off – exchanging one type of cancer for another because of one's chosen treatment plan? Chemotherapy-induced cancers typically occur five to seven years after treatment, and sometimes as much as 20 years later. Of course, after five years and one day, the individual is considered "cured" of cancer, based on the cancer industry's current statistical reporting.

The harsh treatment for Roberts' breast cancer is believed to be the cause of her most recent diagnosis of myelodysplastic syndrome (MDS), a rare blood and bone marrow disorder that led to a bone marrow transplant in September 2012. Following the transplant, Roberts spent weeks in isolation and emerged from the hospital with the fragile immune system of a newborn baby.

She returned to her co-hosting duties in February 2013, and then experienced a brief hospitalization again two months later. According to her interviews, Roberts cautiously uses the word 'remission' and is grateful that she doesn't have breast cancer.

What is wrong with this picture? Roberts received a toxic cancer treatment that gave her a different cancer. Has the point been made?

After spending billions on research, is this the best the cancer industry can offer? Need we say more?

I read a full-page magazine ad that said, "All our focus goes into finding a cure for breast cancer." The colorful advertisement stated:

"The Breast Cancer Research Foundation® funds more than 190 dedicated scientists at major medical institutions around the world, whose research has led to advances in detection, prevention and treatment."

Do women ever wonder about the cure? Where is it? Or why are more women – not less – being diagnosed with breast cancer?

In 2007, I mailed a copy of the book (*Am I Dead? ... or do I just feel like it*) to cyclist Lance Armstrong, seven-time winner of the Tour de France, whose Lance Armstrong Foundation is the largest athlete charity in history. There was no acknowledgement. This was long before Armstrong admitted to using steroids and other drugs.

To give you an idea of how big the business of fighting cancer for Lance Armstrong has been, reported the sports network ESPN in August 2012, consider that his foundation has provided funding to 550 organizations since its inception. The foundation has funded $85 million in grants through 2011, and $470 million is the total amount raised since the foundation began in 1997.

Where's the cure? Where's the outrage? The money is in the medicine, not the cure.

Chapter 25

Why didn't my doctor tell me?

Close your eyes and imagine that you have been told that you have breast cancer. Can you sense the fear? The uncertainty? It starts the very second you hear the word cancer. In our society the fear and uncertainty have become a conditioned response to looking death in the eye.

Now close your eyes and imagine checking into a major, fully-accredited U.S. hospital at 6:15 in the morning as an out-patient, and being finished with a 'cancer cure procedure' by 9:55 – that's three hours and forty minutes to be cancer-free.

This is not your imagination. It's a true story. And it happens frequently, but you probably don't know there is such a treatment option. You may be wondering why a doctor didn't tell you about it.

Imagine checking into the hospital at 6:15 a.m. and being 'released from the hospital' at 12:45 p.m. the same day, and you are cancer-free. That's six and one-half hours. Barring some unforeseen and unexpected complication, you don't have to return to the hospital. The procedure will not be followed by surgery, chemo, or radiation.

- Under many circumstances, a typical woman with breast cancer can be cancer-free in three hours and forty minutes (from the time a woman checks in until the cryoablation procedure is completed).
- A typical woman with breast cancer can be in and out of the hospital on the same day in six and one-half hours (from the time a woman checks in and is then released).
- A typical woman will still physically look and function the same.

Victoria's right breast cryoablation procedure (freezing) was performed on Thursday, April 30, 2009, at Toledo Hospital in Toledo, Ohio, by Dr. Allan Kaufman, interventional radiologist.

"The morning I had my ablation, I remained very calm," Victoria said in a matter-of-fact way.

At this time in her lengthy journey, Victoria believed she was also dealing with a low-level infection. While she felt sharp pains in the right breast, too, she had no suspicion that something foreign might be in her body, or that she could be having an adverse reaction. As for her breast, a cancer diagnosis was all she was hearing from medical doctors to explain the weird feelings and sensations. Other potential causes were not being considered or discussed.

According to the summary of her CT PET scan, done prior to the ablation, "Today's exam demonstrates mild diffuse increased hypermetabolic activity involving a major portion of the right breast with a focal area of intense hypermetabolic activity. These findings are consistent with the patient's *known* right breast cancer. In addition, there is hypermetabolic activity in the right axilla consistent with a pathologic lymph node."

The statement about her "known right breast cancer" goes all the way back to her biopsy in January 2008; she disclosed the results to each doctor before a new test was performed. It would be several years before she would fully understand the power of suggestion, and how detrimental it was to her health and each succeeding diagnosis.

Victoria's questionable lymph node was near "many nerves and blood vessels, making it too risky to perform cryoablation" on the node, according to Dr. Kaufman. The node thus was treated in other ways, much of which involved dietary and supplementary regimens that Victoria was already using, plus detoxing, smoothies and exercise.

During her journey, no doctor ever volunteered that swollen nodes can be caused by infections.

Some women may prefer the choices of lumpectomy, mastectomy, chemotherapy, radiation, or combinations of these treatments. That is what works for them. Victoria did not want any of those options. She wanted a totally non-toxic treatment. And she wanted the freedom to make that choice.

If a movie star has a choice, why shouldn't a housewife or a businesswoman have the same rights?

The world learned of Angelina Jolie's double mastectomy in a May 2013 *New York Times* op-ed article, titled "My Medical Choice." She made the decision to have the "preventive" surgery after learning that she carries a mutation of the BRCA1 gene (breast cancer susceptibility gene). The movie star's mother died of ovarian cancer at the age of 56. Jolie is 37.

"I chose not to keep my story private because there are many women who do not know that they might be living under the shadow of cancer," Jolie said.

The immediate reaction from television news anchors and Hollywood celebrities was predictable. It was one of approval: Jolie's decision will empower millions of women. But breast cancer survivor Melissa Etheridge, who also has the 'faulty' gene mutation, felt very differently and declined to call Jolie's mastectomy a brave choice.

It was "the most fearful choice you can make when confronting anything with cancer," said the 52-year-old Etheridge.

Not so fast. Jolie does have an international platform, but is she using it in the best way?

According to CNN, Jolie said she made her decision because her doctors "estimated I had an 87% risk of breast cancer and 50% risk of ovarian cancer." Actually, her doctors used a test patented by Salt Lake City-based Myriad Genetics that saw its stock price skyrocket after Jolie's public announcement.

What kind of science is behind the expensive BRCA1 gene testing that costs between $3,000 and $4,000? Is it the same science that led to a faulty AIDS test, or a faulty PSA test for prostate cancer, which is now known to be a defective test? What about the millions of young women who had mammograms, only to learn their dense breasts prevented any real benefit from the imaging, but they absorbed harmful radiation in the process?

These questions were posed by Dr. Richard Schulze, who has authored at least a dozen popular books, including the titles, *There Are No Incurable Diseases* and *20 Powerful Steps to a Healthier Life* (HerbDoc.com).

Schulze entered the public debate when he published a commentary on his internet blog several days after Jolie's announcement. In a decade or two, he said, "surgically cutting off healthy breasts because someone tests positive for the BRCA1 gene will be seen as a huge horrific medical mistake." Dr. Schulze said he didn't mind the movie's star's ignorance, "but what I do mind is her preaching her ignorance." He added, "The only reason a woman would cut off her healthy breasts is fear."

"And fear makes for poor choices," says Victoria.

How many women who admire Angelina Jolie will needlessly have their breasts surgically removed without having a hint of cancer? How much money will breast and plastic surgeons see in profits as they cut and reconstruct women's breasts?

Mike Adams of Natural News (NaturalNews.com) reported a more sinister motive than fear in an opinion piece, saying it all coincides "with a well-timed for-profit corporate P.R. campaign that has been planned for months and just happens to coincide with the upcoming U.S. Supreme Court decision on the viability of the BRCA1 patent."

("The Supreme Court ruled that human genes are a product of nature and cannot be patented and held for profit, a decision that medical experts said will lead to more genetic testing for cancers and other diseases and to lower costs for patients," reported the *Chicago Tribune* on June 14, 2013.)

An article published by the *Financial Times* on May 28, 2013, placed an $83 billion value on the biotechnology industry that surrounds gene patents.

Regardless of Jolie's motives, the title of her op-ed should evoke the most concern for women – "My Medical Choice." Jolie made her choice, a choice of radical surgery and reconstruction, and she's entitled to have that freedom, and she's entitled to have larger breasts also.

"When you have to cut off normal body parts to prevent a disease, that's really pretty barbaric when you think about it," said Dr. Susan Love in a *New York Times* interview. She's a breast surgeon and author of *Dr. Susan Love's Breast Book.*

That was not Victoria's choice, but Victoria was not given any other options by her oncologist because the catch phrase Standard of Care was invoked.

Why do patients not have options? It's largely because of the "overt and inappropriate influence of the health care trade unions [in each state], to the detriment of the unlicensed health care community," according to an article distributed by the Texas Health Freedom Coalition. In Texas, for example, there were over 1,500 complaints filed in 2012 with the Texas Medical Board against "non-licensed practitioners" for alleged violations of the state medical practice laws.

But the aggressive laws are created by medical boards and they keep the unlicensed health care community under constant threat, and compromise the ability of individuals to access health care treatment of their choice.

Aside from the monopoly exercised by state medical boards, there is the legitimate concern about public safety. This question is addressed by the Texas Health Freedom Coalition.

"For those who raise the warning flag of safety, we would point out that, currently, the most heavily licensed occupation in the country, physician, is directly or indirectly responsible for over three-quarters of a million U.S. deaths annually. The fact is, licensing does very little to 'protect the public' (as its advocates inaccurately assert), but in fact primarily protects only the practitioner, from prosecution and litigation in the event of an adverse health event for the patient and confers an unfair and undeserved monopoly on the trade unions."

Victoria found an option because of her own diligence, but no medical doctor told her about it.

A cryoablation procedure like Victoria's is a rather straightforward process. Here's a condensed accounting of what happened the morning of her ablation, in her own words:

No food or drink past midnight including water. Left hotel at 6 a.m. Arrived at hospital at 6:15. Checked in at Admissions. I was there for 25 minutes. Got copy of admission record.

I was escorted to Interventional Radiology Department where I introduced myself to Michelle. Gave her copy of written results for my CT PET done on April 16. Was taken to pre-op/recovery room that had about 11 beds. Was told to take off all clothes and put on hospital gown. Amber and Diane were my attending nurses.

They gave me a saline intravenous drip at 6:45 a.m. It consisted of something for pain, steroids, antibiotic, Benadryl. They told me the procedure would take two hours, and three hours for recovery.

Dr. Kaufman arrived at 7:50 a.m. He explained the procedure. He would insert two probes into lump (long needles with a hollow core that carried gas into the lump) that will form an ice ball around lump. After the ablation, he said the tumor could form scar tissue or could be absorbed back into body.

I was asked to make a black mark above right breast. It was hospital requirement. I was wheeled down on a bed for procedure at 8:17 a.m. Kevin took me down. I changed over to the CT scan bed. Had to raise arms above head. Blood pressure cuff was placed on left arm by Meg. She was person that was administrating pain medication, and keeping me comfortable.

The only glitch in the whole process was a misplaced consent form that I had signed giving permission for treatment. I had to lower my right arm and sign a new form.

Scanned for precise tumor location. Right breast was cleaned. White grid cloth with black lines was placed over breast. Tumor was located. Probes inserted. Kevin said compressed argon gas was being used for the freezing.

After probes were inserted, I was scanned again to make sure probes were in proper location. Froze tumor for 10 minutes. Kevin kept putting solution around probes so skin outside of breast would not burn. I thawed for 10 minutes. Repeated freezing for 10 minutes. Thawed for another 10 minutes. Rescanned to check tumor status.

I asked Kevin during the ablation if he would recommend this procedure for his mother, if she had breast cancer. He said "definitely, yes, there are a lot of new techniques."

I asked Cindy during the procedure if two probes were typically used. She said they have done "up to eight." Meg told me my blood pressure got to 70 at one point. I told her stretching my right arm back was the most uncomfortable part. "Everyone says that," she said.

Procedure was concluded at 9:55 a.m. I was told everything went great. Right after I got to recovery room, I had the most intense pain. My breast felt like it was frozen. I was given something else in my intravenous drip and told it would feel like liquid morphine. Thank God, I felt much better quickly.

About 11:15, my attending nurse, Cindy, put socks on my feet and helped me walk to restroom.

About 11:30, I was very hungry and Cindy brought me a turkey sandwich, fruit cup and three sugarless cookies. I also drank lots of water and orange juice in recovery. Cindy put ice pack on my breast to help with swelling. I was given prescriptions by Debbie, head nurse, which were prescribed by Dr. Kaufman.

Cindy asked me about 12:45 p.m. if I was ready to leave. I said yes. She told me not to drive or climb stairs for rest of day. Gave me copy of discharge instructions. Got dressed and left. Hospital staff was very kind to me and professional. Dr. Kaufman had good bedside manner and I felt comfortable in his hands.

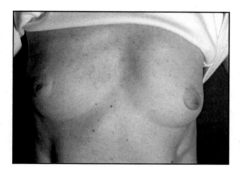

The physical appearance of Victoria's breasts appeared normal in this May 2009 photo taken several weeks after her cryoablation, but the picture does not show the internal turmoil and pain created by the biopsy in January 2008.

Chapter 26

Free boob job

About the time Victoria's cryoablation was scheduled, her friend Thelma (not her real name), whom she had met in Las Vegas in 2001, was consenting to a radical mastectomy. It was a process that Thelma was not prepared for. In fact, most women are not prepared for the aftermath of a mastectomy.

Full recovery – physically, mentally and emotionally – is a long, hard road.

"She thought she was getting a quick fix and would not have to come to her own party to get healthy," Victoria observed. "She will stay in the hospital two days and take six weeks off work, and she will be back to normal. Nothing could be further from the truth."

In Victoria's mind, Thelma was putting a bandaid on an amputated finger. "It wasn't going to solve her problem and it certainly wasn't getting to the source of it. I tried to tell her!"

"I felt guilty. I didn't tell her that I had the ablation and still had my breast. I didn't trust her not to tell my mother. It was my gut feeling. However, I was only trying to help her, and she was placing all her trust in the doctor; yet, I had lived it."

Victoria suggested that Thelma read the book, *Am I Dead*. "I gave her the phone number to order and told her how much it would be."

Victoria frequently bought extra books and gave them to friends or family members to read. In this case, unless Thelma took the initiative to order and read the book herself, Victoria considered it a waste of her own time and money.

Victoria encouraged her friend, also age 54, to change her diet, stop smoking, and "ask your doctor if you can have an ablation." Thelma consulted with two doctors. One of them, a doctor in Connecticut, had heard about ablations, but claimed the friend's tumor was too large for such a procedure.

Was it the doctor's insistence that Thelma's tumor was too large that prevented an ablation? Or were more sinister financial motives at play? There was an opportunity to perform two surgeries instead of one – remove the diseased breast, and then reconstruct both breasts.

This motive involves money, lots of it. Ablation would most likely have required Thelma to pay out of her pocket, whereas the surgical removal of her breast and the reconstruction would be paid by her insurance company.

And it wasn't just one breast that insurance would pay for. Insurance would pay for reconstructing – larger or smaller – both breasts. "For my friend, it was a free boob job." For the surgeons, it was a huge chunk of change.

Her friend's situation continues to infuriate Victoria. "They took two of her lymph nodes to see if they were cancerous," she said. She will need all her lymph nodes to help her immune system." No cancer was found. After the surgery, the friend reported having intense pain in that area.

Thelma had cancer in one breast, yet she eagerly chose to have both breasts surgically reconstructed.

"She's also telling me that she's feeling sensations where the nipple used to be, I guess like a phantom leg," Victoria speculated.

Over Victoria's objections, Thelma immediately underwent reconstruction. Victoria encouraged her to apply common sense and allow her body to heal. That didn't happen. The truth is, very few women are in a state of mind with a cancer diagnosis to make a good judgment call.

Thelma wasn't listening because she had a specific motive for instant breast reconstruction. "I don't want to get off the table with a flat tire," Victoria quoted her friend as saying. "Our culture is in such a hurry that good reasoning goes out the window."

"As soon as they finished the mastectomy, the doctor turned her over to the plastic surgeon." She remained on the operating table, and the plastic surgeon began his procedure.

Not long after the surgery, reality was setting in for Victoria's friend. "She was so depressed on Saturday night when I spoke with her. She is single and was telling me she knows she will spend the rest of her life alone. It was so sad."

A few months after the reconstruction, Victoria's friend looked at her scars where her breasts were removed "and told me how ugly it is. These doctors never cease to amaze me. I feel so grateful I was able to have the ablation."

"Another thing, you have to have a lot of energy and be dedicated, to do what I did. I had to give my life to this breast condition. She doesn't have that dedication like I have. She was getting tired after two months of doing the juicing. She's going to take the easy way out, so she thought. In the end, it was an exhausting experience that will have repercussions for the rest of her life."

According to Victoria, "When you're going to try and make yourself healthy again, it's not like taking a pill or cutting off your breast. It's a process and you have to work at it."

"I think I feel more sad than guilty," Victoria finally admitted, "because I spent a lot of time trying to convince and help her, but she didn't listen. I'm sure you know that story."

Victoria's friend was not told until after the surgery that her cancer had turned into "invasive." It was starting to spread. "How do you know that where they did the biopsy isn't where it started to spread?" Victoria asked her friend. Thelma replied, "I thought of that myself."

Thelma's original diagnosis came from the family doctor that also treats her sister. The doctor took it on himself to write a letter to Thelma and Thelma's sister, without Thelma's knowledge or consent, and stated that Thelma was going to die if she did not do the prescribed treatments.

To her credit, Thelma got a new doctor. "She didn't like that first doctor anyway," said Victoria, who participated in a conference call with the doctor and Thelma because Thelma needed moral support and wanted Victoria to hear what the doctor had to say.

Thelma didn't know that Victoria had already heard this well rehearsed, same song and dance.

Make no mistake about it, the doctor's letter to his patient's sister was a criminal act, but it happens all the time. Generally disclosure of confidential clinical material to someone other than the patient is an actionable breach of confidence. No

doctor has a right to disclose any information about his patient without permission from the patient.

There are many good reasons and situations why patients like Victoria do not want their medical information relayed to family members.

Back at the doctor's office during the process of reconstruction, Thelma learned that the severe pain she was experiencing in the chest area was the result of too much saline which was used for breast expansion. "Are we surprised?" Victoria asked.

Thelma caught a severe infection during the breast reconstruction process.

The plastic surgeon worked on the incision from the original surgery and attempted to make Thelma's surgical scars less ugly.

At the end of July 2009, Victoria flew to Massachusetts and ate lobster and toured the city that was the site of so many crucial events in the American Revolution – Boston Tea Party, Paul Revere's 'midnight ride,' and the Boston Massacre.

The word massacre could easily be used to describe Thelma's ordeal, but not Victoria's. There was one good purpose in the vacation beyond relaxation.

Victoria visited her friend, Thelma. They met at Mystic Seaport in Connecticut, where Victoria heard the horror story in person for the first time. "God, I'm so lucky," she thought to herself.

"I felt so relaxed. I felt like the worst was behind me," she wrote in her journal. In reality, Victoria was living in an illusion and the worst for her was yet to come.

Chapter 27

Place your bets

Victoria's post ablation experience on April 30, 2009, was very different than women who have a mastectomy. Although she experienced some discomfort, she was not hospitalized and she wasn't connected to feeding or drainage tubes.

It was 32 days before Victoria regained all of her strength and the soreness and swelling in her right breast was gone. During that time, she remained thankful. "I have my breast to be swollen and I thank God for that," she said.

With a half-grin, she added, "I don't know of any women that have had their breasts removed and then went to a Kentucky Derby party two days later. I wasn't my usual self, but I stayed a little while and had some fun. I was happy I could get up out of bed, take a shower and put on my makeup."

The day after the ablation, Victoria dressed in a loose fitting top but did not wear a bra. Clothing was not a problem, she said, but her vehicle's shoulder harness was. "It hurt."

Five weeks after the ablation, she still wasn't wearing a shoulder belt. She was not carrying the weight of the world around on her shoulder either. "Since I am not under such stress trying to figure out what to do because of the lump, I feel like my spirit has been lifted," she related. "The trauma is more than you realize. A cancer diagnosis leaves a dark cloud hanging over your head."

Here are some snippets about what happened that afternoon and the next day. Victoria's comments, in quotes, are interspersed in this chapter.

"Left hospital at 1 p.m. Filled prescriptions. Picked up food to take back to hotel. Ate lunch. Iced down my breast. Slept for a while. Dr. Kaufman and Debbie, the managing nurse, told me some places to have dinner, but I really didn't feel like going out. I also thought it was important to keep my breast iced down. It was swelling so much."

"I used room service to order a salad with salmon and enjoyed a peaceful evening relaxing in the room. At this point the most discomfort I was having was the swelling in my arm pit area. Tried to keep ice on that area as much as possible. Took pain pill and slept well."

The day after the ablation was May 1, 2009.

Regardless of its ancient history, most Americans over age 50 remember watching or being part of a May Day celebration, highlighted by youngsters weaving in and out as they tied the maypole with colorful streamers or ribbons.

In a very real sense, May 1 was a festive day for Victoria. After all, she had both breasts and no disfiguration. So what if she was experiencing a "little" discomfort, she thought.

"I took my shower and took the bandage off. At first I was scared to look, but when I saw how small the two incisions were I was relieved. My right breast had swollen about five times its normal size."

"Our Lady Queen of the Most Holy Rosary Cathedral was located between the hospital and hotel. I went inside this beautiful place to thank God for allowing me to get rid of a breast lump that had dominated my life for 14 months. I was blessed."

"It's back on the road to Lexington, Kentucky. I felt more relaxed than I had felt in such a long time. Within the hour, had to swerve to miss an 18-wheeler that pulled into my lane. Unable to wear a shoulder belt, I was jerked around. I was glad Dr. Kaufman had given me pain pills. I felt a lot more discomfort than I did four hours earlier."

"Since I had never told anyone in my family about the lump, I had to have some kind of excuse about why I was gone for several days. It was Kentucky Derby weekend and I told everyone I was going to Lexington for the Keeneland Race Track's Kentucky Derby Party. It was nice to get to stop driving but I was concerned about the size of my right breast."

"Arrived Lexington in the early afternoon and checked in to a hotel. I thought some walking would do me good so I found the track. It was a beautiful place. Had dinner and went back to the room. I was getting tired and wanted to ice down my breast again."

Saturday, May 2, 2009

Victoria considered herself to be in good shape. "There had to be a source that had caused this lump."

"Swelling in the breast had gone down some, but it was still very swollen. Felt very optimistic about life again. I knew I still had to deal with my dental issues."

It's important to put the time line into perspective. Three days after her ablation, Victoria was at a Kentucky Derby party. Three days after Thelma's surgery, her friend remained in the hospital and her future was bleak and uncertain.

Sunday, May 3, 2009

"I noticed since the ablation, my energy was good in the morning, but I would tire out in the afternoon. I was also trying not to lift anything on my right side. My breast was still very swollen."

"Saw some beautiful horses at the Kentucky Horse Farm. Lexington is a majestic place. Drove back to North Carolina."

Monday, May 4, 2009

"Woke up in new house. Took a 'jet tub' and relaxed. I used to sit in my tub and cry because of the lump and the options I had been given by the oncologist in order to live. That bath felt so relaxing."

"Stopped by my Mom's. I made sure I wore a jacket because I didn't want her to see my breast was swollen. I still wondered when she looked at me, would she know I was hiding something. You know how mothers are. Breast swelling was going down daily."

Wednesday, May 6, 2009

"Felt like I had a little more energy this morning.

"I started back on my organic smoothies. For example, today in my smoothie I put bee pollen, goji juice, enzymes, beet, carrots, apple, and a half of a lime. My pH on Tuesday had been 5.0; it is normally 7.0. I knew this smoothie would also help that."

Friday, May 8, 2009

"Finally had a good night's rest. Had a smoothie. Went shopping with a handicapped friend and I normally lift heavy items for her, but knew I shouldn't today."

Saturday, May 9, 2009

"This was the last day my energy level was zero. I love to garden, but knew I shouldn't pull weeds or anything like that with my right arm. My breast was still swollen."

Chapter 28

Where is your dining room table?

It was May 10, 2009, and America's annual Mother's Day recognition was beginning its second century, having been celebrated for the first time in 1908. Victoria was experiencing a renewed spirit.

Most people can remember their own birthday, but far too few of us can remember anyone else's. It's second-nature for Victoria. This day, May 10, had been kind to many historical events, and now it was being kind to Victoria.

- The First Transcontinental Railroad, linking the eastern and western United States, was completed at Promontory Summit, Utah. The Golden Spike was driven on May 10, 1869.
- Bill Haley & His Comets released "Rock Around the Clock" on May 10, 1954, the first rock and roll record to reach number one on the Billboard charts.

"Today was the turning point with my energy," Victoria declared. "I felt great. It was Mother's Day."

"My inner core belief was that I didn't have to damage my health to get well. The cut, burn, and poison theory brought me to my knees in fear. I believe the American medical establishment makes billions of dollars with breast cancer victims. I wish I had read the book, *Am I Dead?*, before my oncologist told me that I needed a biopsy, mastectomy, and radiation."

"Women now have a source for the cure of breast cancer that is done with the most respect for their health and dignity as a woman. If only I had known sooner about other treatment options, and, most importantly, the ramifications of having a breast biopsy."

"The lump has taught me things about life I really didn't understand before. You don't have to work yourself to exhaustion every day to give yourself permission to do what you just want to do. I also have to make my health my top priority and take time to make myself a smoothie or do some exercise or just have some fun."

Victoria celebrated Mother's Day by taking her mother to church, brunch, shopping, and an afternoon movie in a quaint theater setting – Flat Rock Cinema – in Flat Rock, North Carolina where patrons sat in cushioned chairs on rollers with high backs at small round tables and enjoyed food and beverages as they watched the film.

Showing was the 2008 American comedy-drama "The Great Buck Howard" starring Colin Hanks and John Malkovich. Suddenly, Victoria recognized a scene in the movie. As big as life, there was the bridge over the Ohio River at Cincinnati, the same bridge that she had driven over 10 days earlier en route to the Toledo Hospital.

Cincinnati bridge scene in movie "The Great Buck Howard" starring John Malkovich (left), distributed by Magnolia Pictures.

No one in Victoria's immediate family had been told yet about her breast. "Every time I hear about a family member's intervention, I know I am doing the right thing not telling mine," she stated.

"My mother would die if she knew that a few days ago I drove north and south over that bridge, going to and from a breast ablation in Toledo, Ohio."

Victoria waited another nine months before telling her mother, and she delayed telling her siblings until November 2010. Why she waited will become apparent.

More than a year after moving into her new home, Victoria wasn't finished with touch-up painting and three rooms had not been completely decorated. Only a few pieces of art had been hung. This was so out of character for Victoria.

"The lump had taken top priority. It was simple, if I wasn't alive, who cared if my home was completed. This also baffled my mother and sister since they knew I would exhaust myself to get something finished. 'Have you picked out your dining room table yet?' they asked constantly."

Monday, May 11, 2009

"As of today it has been 11 days. I just looked at my breast and it is probably twice the size it normally is. It is still very hard. It has a slick appearance. I thought it was something sticky from the grid placed on my breast during the ablation. I have on several occasions tried to wash this off, but it still seems to stay on my breast. Of course I am not applying much pressure."

During her constant battle, Victoria was frequently heard saying, "I have to keep my sense of humor." And she worked at it. Today was no exception. "I bet on the wrong horse. If only I had won at the Kentucky Derby party, it would make for a great story! I felt really good yesterday. My friend that had her breast removed is still in bed. I try everything in my power to stay healthy."

Three weeks after her ablation, Victoria started a regimen of low-dose Naltrexone (an immune system booster), and continues to take a 4.5 mg tablet daily at bedtime. The little pill in such a small dose has no known side effects and numerous benefits as reported in published articles in U.S. medical journals, peer-reviewed research, and news stories on TV, newspapers, and even college campus publications.

The swelling in Victoria's breast was visibly decreasing daily. Finally, on May 28, 2009, she witnessed a normal breast again. "My breast swelling has gone down to my original size," she wrote in her journal.

"I get strange sensations sometimes, sometimes painful, but this has been the case since the biopsy in January 2008," said Victoria. "Today it has been itching. Today I did some gardening, but I am still being careful not to pull too much on the right side of my body. It causes me discomfort. I still respect I had the ablation. I haven't done a task such as vacuuming because I think it would pull my body too much. I am trying to

let it heal as much as possible before I start doing physical things as I normally would."

"My breast at first was so hard; the feel of my breast is softening as it should be. I have discomfort under my arm. I hope it has nothing to do with the lymph node. I will be glad we will be doing some follow-up just to see what is going on. I know my breast is getting better on a daily basis."

"Of course, compared to my friend's story in Connecticut who had the mastectomy on May 5, this is a cake walk. Just two days ago doctors removed the drains from where they had cut her lymph nodes out and she cries to me a lot. I know how blessed I am."

June 1, 2009

"I've had a fabulous weekend. I finally feel like I have moved into a new house and I'm hanging art, cleaning the garage, putting away storage containers. It is how I should have felt in January 2008, but I did not know about other options."

"My physical energy is great and I felt like my old self yesterday when I was lifting boxes and mopping my garage floor. Yesterday I removed the contractor's paper I had put on my garage floor to stop the sub-contractors from destroying it. Without the lump in my breast I would have done that long before now."

"The thing I am enjoying the most about my life again is thinking about something besides a lump in my breast. It is like a switch went off in my mind and the world as I knew it has returned. I thanked God yesterday when I was looking at the beautiful blue sky."

"I'm keeping my weekly appointments for intravenous vitamin C treatments. I want to keep my body built up until my dental work is done."

Chapter 29

Scared of his profession

After her breast ablation, Victoria was so excited to tell her dentist, Dr. Matthew Young, about the problems with root canals and cavitations that she purchased a copy of the book, *Am I Dead? ... or do I just feel like it,* and hand-delivered it to his receptionist along with a personal note on May 12, 2009.

Nearly five years after her Christmas morning 2007 discovery of a lump in her right breast, Victoria was still having trouble accepting the inescapable fact that many health practitioners in western North Carolina were aware of alternative breast protocols and new developments in breast cancer research, diagnosis and treatment, but they were tight-lipped about it.

Why didn't Victoria's journey bring her to practitioners willing to share this information with her? She was dumbfounded.

Some of them obviously had at least heard about ablations. Victoria's mind thinks logically. Why didn't someone tell her? Why wasn't she offered at least the option of considering a path that was different from slash, burn, and poison (radical surgery, radiation, and chemo)?

In her mind, the most logical person to point her in the right direction was her dentist, who practices in a mercury-free office and is a member of the International Academy of Oral Medicine and Toxicology, whose 700-plus members in North America have already taken a tough stand against "silver amalgam fillings" that are loaded with mercury.

At Dr. Young's advanced dental office, special filters are used to remove mercury waste using an in-house mercury separator. Dr. Young understands the concept of tooth meridians and offers patients metal-free restorations. According to his website, he uses a phase contrast microscope to show patients "dangerous bacteria that lead to gum infection and heart disease."

Dr. Young recommended that Victoria see Dr. Meg Colgate for a meridian analysis. In fact, he was receiving reports from Dr.

Colgate indicating that Victoria's upper right front root canal (tooth #8) should be closely monitored.

A one-page handout given to Victoria when she started seeing Dr. Young in 2006 at his Hendersonville, North Carolina office stated: "We consider the health of the mouth and gums a vital part of overall health for the body since up to 90% of all chronic diseases begin with inflammation in the mouth."

This is a positive admission that most patients do not usually get from their dentist – an assertion that there is a very real association between the health of the mouth and the long-term health of the body. Victoria was impressed.

There's also a very real association between the health of the mouth and cancer. Victoria had never heard this, either.

When Victoria went to Dr. Young's office to have her teeth cleaned in January 2008, it was about three weeks before her life-altering breast biopsy.

Dr. Young knew about the root canal in her front tooth and he knew she had found a lump in her breast. The dentist was getting reports from a Meridian Stress Assessment that had already revealed a connection between the tooth and the right breast. And Victoria was refusing dental x-rays because she didn't want to be exposed to more radiation.

"By knowing about the information in this book (*Am I Dead?*), I believed Dr. Young could help so many women with this dental connection," said Victoria.

Her dentist called that afternoon (May 12, 2009) to let Victoria know he had received the book, and that he had read it previously. He had received a copy from his friend, Dr. Gary McCown, a holistic dentist in Knoxville, Tennessee. Dr. Young told Victoria he had referred some patients to Dr. McCown.

As the months passed after her ablation, Victoria stewed over the timing. When did Dr. Young read the book? If he had read the book when she was at his office in January 2008, why didn't he tell her. "The more I thought about it, the more irritated I became."

It was January 7, 2010. This was the first time she had been for a cleaning since she delivered a book to his office in May 2009. After the cleaning, Dr. Young checked her teeth and as he started to leave the room, Victoria grabbed his arm and looked him in the eye and asked when he got the book. "He said about three years ago, Dr. [Gary] McCown gave it to him."

"Why didn't you tell me about the book in January 2008?" Victoria asked.

Victoria's journal states that Dr. Young told her he had tried to tell a couple of people things and had gotten in trouble. He did not elaborate. Victoria would have been happy with the mere mention that a researcher was claiming to have undeniable evidence that breast cancer and infected root canals are connected.

By this time, Dr. Young knew that Dr. McCown had extracted her front root canal tooth (#8).

"I could have avoided a life-altering biopsy had Dr. Young merely suggested I read the book (*Am I Dead?*) published in 2007," she said. Victoria would have been even happier had her hometown dentist referred her to Dr. McCown as soon as he knew she had a lump in her right breast and a root canal tooth in the right side of her mouth. "He could have done that without any repercussions."

She described Dr. Young as a nice man and a very competent, very cutting edge dentist. She also understands his hesitancy at pointing her in the right direction. "If he wasn't afraid of repercussions, I feel sure he would have told me. He probably wanted to tell me, but he got scared of his profession."

Victoria paid a heavy price because of the dictatorial-like power and control wielded by state dental boards and the American Dental Association that keeps so many dentists from being healers. This power is a crime against humanity.

Victoria added: "If you don't take a stand against something you know to be wrong, then you're part of the problem. That's why I feel so strongly about taking a stand."

Strangely enough, Victoria found a book at her home in 2012 which Dr. Young had given her five years earlier in 2007.

On Page 109 of *Choices and Illusions*, Victoria found a quote from O.A. Battista: "An error doesn't become a mistake until you refuse to correct it."

Chapter 30

The Body Farm

In June 2009, when Victoria exited off I-40 in Knoxville and headed south to the dental office of Gary McCown, DDS, on Alcoa Highway, she could see the light clusters on tall steel poles overlooking Neyland Stadium where the Volunteers play football and she passed by the University of Tennessee Medical Center. She was totally unaware of the school's Body Farm nearby.

Dr. McCown is an assistant professor at UT's Department of General Dentistry, who maintains a private practice a couple of miles from the Body Farm.

As she was driving, Victoria was also unaware that the Body Farm, created in 1981, was contributing to new oral discoveries and that her dentist was one of the key researchers.

The Body Farm's official name is the Anthropology Research Facility founded by Dr. William M. Bass, a forensic anthropologist and author, to allow for the systematic study of human decomposition. The facility is utilized by researchers and law enforcement as a scientific research lab. Every manner of human decay is fully explored for the sake of science and the cause of justice.

The University of Tennessee may be the only place in the world where forensic science is systematically being used to solve dental mysteries.

A hint of this specialized research first appeared in the Winter 2012 edition of the university's magazine *Advance,* a biannual research digest produced by UT's Medical Center and Graduate School of Medicine. The medical center and graduate school are involved in collaborative research with other institutions.

Writing in the digest, Mitchell Goldman, MD, assistant dean for Research, said UT's research enterprise "has grown so vast that partnering with different organizations often is the most robust way to focus diverse expertise on a single problem."

According to the article in *Advance*, "Dentists have long been able to see how diseases of the teeth and gums affect the body, but now, our research is revealing that systemic disease can first be spotted in the mouth."

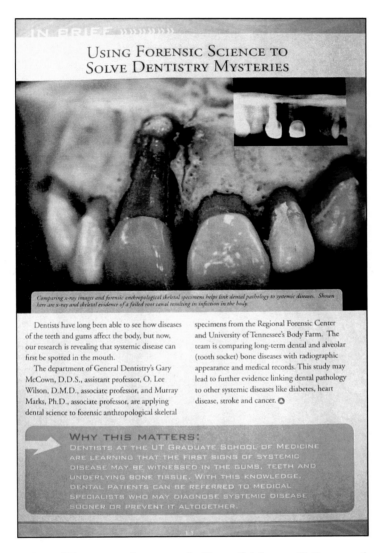

USING FORENSIC SCIENCE TO SOLVE DENTISTRY MYSTERIES

Comparing x-ray images and forensic anthropological skeletal specimens helps link dental pathology to systemic diseases. Shown here are x-ray and skeletal evidence of a failed root canal resulting in infection in the body.

Dentists have long been able to see how diseases of the teeth and gums affect the body, but now, our research is revealing that systemic disease can first be spotted in the mouth.

The department of General Dentistry's Gary McCown, D.D.S., assistant professor, O. Lee Wilson, D.M.D., associate professor, and Murray Marks, Ph.D., associate professor, are applying dental science to forensic anthropological skeletal specimens from the Regional Forensic Center and University of Tennessee's Body Farm. The team is comparing long-term dental and alveolar (tooth socket) bone diseases with radiographic appearance and medical records. This study may lead to further evidence linking dental pathology to other systemic diseases like diabetes, heart disease, stroke and cancer.

WHY THIS MATTERS:
DENTISTS AT THE UT GRADUATE SCHOOL OF MEDICINE ARE LEARNING THAT THE FIRST SIGNS OF SYSTEMIC DISEASE MAY BE WITNESSED IN THE GUMS, TEETH AND UNDERLYING BONE TISSUE. WITH THIS KNOWLEDGE, DENTAL PATIENTS CAN BE REFERRED TO MEDICAL SPECIALISTS WHO MAY DIAGNOSE SYSTEMIC DISEASE SOONER OR PREVENT IT ALTOGETHER.

The University of Tennessee's research digest "Advance" discussed a failed root canal and other dental research in the Winter 2012 issue.

Many people don't realize that the Body Farm is a real place. It gained notoriety in the movie "The Blind Side," when actress Kathy

Bates, who played Miss Sue, mentions the skeletal remains to her pupil, Michael Oher, as he plans his future football career.

The forensic research center once made Popular Science magazine's list of top summer destinations for "Geek Getaways" and prompted Global Travel Industry News to use the headline, "Tourists dying to get in the Body Farm."

In spite of hundreds of requests, tourists and the curious are not allowed.

Not only are there bodies exposed to the environment at the Body Farm, but after the decomposing is complete, the skeletons are stored for later reference and analysis in a facility under the football stadium known as the Bone Library. There are 1,167 boxes, all cleaned down to skeletons.

Dr. McCown is doing the research with two UT professors, O. Lee Wilson, DMD, chairman of the UTMC General Practice Residency, and Murray Marks, PhD, a forensic pathologist. Working with a grant that started in June 2010, they are comparing long-term dental and alveolar (tooth socket) bone diseases with radiographic appearance and medical records. "This study may lead to further evidence linking dental pathology to other systemic diseases like diabetes, heart disease, stroke, and cancer," the research digest reported.

The Bone Library has a librarian, just like a book library, and maintains medical records for the specimens as well. The bones can be checked out for research purposes, and they are used mostly by anthropology students and faculty. It's the largest collection of contemporary human skeletons in the U.S.

Dr. McCown was given permission to check out samples, take them to his nearby dental office, and x-ray the jawbones. "It's intensely time-consuming," he said. "We can only check out five skulls at a time from the Bone Library for panoramic x-rays and we want to complete one hundred."

On an x-ray, a dentist might only see a black spot indicating infection. When the actual jawbone is observed and photographed, "you see a larger area of infection," a problem not revealed in the x-ray, the dentist explained.

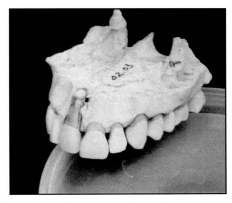

Photo of root canal-treated tooth shows missing bone from jaw (eaten away by toxins).

If inflammation leads to systemic disease and most primary inflammation begins in the mouth and goes undiagnosed, imagine the potential health benefits of integrating dentistry and medicine. It's already being done in other countries, but the U.S. is way behind.

Dr. McCown is trying to find a way to integrate dentistry and medicine, and he sees the University of Tennessee as the best place in the world to make it happen.

Famous Appalachian Trail thru-hiker Bill Irwin, who wrote the Prologue for this book, and his wife, Debra, agree. They have completed the Body Donation Document and Biological Questionnaire required by the university's Forensic Anthropology Center for a body donation. Send email inquiries to donateinfo@utk.edu, or submit an online search using the words "donate body to University of Tennessee."

The donation of their bodies is for Dr. McCown's research, said Bill Irwin, "and that of any other dental and/or medical professionals who are also looking at integrating dentistry with medicine in conquering stealth bacterial mysteries of the body. I have an idea that the issue is in its infancy in discovering what really is going on with this mysterious dark side of science."

On the university's 'body donation' website, the research program refers to the donation of a person's body after death as a "tremendous gift." The donation of Bill Irwin's body to UT will be uniquely different. He is the only person in the world to meet all of the following criteria. He had 24 root canal teeth and eight implants, and was wrongly diagnosed with cancer on two separate occasions, and walked the full-length of the Appalachian Trail with a Seeing Eye™ dog while totally blind.

Unlike medical schools, which remove designated organs from donors and then return the remains to the family, UT does not return remains. "The skeletal remains are a very important component to our research and teaching program," the website says. "The first donation made to our program in 1981 continues to be studied by researchers today."

UT's Anthropology Research Facility does allow the removal of organs for transplant. "We both would like to have any organs that could be salvaged for transplant to be immediately excised for that express purpose," said Irwin, then the bodies would be shipped to Knoxville.

According to Dr. McCown, "The oral-systemic disease connection is real, has been researched and documented since the early 1900s and is still largely ignored by both the dental and medical professions."

How can this integration between two different health disciplines be accomplished?

Dr. McCown is proposing the creation of a Department of Oral and Systemic Medicine at UT. His plan incorporates 10 specific goals.

Dr. McCown used remarks made by Orlando Montero da Silva in the Journal of the International College of Dentists to make three key points about integrating medicine and dentistry.

- The mouth is not separate from the body.
- Viewing oral health as separate from general health is obsolete.
- The dental profession must adapt a more inter-professional approach in relation with other health professionals.

Dr. McCown believes that "root canals" (endodontically treated teeth) are the only place in any field of medicine where one can keep a body part with no blood supply. One of his most dramatic findings is the visual comparison of a skeletal specimen and the corresponding x-ray of the jawbone that links dental pathology to systemic diseases, and further links a failed root canal tooth to infection in the body.

Root canals do not just remove the nerve and make the pain go away. They remove the artery, vein and nerve from the dental organ and precipitate a condition called "gangrene," said McCown. "There's no blood pressure after the blood is severed and the tooth dies, therefore the tooth can no longer be self-cleaning."

Very few people have a sufficiently strong hereditary immune system to prevent their bodies from developing cancer or some other serious systemic illness due to the bacterial infection caused by the lack of blood supply in a dead tooth, the dentist said.

"In over 22 years, I have never seen a woman with breast cancer that did not have a dental infection on the affected side!"

It's getting more difficult to find someone who doesn't have at least one root canal-treated tooth. Victoria is a prime example of Dr. McCown's experience. She had a lump in the right breast. She had dental infections on the right side – a root canal on the right side at tooth #8, and cavitations on the right side where wisdom teeth were extracted (teeth #1 and #32).

This connection between cavitations and root canal infections and breast cancer is being made all over the world, yet it's being ridiculed and opposed in the United States.

Dr. McCown asserts that root canals are an archaic treatment that should be eliminated except for the temporary relief of pain. Tooth removal and modern dental implants are safe, effective alternative treatments at about the same cost, in his opinion.

Research indicates that a single implant can cost from $1,000 to $3,000, but the procedure can also cost from $4,000 to $10,000 or more if additional procedures like extractions or bone and tissue grafts are required.

In his proposal to the University of Tennessee, Dr. McCown included a 12-page paper prepared by Dr. Ronald S. Carlson, DDS, who estimated that 420 million teeth have been root canalled in the U.S. suggesting an average of 2.2 root canal-treated teeth per adult.

But with the advent of "modern endodontics" in the early 1950s and the commercialization of the dental profession, dental schools taught and encouraged the retention of the dead dental organ's shell – root canalled teeth – leading to the "save the tooth at all cost" era of dentistry, said Carlson.

It is Dr. Carlson's contention that the "magnitude" of the pending issues with root canals has not been fully comprehended "as to its impact upon the general health of the individuals."

"For more than 135 years there have been attempts to retain teeth whose nutrient canals have been destroyed by placing gutta-percha or other sealants within the canals," said Dr. Carlson. Overlooked in this process, he explained, is that even if sealants could effectively seal a tooth, the root canal tooth itself becomes a nesting site for microbes that migrate through the dentin and find their way into the circulatory system and tissues.

Dr. Carlson cites a 1967 study where "complete healing after root-filling occurred in only 7% of the cases." Stated another way, 93% of root canal-treated teeth were not healed and still had diseased tissue present.

Dr. Carlson referred to another study of 111 people from 2001-2008 where all 139 teeth with root canal fillings were found to have an inflammatory condition that was identified by a board certified pathologist at Queens Hospital Pathology Department in Honolulu, Hawaii.

Dr. Carlson's paper draws two other interesting conclusions:
- In one study of 1,412 people with rheumatoid arthritis, 62.5% had advanced periodontal disease.
- In 2001, the examination of 50 plaques scraped out of human arteries revealed that 72% contained periodontal pathogens.

If more medical centers can successfully integrate medicine and dentistry, and improve patient outcomes, Dr. McCown believes those institutions will become the nation's premier treatment centers. He proposes instituting an admission protocol that includes a dental examination, a digital panoramic radiograph (x-ray), and treatment recommendations by a dentist.

The admission protocol would look at dental infections, periodontal disease, abscessed teeth, failed root canals, and cavitations (NICO – Neuralgia Inducing Cavitational Osteonecrosis).

By definition, a cavitation is a hole in the jawbone where healing did not take place properly. They form for two primary reasons, and the number one reason is that "healing is all about blood supply," says McCown. Most dentists use a product that restricts blood flow; an anesthetic injection containing epinephrine is most common. Dr. McCown uses carbocaine without epinephrine most of the time.

Secondly, most dentists do not remove and clean the periodontal ligament from the bone around the extraction site. "I prefer to hand curette it because I can feel what I'm doing," he explains. He prefers to not use a dental bur. The only time he uses one is when he needs to establish bleeding, and he'll take a bur and drill a few holes in the bone "and tap into some blood flow."

In his proposal, Dr. McCown mentions that inflammatory oral infections have also been linked to inflammatory bowel disease, kidney disease, osteoporosis, rheumatoid arthritis, Alzheimer's disease, chronic respiratory disease, MS, Lou Gherig's disease, seizures, poor memory recall, and other neurological disturbances. The list goes on to include emotional conditions including unexplained anger, irritability, and depression.

McCown's final point is that regular dental care, dental education, diet counseling, and preventive care are important in preventing systemic illness. "Compliance and access to care in low income populations are a continual concern to our profession."

Why is Dr. McCown's proposal so important for Americans? The research digest paper asked the question, why does it matter? Here's the answer as printed on Page 11:

"Dentists at the UT Graduate School of Medicine are learning that the first signs of systemic disease may be witnessed in the gums, teeth and underlying bone tissue. With this knowledge, dental patients can be referred to medical specialists who may diagnose systemic disease sooner or prevent it altogether."

Dr. McCown believes that maintaining good dental health is essential to continued well being. Regular check ups and cleanings are the key to good dental health, he said. "It is cheaper to change your oil than buy a new engine!"

The dentist concluded his proposal with a quote from a German philosopher, Arthur Schopenhauer: "All truth passes through three phases: first it is ridiculed; next it is violently opposed; and finally it is accepted as self-evident."

The evidence is in. The dental connection is self-evident.

Chapter 31

No diagnosis, no treatment

Sam was a 10-year-old boy with severe arthritis on the left side of his body. Thousands of dollars had been spent on tests at a hospital. Doctors told the mother that there was no known cause, and Sam would have to take high levels of steroids for life, resulting in stunted growth, no marriage, and early death.

The mother wasn't satisfied. She took Sam to see a chiropractor who traced the boy's problem to a primary tooth with a pulpotomy – a baby tooth root canal. Three dentists refused to pull the tooth.

Three days after a willing dentist extracted the infected tooth, all of the boy's symptoms were gone. He was still doing fine six months later.

Why did three dentists refuse to extract the tooth? You are about to find out!

I don't pretend to know the thinking process of these dentists, but my educated guess is that their refusal to extract the boy's tooth, even with his mother begging them to do so, falls into one of three categories.

The first reason involves mind control. Dental students are taught to drill, fill, and bill. It's a good business plan that creates a never ending cycle of patients. Dental students are given no reason to question this practice.

The second reason involves professional control and the concept of Standard of Care. Dental schools not only teach but state licensing boards demand that dentists utilize only an 'approved' option to save a tooth. Let's see, if a cavity can't be filled or a crown can't be used, there's only one option – root canal.

Dentists have been basically taught that the mouth does not affect the rest of the body. If a tooth isn't abscessed and doesn't hurt, how could it be the cause of a problem somewhere else? Dentists are no different than the rest of us when it comes to placing a value on their education. Dentists want to believe their investment of time, money, and effort was wise and the instruction was valid.

After all, they are the professionals with a doctorate degree and years of additional training and experience.

The third reason involves money. Always follow the money trail. According to one website (CostHelper.com), the average cost of a non-surgical tooth extraction varies widely across the country but generally falls between $75 and $300. The cost of a root canal varies widely as well but a reasonable average is $1,184.

If a tooth is extracted, it's gone. If a tooth is filled with a silver amalgam at an average cost of $89, there's opportunity for future fillings. A root canal-treated tooth provides opportunity for retreatment in the future if the original treatment fails. (Eventually, it will fail.)

Check the internet and you'll find many postings asking the same question: Why do dentists refuse to extract a tooth? The following scenario posted on yahoo.com is still awaiting an answer:

"We already knew that it was probably bad enough to where he would have to get a root canal," said a woman who was describing her husband's five-day toothache. "Problem is, we don't have the money for that," she said. The dentist stated that she "knows it can be saved," said the woman, and the dentist refused to extract the tooth.

"So what, he didn't want it saved. It's his tooth. He should have the right to choose what he wants done with it. So the dentist would rather let you suffer and possibly get a really bad infection just because they don't want to pull it," the woman complained. "I personally feel it's a money issue. Also, no dentist can guarantee a root canal … just because you have a root canal doesn't mean that tooth is fixed forever."

Sam's story is not an isolated case. Similar "healing miracles" are happening in dental offices across America. Why don't you know about it? Why isn't this level of healing happening everywhere? Has it ever happened in the office of your dentist?

These miracles are not happening by accident. They are happening because a few dentists are willing to question their dental school training and challenge the rigid rules of their profession that typically prevent miraculous outcomes.

One such dentist is Wendell Robertson, who served in the U.S. Army in Germany from 1987-1991. Although he was a general dentist, his last six months were spent performing oral surgery on patients because the army's oral surgeons were waiting for the wounded from the Gulf War conflict that never arrived.

Dr. Robertson returned to Utah and took over his father's dental practice, fulfilling one of his childhood dreams. He was a high school freshman when faced with the career choice of becoming an architect or a dentist. "I couldn't follow both career tracks at the same time so I chose the science path that led to dentistry," he said.

Robertson worked hard, took the toughest courses and maintained top grades. He was an athlete, class president, student body president, "and earned all of my clothes and gas money with summer and part-time jobs after school." He did well enough in college to get accepted into every dental school to which he applied, and he looked forward to becoming a graduate student, in a professional/doctorate program.

Little did he know that 20 years later he would assist a totally blind 59-year-old man from Montana into the dental chair at his Spanish Fork, Utah office, and watch the man get out of the chair and start recovering his vision within days, all because Dr. Robertson corrected some oral pathology.

After two months of testing, doctors could find no cause for Danny's blindness. Danny's wife located a master homeopathic who referred Danny to have mercury-loaded amalgam fillings properly removed from his mouth.

Two weeks after extracting a pair of infected root canal-treated teeth and removing two mercury alloy fillings, Danny could see light and sense movement visually, like someone walking through the light in a doorway or by a window.

When two additional mercury fillings were replaced, almost immediately Danny could read the title of a magazine and the numbers on the hotel rooms when he returned to his lodging. Before returning to Montana, three more mercury fillings were replaced.

Victoria could relate to Danny's root canals. When her root canal tooth #8 (upper right incisor) was extracted, Victoria experienced a unique sensation. She felt a strong physical connection to her right breast, as if the tooth were being pulled by a string out of her right breast and coming up her chest and out her mouth.

230

When Danny's wife called to say how he was doing, she reported that he was mowing the lawn and had great improvement in his eyesight.

How did this happen?

Dr. Robertson did not perform magic. He used no secret potion or patented pills. He used the tools of his trade bolstered by the common sense that seemed to evade his dental school professors.

"My first day of dental school was a total shock, a harsh awakening of what was in store," Dr. Robertson recalled. "A faculty member of the operative dentistry department gave an orientation. I expected this fifty-something, distinguished looking doctor with grey/black hair in a white coat and tie to warmly welcome us into the program."

"His attitude and demeanor gave a clear message that we were not welcome at all, rather we were 'privileged' to be in his presence."

Dr. Robertson described how a rambling 90-minute speech skirted from one subject to another about how arrogant dental students are and how they have to be taught a lesson. "He told personal stories of conflicts he had with past dental students and how he had 'skillfully' handled and managed these people and put them in their place."

Robertson specifically remembers the professor's concluding paragraphs that went something like this:

"You think that you are so smart because you have written research papers, and you have been doing calculus and physics. You have been encouraged to think and grow like little flowers. And you think that you are going to continue on this path as you become a doctor.

"I am here to warn you that you need to leave all this behind. You need to learn what we are going to teach you and not ask any questions. Everything has already been figured out over hundreds of years; we have all of the answers. All you need to do is learn what we are going to teach you and nothing else.

"You are proud that you are future doctors, but you need to put this in perspective. You are not doctors in embryo, you are just zygotes

231

(produced when an egg and sperm meet), and you know what a zygote is, don't you? It means that you have just been f____."

Then the professor sat down "with a smug grin on his face," said Robertson.

"I was shocked. I had not seen a respected professional act this way. I would expect it of an alcoholic on the street, or construction worker who just hit his finger with a hammer, but not from a professional faculty member who had time to prepare a speech. What was going on?"

Indeed, what *was* going on? And why are most medical doctors so afraid of looking in the direction of oral pathology for answers, and why aren't more dentists focused on whole body healing?

Even at age 15, Victoria was being set up for a health problem later in life when her front tooth was root canal-treated. Her immune system was compromised by the tooth treatment, and her system was further compromised with each succeeding stressful crisis in her life. Twenty-four years after the root canal, a lump appeared in her right breast for the first time, and eventually went away on its own. Thirty-eight years after the root canal, another lump appeared. She could associate both lumps with divorces – extreme stressful situations.

Dr. Robertson knew that dental school would be tough. His father was a dentist. In late August 2012, Dr. Wendell Robertson extracted Dr. Don Robertson's second molar in the upper left (tooth #15) and submitted the root canal-treated sample for testing at the Dental DNA lab in Colorado Springs.

On September 14, 2012, the lab issued its report and identified 33 separate bacteria in a single tooth. Many of these bacteria have become resistant to antibiotics. The names themselves are scary. Here are eight examples: enterococcus faecium, escherichia coli, fusobacterium periodonticum, porphyromonas gingivalis, streptococcus gordonii, campylobacter rectus, enterobacter cloacae, and fusobacterium necrophorum.

For patients whose oral infections are being associated with other health issues, it's important to identify the enemy and enlighten the patient.

Dr. Robertson frequently sends extracted teeth for lab DNA analysis. Because of the hefty cost – about $300 per tooth – many patients decline the service, in which case the dentist asks them to smell the extracted tooth immediately upon removal, a type of free but convincing test. "I promise them that there is nothing that could harm them by smelling that isn't a million times worse in their bone marrow. When they agree to this they are always disgusted; they always say it smells like a dead animal or feces. I actually feel this is more effective than the DNA test for a hesitant patient."

Doctors at acute care clinics were scratching their heads. Perhaps Nathan, age 9, had a mysterious illness. Whatever the cause of his sickness, it was apparent that no conventional doctor was going to leave his comfort zone and identify the problem.

After consulting with several medical doctors, the boy's mother, an RN, felt she had exhausted all options, except at a pediatric hospital where she felt the doctors would probably have recommended extreme treatments. The mother decided to pursue an alternative.

Using advanced healing techniques in alternative medicine, a doctor traced the source of Nathan's problems to a primary (baby) tooth that had been treated with a pulpotomy (incomplete root canal treatment that leaves dead tissue in the canals of the primary teeth) and a stainless steel crown containing 71% nickel.

Nathan's mother scheduled with Dr. Robertson for the tooth removal. The tooth itself was asymptomatic and even when x-rays do show bone loss and disease, baby teeth are not usually removed as they don't have symptoms of pain associated with the teeth themselves.

Upon removal of the tooth, however, there was a foul odor of decaying flesh similar to the smell of a dead animal. The day the tooth was removed, Nathan was gray in color.

In the two weeks prior to meeting Dr. Robertson, Nathan had a fever that wouldn't respond to any medications. The boy's fever broke within hours of the tooth extraction.

The youngster's next blood test indicated that his high white blood cell count had dramatically dropped to nearly normal. Nathan has no sign of systemic disease.

A year after his single tooth extraction, Nathan is a totally healthy youngster with a full, normal life ahead of him.

What was really happening to Nathan and Sam, ages 9 and 10 respectively, and Danny, the 59-year-old man?

The answer is found in their true stories. Most traditional medical doctors refuse to give any credence to the possibility that an oral infection in the mouth, and especially the jawbone, could be causing severe medical conditions.

This is exactly what happened to Victoria when she first went to an integrative medical center with a small lump in her breast. In Europe, the doctor would immediately have looked at her mouth. But this does not happen in the USA.

We can't blame the medical doctors exclusively, however. Most of Dr. Robertson's dental peers would take the same position, and deny that an infected root canal or mercury toxicity – the direct result of so-called silver amalgam fillings – could be a contributing cause, much less the sole cause for a debilitating or life-threatening illness.

After all, Dr. Robertson wasn't taught this in dental school. In fact, it was after his formal dental school training that he learned about total body postural balance using a process called "Chirodontics," a combined art of chiropractic spinal and cranial treatment with dental TMJ and occlusion treatments.

It was after his formal dental school training that he studied "Biomimetic Dentistry" and learned techniques for stopping the "dental downward spiral."

It was after his formal dental school training, and years of practice, in May 2010, that he heard Dr. Thomas Levy, cardiologist, make the oral pathology connection with heart disease.

And it was after his formal dental school training that he read the book, *Am I Dead? ... or do I just feel like it*. The book soon became instrumental in saving the life of one of Dr. Robertson's patients.

If all of these processes and technologies were learned after his formal dental school training, what did Dr. Robertson actually learn in dental school?

He had his own dental problems in 2010 that required removing some infected bone in his jaw where a tooth was extracted many years earlier. After experiencing his own cavitational surgery in the chair of Dr. Gary McCown, a holistic dentist in Knoxville, Tennessee, this Utah dentist returned to his practice determined to pay more attention to the specific health issues his patients were facing.

Was he now better equipped to connect the dots? Could he relate some of his patients' health issues to their dental issues? Yes, he could, and he began connecting the dots almost immediately.

Sheila, a 62-year-old female, suffered severe chest pain. In July 2010, the patient made two visits to a hospital emergency room in Provo, Utah at a cost of $10,000 per visit. In October 2010, the patient incurred another $10,000 bill.

After three trips to the ER, doctors could not identify any cause for her severe chest pain. Because there was no diagnosis, she was given no treatment.

Eventually, a dentist connected the dots. Three infected root canal-treated teeth were extracted and two anaerobic infections in the jawbone (cavitations) were fixed. Immediately after the two and a half hour surgery, the pain was totally gone and the patient lifted her arm over her head and exclaimed: "I haven't been able to raise my arm in over a year."

After a few more experiences connecting the dots that medical doctors were not even seeing, much less connecting, Dr. Robertson witnessed another miracle in his office.

Samantha, age 55, walked in using a cane and in severe pain. After surgery to remove a radio opaque area of "condensing osteitis (bone lesion)," the patient walked out without the cane.

No magic, no spells, no potions, no mysterious futuristic technology.

Brandon, age 10, was short for his age and was living with severe midface insufficiency. Dr. Robertson, who specializes in a procedure known as "Epigenetic Orthodontics," placed the DNA appliance and freed up the boy's craniomandibular complex allowing pituitary function.

The youngster grew four inches in four months.

235

With the attitudes and restrictions imposed on aspiring dentists by dental schools, it's no wonder practicing dentists are not seeing miracles in their offices every day.

Here is more insight into Dr. Robertson's dental school experience, in his own words:

Our curriculum required that we take all of the classes with the medical students. We were in class with them 18 hours per week plus we had our own dental curriculum in the additional 22 hours of a 40-hour class week. Attendance was required. Missing class resulted in failure.

An interesting point is that the medical students were not required to attend. I specifically remember classes given by researchers from foreign countries that could not speak English well and could not be easily understood. There were no medical students present, only the dental students.

The basic science was solid science such as medical physiology, anatomy, biochemistry, pharmacology, psychology, epidemiology and pathogenesis of disease processes, histology, embryology, and so on.

This work-load was overwhelming, sometimes extremely boring such as having to listen to a dentist take four hours describing how to drill decay out of a tooth. Another spoke for two hours expounding on how mixing alginate impression material is an art.

Then we'd have to stay up until 2 a.m. to study for the quizzes in the next day's classes. Very often there was not time to eat or sleep as we tried to keep up with all of the assignments of 40 hours worth of classes plus another 40-60 hours of study.

We couldn't compete academically with the medical students and the class curve showed that the dental students were academically inferior. I pointed out to my medical student room-mate that we were in class 40 hours per week and I showed him the lists of things we were required to memorize and he was quite surprised to see what we were dealing with.

I also pointed out that he had classmates that had flunked out of dental school and were doing very well academically in medical school. I further mentioned that there are not any medical students that flunk out of medical school and go to dental school.

Gradually we worked from the solid curriculum of the basic sciences to the dental curriculum. We assumed that the scientific value of what we were learning was of the same integrity as the science developed with the basic sciences, and how we were being taught to fix teeth with mercury mixed with powdered metal was as scientific as the Krebs citric acid cycle.

And we learned not to ask questions.

- The nail that sticks up is the one that gets pounded down.
- Never volunteer.
- Keep a low profile.

On the subject of mercury, someone dared to ask: "Isn't mercury poison?" The room was silent as death.

The answer from the faculty: "What makes mercury so dangerous is exactly what makes it safe. Its affinity to bind with other elements in its molten-at-room-temperature state means that when it binds, it binds very strongly and is totally stable."

We were well trained not to ask questions, or more specifically not to question the doctor. The doctors are always right.

One day a group of us were sitting at our lab benches practicing cutting Ivorine plastic teeth down for crowns. A discussion ensued resulting from the question: "How can a pre-molar (bi-cuspid) tooth survive being cut down so much?"

In our minds based on the physics classes we were required to take before dental school, it just didn't make sense that cutting away 60-70% of the tooth to make room for a crown was the best way to "fix" a tooth.

It didn't make sense to us to cut all of the enamel off of teeth. Wouldn't that harm the living root canal system and the cells inside the tooth that have cytoplasmic extensions all the way to the enamel? Wouldn't it result in dying teeth and root canal treatments?

(We were 100% right.)

But we did as we were taught and got "A's" on delicately sculpting teeth down to "preparations" that were precise and exact in form.

One day, a professor was describing the "Dental Cycle" which was illustrated by slides on the classroom screen. The dental cycle starts out with a little filling, that must be replaced with a larger filling, and then a larger filling, eventually a crown, and then a root canal treatment, and then loss of that tooth to be replaced with a bridge that requires cutting down and crowning the adjacent teeth, and then loss of those teeth and partial dentures and finally dentures.

The professor's point was that if we do a good job on the first filling and the second then maybe the patient will not move along in the dental cycle.

"So do quality work!" he told us. I couldn't help it, I raised my hand and said, that isn't a cycle, we're not sharks, that is a spiral and its direction is downward. The professor nodded in agreement; I had added to the importance of his point. A tooth only gets one chance and we don't get a new one when it is lost.

So the point of reliving these memories is to try to understand why so many of my "doctor" colleagues are content to do what they were taught 30 years ago, as if it is the sacred tenet of a holy faith.

How can they continue to use mercury and not even think that something just isn't right about all of this? If the EPA was really concerned about the health of individuals it would be inspecting dental offices for toxic mercury contamination.

How can a dental profession completely ignore the massive volume of science that condemns leaving dead teeth in bone by doing root canal treatments and continue to do something that is so potentially harmful, and even deadly, for their patients?

The answer is found in dental schools. Unlike ancient Greece, where students were taught to love knowledge, to debate, to embrace new thinking, much of higher education teaches blind acceptance of the status-quo. Perhaps one of the most dangerous concepts that the schools teach is not to question, but rather to accept that "it has all been figured out and we have all the answers."

As students we study and learn. We work hard to master what we are taught and in the end we get a doctorate degree. We become one of the masters. A missing part of this is that we have lost the curiosity, the questioning, the challenging of the status-quo; we don't debate or participate in dialogue or differing positions. We are the masters of one-track thinking.

I am very proud of my education and greatly respect my professors, many of whom are authors of textbooks and inventors and patent holders, as well as founders of revolutionary improvements in dental techniques. I doubled my requirements for graduation in the art of endodontics (root canals) and received an award from the Children's Dentistry Department. In the U.S. Army I was able to do procedures that dentists who had spent a year in residency were unable to do, yet, there was a flaw.

There wasn't room for change. The established practices were taught as absolute fact. Victoria faced the same hurdles with her doctors.

Chapter 32

Chemo drugs not accepted here

Ablation of a breast tumor is not suitable for all women or in all circumstances, but it's a viable option worth considering. Why do so many women reject the procedure without knowing anything about it?

- Is it disbelief? Women can't believe there's a viable option and most medical doctors will not discuss it.
- Is it lack of knowledge? Women simply don't know about it.
- Is it misinformation from mainstream medicine? Negative and sometimes caustic comments are made by everyone from the American Medical Association to oncologists.
- Is it intimidation by oncologists and surgeons that are selfishly opposed to the procedure? Financially, the cost of an ablation is peanuts compared to surgery, chemo, and radiation treatments.
- Is it because medical insurance will generally not pay for it (calling the procedure investigational)?
- Is it because of pressure from friends and loved ones who are uninformed?
- Is it the unknown? Women don't know what to expect.

Actually, it's a combination of all of the above.

"I know from my experience you get so exhausted, you are just worn down. You don't want to die. Desperation makes for bad choices," acknowledges Victoria, who is particularly sensitive about her family.

She stands by her choice and remains adamant that not telling them up front about her diagnosed cancer or the ablation was the correct decision for her.

"Family means well and loves you but can give you lots of pressure," she says. She did not want her family to worry. "We are all very close and it would be very upsetting to all of them. Diagnosed cancer is enough pressure. I didn't need to worry how they were taking this. Plus I am strong and don't want to feel like a victim. Only years later did I learn that I didn't have all the facts about my breast biopsy either."

But Victoria's stronger point is very basic to her and should be to all women: "It is my body, my quality of life, and I get to make the final choice."

Time after time, women are approved for an ablation procedure and then resort to the surgical removal of their breasts. More often than not, it's the direct result of family pressure from well-meaning loved ones coupled with the realization that there's a strong financial incentive to not have an ablation.

Aside from what Blue Cross and Blue Shield of North Carolina paid, Victoria shelled out $69,314.46 over the course of four years.

Health insurance plans basically offer cancer victims three options – surgical, radiation therapy, and chemotherapy. Virtually every natural or alternative cancer treatment protocol will require the cancer patient to pay out of their pocket, with a few rare exceptions.

There's also a mind control game at work. Women who have been told they have breast cancer are generally in a state of shock. In other words, they are vulnerable to intimidation and persuasion. And oncologists are good at both. They have to be. Their specialty is treating cancer patients and they are basically restricted to using dangerous and painful treatments. To sell such danger and death, they have to be the best salesmen on the block.

We all know some used car salesmen who are impeccably honest. But let's face it; the stereotype used car salesman has a reputation of being sneaky or underhanded to make sales. In contrast, a typical oncologist relies on fear to sell surgery, chemo, and radiation. This characteristic is not necessarily a personal trait of the oncologist as much as it is part of the job.

The cancer prescription is a drug so dangerous that the Environmental Protection Agency (EPA) has drafted hundreds of pages describing precisely how the drugs are to be handled in a medical setting as well as disposed of properly. Even people being treated as out-patients are given strict guidelines regarding methods for cleaning or disposing of their clothing to keep others from becoming contaminated. And they're told not to touch loved ones.

The guidelines cover chemotherapy waste bags, empty vials, tubing, gowns, gloves, needles, and other sharp objects.

Most people would question the claims of a used car salesman, yet hardly anyone questions the claims of an oncologist. Isn't this strange?

Actually, it's not as strange as the radio report Victoria heard on the morning of April 4, 2013, when a spokesman for the Henderson County (North Carolina) Sheriff's Department announced an on-going pharmaceutical drug disposal program. She was listening to WHKP AM 1450 when Major Frank Stout, public information officer, reported about a permanent collection box in which citizens may deposit unused pharmaceutical medications.

There is one catch. Chemotherapy drugs are not accepted in the collection box. Patients put these dangerous drugs in their bodies as per their doctor's instructions, and the same drugs are not even allowed in a public depository for unused pharmaceutical drugs. Isn't this strange?

Pharmaceutical compounds and hormones are considered to be 'toxins of emerging concern' because they are finding their way into the nation's water supply. Chemotherapy wastes contain powerful drugs, far more dangerous than your leftover antibiotics or Valium.

Women who have heard the cancer pronouncement from a doctor will tell you that the prospect of chemo or immediately facing the surgical knife can leave a female somewhat crazed out of her mind. "With the pressure of the doctors, you don't need more pressure making a decision," said Victoria.

- It is the woman's life.
- It is the woman's breasts.
- At the end of the day, the woman will look in the mirror and she will examine her soul and she will have to face the consequences. She must do whatever serves her best.

For those women who find themselves overwhelmed and praying for a miracle, try going back to basics. Some researchers believe that doing nothing is better than the 'rush to judgment.' It may not be easy to recover once you have damaged your body with radical surgery, chemotherapy, or radiation.

Victoria found a very calming release after reading the book, *Cancer Is Not A Disease*, by best selling author and internationally acclaimed health expert Andreas Moritz (cancerisnotadisease.com).

It's a survival mechanism, says Moritz. He claims that medical intervention "attempts to remove the symptoms of disease with almost complete disregard to their cause(s). This is not only unscientific and unethical, but also life endangering."

"Each year over 900,000 people in the U.S. lose their lives needlessly to medical treatment," he says on his website. "Even one single dose of chemotherapy or radiation can be fatal for both the tumor and the patient."

It was while showering on the morning of May 15, 2009 that Victoria noticed the swelling in the right breast was virtually gone. "Every day it was going down and getting softer."

Although the swelling and soreness – symptoms almost always associated with a cryoablation – were disappearing, the original focal point of the pain in the right breast never went away. The pinpoint pain started immediately after the biopsy in January 2008, and although there was some ebb and flow to the pain, it was always there. The pain associated with the ablation procedure was in a different location, and once healed, there was never any pain or discomfort at that location again.

There are two notable points to be made about a breast cancer tumor and hardness. One is that as cancer tumors grow, the tumor's outer surface tends to get harder. Following an ablation, a tumor or mass will either partially or fully dissolve or remain hard – dead, but hard. There seems to be no way to predict the outcome.

Chapter 33

Mother, it shocked me also

It was dusk on Saturday, February 27, 2010, when Victoria backed out of her garage and drove several hundred feet down the hill to her mother's house. She usually walked but she didn't want to walk home alone in the dark or the cold.

"I needed her support. I was getting worn out. I'm tired of lying to my mother."

Her brother Greg was visiting her brother Woody in Palm Springs, so her mother was alone. A short while earlier she heard the television news reporting that San Diego, several hours away from Palm Springs, was under a tsunami warning triggered by an 8.8 magnitude earthquake in central Chile, the sixth largest quake ever recorded by a seismograph.

She was uneasy about her brothers; it's that 'mother instinct' she has with her siblings. She didn't like the news that a tsunami could be headed for California. She didn't like her Saturday afternoon mission either. She was anxious. She was about to confess to keeping her cancer diagnosis secret for two years. How would her mother react?

Emotionally, Victoria was at peace knowing she only had a breast infection. "When someone is told they have cancer, too often good reasoning goes out the window. I was cancer-free. I was dealing with an adverse reaction and an infection. How could I make my mother understand this?"

Victoria sat on the couch, her mother in a recliner. Two agonizing hours passed. "It was such a complicated and confusing story," she said. In the process, Victoria had to "swear my mother to secrecy, which was very hard for her to do."

The norm in the mother-daughter relationship usually went something like this: Tell mother something private, moments later, sister knew all about it, but would be confused.

Cautiously, Victoria proceeded. "Mother, do you remember when you had to talk to your mother about something that had to stay between you and her? Mother, I need to talk to you and I will only tell you if you promise me it will stay between the two of us."

"My mother is normally not at a loss for words. She had a shocked look on her face. She was in a daze. She was in total disbelief."

Aside from completely and totally baring her soul, there was one overriding thought in the back of Victoria's mind: "I knew she would be the support I needed. I didn't need the pressure of her believing or worrying that I had cancer. In our society, a cancer diagnosis is usually interpreted as death. I did not want my mother falsely and needlessly believing I was going to die."

As it turned out, "my mother was good about it. I felt relieved."

It took several days for Victoria's mother to comprehend the gravity of her daughter's silent and sometimes lonely battle with her cancer diagnosis. She finally opened up. "Of all my kids," she told Victoria, "I would never have thought something like this would happen to you. Victoria, you were so healthy and you always took care of yourself."

"Mother, it shocked me also," Victoria responded. "This is why the dental issues are so important. They can cause your breasts to get lumps." Victoria's mother had traveled with her to Knoxville when her two root canals were extracted. Even as secretive as Victoria had become, it's hard to disguise a missing front tooth.

Victoria knew she should write a letter to her brother in California and sister in Louisiana so they would have time to digest it before there was a conversation. "This is something I needed to tell my siblings myself and not have my mother communicate the story. The story was so complicated. I felt I needed to explain it in writing, but I didn't do that for nine months."

Chapter 34

Do you want to dance?

For four years, Victoria steadfastly believed that she was dealing with an infection, and the root source of this infection was the biopsy procedure.

How was she feeling in January 2008 before the biopsy? "Great," she said, "I was excited. I was on top of the world." The lump she felt on Christmas Day 2007 did produce a sudden rush of fear, "mental and emotional agony, but not pain. There was a slight discomfort. That's all. It was the fear." Fear pushed reason and logic out the door.

Then came the biopsy. Nothing was ever the same after her biopsy. Nothing!

On a scale of 1-10, the pain or discomfort in Victoria's breast on the morning of January 23, 2008, was hardly a 1 – barely noticeable.

When she walked out of the Hope Cancer Center at 1 p.m. that day, after the biopsy, the pain or discomfort level in her breast was an 8. That might have been expected – pain and discomfort for a few days. But Victoria did not experience a sustained recovery.

No doctor was able to explain the pain and discomfort.

After the biopsy, Victoria always had pain and discomfort that was never there before, and although the level of pain and discomfort varied over the next several years, it never went away. There was an ebb and flow to the pain and discomfort. Pain and discomfort were present prior to and after her cryoablation done on April 30, 2009.

She experienced strange sensations in her breast and chest wall, sensations she had never felt before. Certain movements and stretching were uncomfortable, if not painful. She noticed swelling in the right breast that would come and go. Nearly all exercise movements that involved her chest and right arm brought her attention to the right breast. A tight hug triggered sharp pain. Antibiotics always helped the situation. But she wasn't interested in living on antibiotics.

What caused these pains, some of which were often sharp like a knife cutting her, or something metallic cutting into her tissue, or something metal with a sharp point that was jabbing her in the ribs?

In the first half of 2009, after extensive natural treatments and a cryoablation, Victoria generally felt good and remained very active. Her journal entry on May 28 reminded her that she had accomplished the "finishing touches" on her new house, resumed her smoothies, and planted her garden. "I'm going to get my life back on track."

It was time to deal with the root cause of the lump in her breast. On June 23, 2009, she drove three hours by herself, north on I-26 and then headed west to Knoxville, Tennessee on I-40 through the Pigeon River Gorge near the North Carolina state line which is notorious for rockslides and boulders the size of houses falling on the highway.

Her angels were with her. Two years earlier, a rockslide closed the interstate highway in western North Carolina for nearly six months. About 14 weeks after Victoria finished her dental work in October 2009, another rockslide closed the highway. Some people claim this section of interstate is twice as dangerous as any other interstate location in the U.S.

Victoria slipped through The Gorge, as it's locally known, on two occasions in the summer of 2009 without incident. Two minutes before pulling into the parking lot, she passed by the famous Body Farm at the University of Tennessee.

It was Victoria's first meeting with Dr. Gary McCown, a dentist who has seen more than 800 cancer patients in the past 20 years and never found one that did not have a contributing anaerobic infection in the jawbone. Dr. McCown and I have worked closely together for eight years comparing his patients' digital panoramic x-rays with their thermal images.

Victoria had two separate appointments. The first visit was for the purpose of cleaning up two cavitations. In July, she was to return to have two infected root canal teeth extracted.

She wasn't looking forward to the extractions. "Everything doesn't have to be as perfect now. I used to be a lot more vain before I was diagnosed with cancer. Now I understand the dangers of root canals. I had to have them extracted."

Dr. McCown is much more than a good dentist. He has earned the respect of his patients who know him as a true healer. He made the same impression on Victoria.

Victoria's wisdom teeth on the right side were extracted at the age of 20, after she moved to California. Her wisdom teeth on the left side never developed.

Dr. McCown used an injection of Citanest Plain (carbocaine without epinephrine) to deaden the area at tooth #1 and #32. He was fully aware of Victoria's unique sensitivities. Epinephrine restricts bleeding long after surgery and Dr. McCown tries to use as little as possible with his patients. It's one of the keys for healing, he says.

"She tested better with it," the dentist observed. Because Dr. McCown acknowledged that Victoria could have problems with many dental materials, he had recommended a Meridian Stress Assessment to check the compatibility of his dental materials and anesthesia. "Dr. McCown and Dr. Heltzel in Las Vegas were the only two dentists in my life who recognized that I could have a sensitivity to certain dental materials," Victoria said.

The dentist rated the bottom cavitation as a "6 or 7" on a scale of 1-10, with the larger number being the worst.

The upper cavitation was another story. The jawbone contained a "huge amount of oil plus yellow drainage," the dental records state. Victoria was in reverse of the typical patient. The bottom cavitation usually proves to be the worst infection. In Victoria's case, the dentist rated the upper site as an 11, off his chart, so to speak.

"The moment he did the upper cavitation, I had a feeling come over me like my spirit had been lifted. I just felt lighter all over. At the end I had tears of joy because I knew he is helping to save my life. In fact, in nearly two dozen years of doing cavitations, my upper one was the third worst he had ever seen," Victoria said.

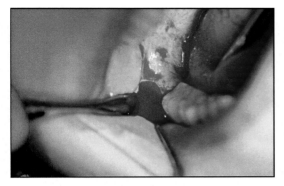

Photo was taken during the cavitation surgery at Victoria's wisdom tooth extraction site (#32). The technical term for a cavitation is "neuralgia inducing cavitational osteonecrosis," often referred to as "NICO." All the dark spots are the "oil" that is bacterial waste indicative of a bacterial infection, explained Dr. Gary McCown. Dr. Jerry Bouquot, a licensed dentist since 1971, board certified oral pathologist, and director of research at the Maxillofacial Center for Diagnostics and Research in Morgantown, West Virginia, is the nation's leading proponent of NICO. "Dr. Bouquot told me, 'If you find the oil, you found the problem,'" said Dr. McCown. Cavitations are thought to be the result of extractions using too much epinephrine (anesthesia administered by injection), which restricts blood flow for several hours, and not removing the periodontal ligament which connects the tooth to the jaw bone.

"The moment he did the upper cavitation, I had a feeling come over me like my spirit had been lifted. I just felt lighter all over. At the end I had tears of joy because I knew he is helping to save my life. In fact, in nearly two dozen years of doing cavitations, my upper one was the third worst he had ever seen," Victoria said.

Victoria's testimony about how she felt following the cavitational surgery "should have been on tape," said Dr. McCown. "Incredible!"

Victoria felt so good, so quickly, that she almost embarrassed herself. "Well, he is handsome." She sat up in the dental chair and asked, "Hey, do you want to dance?"

Driving home that day, she stopped frequently to change the gauze in her mouth. "I was glad to get home," she said. "That last hour was hard. This tumor has dominated my life for so long. It was painful. It kind of drained me. All this takes a toll on you but it sure beats a mastectomy."

At home, Victoria's mouth was still swollen when she heard the news on June 25 that pop singer Michael Jackson and sex symbol and pop culture icon Farrah Fawcett had died on the same day. The circumstances and timing of Jackson's death were compared to those of Elvis Presley and John Lennon and seemed to push Fawcett's death from cancer into the background.

"I thought that she was a very beautiful woman who died a tragic death, and before she died, medical doctors ruined her looks," said Victoria. "They killed her spirit and her looks at the same time."

Fawcett rose to stardom in 1976 after portraying the role of a private detective in the hit TV series, "Charlie's Angels," and her swimsuit poster sold a record-breaking 12 million copies. Victoria's shoulder-length hairstyle in the 1970s and 1980s was quite similar to Fawcett's, believed by many fans to be the most famous hair in the world.

However, Victoria's fascination with Farrah Fawcett had more to do with cancer than her imposing white teeth, sculpted hair, and contoured body. Diagnosed with colorectal cancer in 2006, Fawcett, who could afford any treatment in the world, submitted to chemo and surgery. Four months later, the Associated Press reported that she was cancer-free.

Another four months passed and, in May 2007, Fawcett was diagnosed with a malignant polyp where she had been treated for her initial cancer. She rejected a colostomy and, instead, traveled to Germany for a novel treatment protocol that became the basis of a two-hour documentary, "Farrah's Story."

In Germany, doctors discovered Fawcett's cancer had metastasized to her liver.

Controversy surrounded the documentary as some of Fawcett's associates claimed the film's editing omitted the exploration of rare cancers and alternative methods of treatment that the 62-year-old star wished to portray.

Victoria was thankful for alternative forms of treatment. She was feeling refreshed after her July 1 birthday bash with family. She spent all day on July 4, 2009, cleaning at home. But she was anything but independent. She was tied down by an inflamed breast and no medical doctor was willing to help her. She didn't know it at the time, but she was a long 33 months away from freedom.

"Finally got the house put together. Today was a wonderful day. I got my kitchen table put in with 'rooster pillows' on the chairs. I vacuumed and mopped the house, just loving every second of it. Now there are no contractors, paper, plastic or plastic containers in this house. I got on my knees and thanked God. I like the peacefulness of my life now." That's how Victoria felt on July 4, 2009.

July 7, 2009 came quickly. Victoria headed off through The Gorge, this time accompanied by her mother, who still did not know about her daughter's diagnosed breast cancer. Victoria thought about the significance of her sharing a motel room with her mother, and not having any hint of a breast issue. Her cryoablation procedure was done nine weeks earlier; she still had her breasts, her hair, and her health. Imagine if she had submitted to any other type of radical surgery.

Dr. McCown had agreed to schedule Victoria quickly because her ablation was behind her and he was booked solid into the near future. "He was so kind to me coming in on his day off Wednesday, July 8, with his dental assistant to extract my two root canals."

Victoria's #14 was taken first, "The shot hurt," she wrote in her journal. The tooth had three long roots and the infection was still developing. "With the right root canal extraction (#8), I felt the intense feeling in the core of my right breast. It did not bring a feeling as much over my complete body as the cavitation did."

Victoria's right front tooth is the infamous root canal tooth previously described in Chapter 9 of this book, where Dr. McCown found the tip of the file used by the dentist when her root canal was done at age 15. For years, she had been having an allergic reaction to the nickel in the stainless steel file. Remember the red spot on her upper lip?

"My meridian was finally opened up after all this time. It was as though a heaviness was taken from that area."

"Since that root canal and my wisdom teeth were done so long ago, I had forgotten what my complete body should feel like if everything was functioning as it should. My body had not forgotten, and was so delighted to have all my energy systems functioning the way they should be."

There's a paradox associated with women like Victoria who have root canal infections and diagnosed breast cancer. The dentists who are trained to diagnose and treat such lesions in the jawbone are few and far between. Yet the bulk of dentists, who are not properly educated and trained in the nuances of digital panoramic x-rays and thermograms, fail to realize that their lack of training should disqualify them.

These dentists should never be telling a woman with breast cancer that she has no oral pathology – no cavitations and no infected root canal-treated teeth – because they're not trained to see it or find it, and the infections are not always obvious or apparent on an x-ray.

Dr. McCown needed to fashion a cantilevered bridge to secure tooth #8 without closing the "midline" of her mouth. It's unwise to do a bridge that goes across the midline, he said. "If you tie two bones together they don't flex anymore. It's a craniopathy issue."

Victoria woke up in her own house on July 9, the day after her root canal extractions. "I know now I'm on the road to good health. It was shocking to take the temporary partial out and I see that I don't have a front tooth. Life is strange. If I hadn't been diagnosed with cancer, this would have been harder. Now I'm happy I did it," she wrote in her journal.

Her younger brother was having fun with her swollen face, mocking the Alvin the Chipmunk look. "I'm sure in a couple of days with a little healing I will be feeling great. Imagine having all that infection in my body for 40 years."

It took her a few days to get a grip on the loss of her front tooth. "What choice did I have?" she thought. "Death?"

Victoria walked out of the dental office wearing a two-tooth temporary partial that was replaced six weeks later with two separate permanent bridges. Because of vanity, she was worried about losing her front tooth. In the end, cosmetically speaking, the bridge holding #8 in the front looked much better than the root canal tooth.

By mid-September 2009, her doctor in South Carolina was very happy to observe that the "ablated lump was reduced in size," Victoria wrote in her journal. He examined her breast and told her she should write a book about breast cancer. That was the first time Victoria acknowledged to him that a book was, in fact,

being written. **"How could I learn all this information and not share it with other women? I didn't want another woman to not have the knowledge I now possess."**

But the right breast refused to settle down. Victoria experienced strange sensations in September and by October 2010 she was using a word like "weird" sensations.

"I started having a brown discharge from my right breast nipple," Victoria wrote on October 2. "I had been having pain in my back, under my right arm and right breast a few weeks prior. Crust on nipple, been tired."

She re-filled an antibiotic in mid-October that the dentist had prescribed following dental surgery. She felt better immediately. "The discharge was now more yellow than red." Within a few days the discharge stopped. "This isn't how cancer works," she reminded herself. There was no doubt in Victoria's mind that she was dealing with an infection.

Each time she would finish a round of antibiotics, the infection responded by producing less pain or discomfort. She tried a two-hour ultraviolet light and intravenous hydrogen peroxide treatment at Dr. Rozema's in November 2010 to clean up her blood. "I hope this second treatment does the trick." But the UV light and peroxide did not do the trick.

By December 1, the nipple discharge in Victoria's breast had gotten bad enough that she wrote a journal entry that stated: "I would love to have a break with this breast. The family still hasn't been told."

Dr. Rozema took a discharge sample to be cultured in a laboratory. A week later, a report from LabCorp in Burlington, North Carolina confirmed the infection as staphylococcus, and the antibiotic Tetracycline was recommended. Victoria took the recommended dosage and, as usual, the infection seemed to subside almost immediately, only to return with a vengeance when the prescribed round of antibiotics was completed.

Why? Why could Victoria not arrest this infection with powerful antibiotics? She exhausted herself asking this question, over and over again. What was so different about this infection that heavy dosages of antibiotics failed to kill it?

Chapter 35

Everyone needs a D-Day

Since their first meeting in January 2009, Victoria had become close friends with a certified thermographer, Brenda Kinder, at Proven Health Management (PHM) in Clyde, North Carolina, a screening center that was on the cutting edge of thermal imaging.

The center's use of medical Digital Infrared Thermal Imaging (DITI) technology provided a non-invasive method for men and women to monitor health issues in their entire bodies – cardiovascular issues, for example – as well as for women to monitor their breast health.

Not all thermal imaging centers are the same, however. The key difference at the PHM center was in the emphasis placed on oral pathology and the premise that every woman who has breast cancer has an anaerobic infection in their jawbone, and it will most likely be found in a root canal-treated tooth or a cavitation at a wisdom tooth extraction site. No exceptions have been found.

Even if the oral pathology and cancer connection was only a 50/50 probability, why would any woman fail to use thermal imaging as one of several tools to be sure she did not have a potentially life-threatening infection in her jawbone?

The technology is totally non-invasive. An infrared scanning device is used to convert infrared radiation emitted from the skin surface into electrical impulses that are visualized in color on a monitor and thus quantify changes in skin surface temperature.

This visual image graphically maps the body temperature and is referred to as a thermogram. The spectrum of colors indicates an increase or decrease in the amount of infrared radiation being emitted from the body surface.

Thermal imaging is about symmetry – same heat on one side of the body as the other. Since there is a high degree of thermal symmetry in the normal body, subtle abnormal temperature asymmetry's can be easily identified.

DITI's major clinical value is in its high sensitivity to pathology in the vascular, muscular, neural, and skeletal systems. DITI is unique in its capability to show physiological change and metabolic processes.

The Clyde screening center also utilized its thermal camera to explore the world of EMF's (electromagnetic frequencies), especially as they relate to cell phones, and various stick-on devices that claimed to neutralize the EMF's. Fifteen minutes of talking on a cell phone – with phone to the ear – creates an enormous amount of inflammation in the head. It's frightening when viewed in a thermal image.

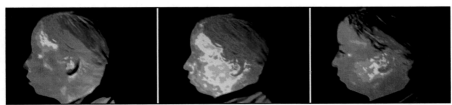

Woman (left) had not talked on a cell phone for hours. After talking 15 minutes on cell phone, woman's head was inflamed (middle). After cooling down, woman again talked for 15 minutes, this time with the cell phone protected by a stick-on electromagnetic frequency device. There was far less inflammation with the EMF device attached (right) than without the device.

However, the most revealing aspect of the center's research was focused on oral pathology. For example, could thermal images of a client's mouth reveal oral health issues that are not readily apparent on a dental x-ray? If so, thermal imaging would be a great assist to dentists.

Could thermal images help doctors and dentists better assess the cause of many health maladies, if the mouth could be connected to the problem?

When thermal images were submitted to Electronic Medical Interpretation, a group of doctors specially trained to read the colorful scans, a medical doctor might describe the heat signatures around the mouth as follows:

"There is hyperthermia over the anterior mandible, with associated bilateral submandibular lymphatic drainage patterns, and over the anterior and posterior maxillae. These findings are consistent with dental/periodontal pathology."

Such language is confusing to most people, especially those who have never used thermal imaging before. It's also confusing to most practicing medical doctors, because they've never had any training in the relationship between the mouth and whole body wellness. Neither have most dentists.

There had to be a simple educational process to help people understand teeth classifications and how infections in their jawbone correlate with organs and systems in their body. This is what PHM became known for.

Because of the book, *Am I Dead? ... or do I just feel like it,* most of the Clyde screening center's clients were already familiar with an ablation procedure that was being used by many women who were diagnosed with breast cancer. As these women would discuss breast health issues with their own network of family and friends, other women became curious.

Proven Health Management became a clearing house for information about ablations. "Women needed to talk to other women about options other than lumpectomies and mastectomies, and most of our clients were very much opposed to radiation and chemotherapy treatments," explained PHM thermographer Brenda Kinder.

(PHM sold its thermal imaging camera in October 2011 because of continued harassment by the state medical board.)

In the big scheme of things, very few women learn about the breast-saving ablation technology until after it's too late. Their breast has been mutilated by some surgical procedure, often described by a doctor beforehand as a "small incision" with a "little bit of tissue removed."

Some women are, in fact, able to go under the knife and their breast will appear normal afterwards. But they are the exception, not the rule. After the typical surgery, most women who have a lumpectomy are petrified at the damage done to the texture and natural shape of their breast. If they are single women, they are even more terrified at the result.

A woman from New Jersey happened to have a conversation with a woman who had already used the ablation procedure to treat her early stage breast cancer and she was given PHM's number. She called Proven Health Management seeking more information about cryoablation.

Brenda Kinder could have given the woman the name and phone number for an interventional radiologist, but she sensed that the caller needed some human intervention, not just hard data. She thought of Victoria.

Brenda knew that Victoria would not mind talking to a total stranger about her own ablation experience. With a quick phone message, Victoria was told to expect a call. "Brenda asked me to explain the process to her."

Victoria was about to solve the great mystery engulfing her right breast.

Why did she have an infection? Why couldn't she get rid of the infection? Why was she having sharp pains in the right breast? Why did she feel like there was an object in her breast, something foreign? Why did this mysterious thing feel hard like metal? Why did it move around? Why did it feel like it had a sharp edge and a point?

Even the tiny lump she felt prior to the biopsy in January 2008 had none of the same characteristics after the biopsy, nor did the original lump feel anything like what she was now feeling. The pre-biopsy lump had flexibility and softness. It definitely was not hard like metal and it had no points or sharp edges that produced pain when she pressed on it. The lump she felt on Christmas morning was more like a soft sponge, not a hard rock with a knife.

There was something very different about the lump after the ill-fated biopsy, especially the pain that always accompanied a tight hug.

It was D-Day!

Every ounce of her being was being used to fight the infection and almost hold it at bay – almost. But she was gradually losing ground.

In spite of some occasional doubts, she knew she was cancer-free. Her integrative doctor knew it. A breast surgeon knew it. An interventional radiologist was very confident that he had successfully frozen the tumor. After all, she was diagnosed with a stage zero precancerous condition that many experts don't even consider to be cancer. Furthermore, Victoria had utilized a number of natural protocols that would deal with any lymph node concerns. Lymph nodes are especially susceptible to infection.

Other than the breast infection and its associated pain, she felt extremely good.

It was Sunday afternoon, June 6, 2010. June 6 is one of the most important dates in history – the Allied invasion of Normandy that signaled a turning point in World War II. Most people know the date as D-Day, which marked the largest amphibious invasion in world history that was executed by land, sea, and air.

Victoria and her younger brother had been working in their garden. Around four o'clock, an earthshaking phone call took place between two women who had never met or spoken to each other before. In the time it took to exchange greetings and a couple of questions, Victoria connected the missing dots.

D-Day was a turning point in the outcome of World War II. Now, D-Day was a turning point in Victoria's search to find the truth about the mysterious symptoms in her breast.

New Jersey resident Ronda Lutfey, 49, had a biopsy in April 2010 and was diagnosed with DCIS in the left breast. Although she is a licensed and practicing pharmacist, she wasn't about to pursue the traditional surgery, chemo, and radiation treatment options.

She had heard about the minimally invasive cryoablation procedure used to kill a cancer tumor by freezing the cancer cells. And she was drawn to the concept of being treated as an out-patient, and leaving the hospital with her breast intact.

The small incision in Victoria's breast, where the ablation probes were inserted, had completely healed. There was no scarring.

The conversation between Victoria and Ronda began with comments about the dangers of root canals and breast cancer.

"What was so bad for me," Victoria told Ronda, "is that a piece of stainless steel was left in my jaw when the root canal procedure was done many years ago, and I'm allergic to stainless steel."

Close your eyes and picture these next words in your mind. For a fleeting moment, turn your imagination loose.

"How did you do when they left a stainless steel clip in your breast after the biopsy?" asked Ronda.

There was stunned silence. Victoria had an instant gut feeling. It was like a punch in the stomach from a prize fighter. She flushed with mixed emotions. She had never heard about a breast clip. She trembled with excitement. "Is this the answer?"

She had been fighting an invisible enemy. Now, perhaps, her enemy had a name. Her mental questions were endless. "Do I have a biopsy marker in my breast? Is it metal? Is it stainless steel? Am I having an allergic reaction? Is a metal clip preventing healing of this infection?"

Ronda's left breast vacuum assisted core biopsy was done on April 26, 2010, by Radiology Associates in Waldwick, New Jersey. The written diagnostic imaging report made mention of a clip in 10 words: "A radiopaque clip was left following the core biopsy procedure." (A medical dictionary says a radiopaque object is visible in x-ray images and under fluoroscopy.)

Victoria, who began affectionately referring to Ronda as her "clip angel," made a journal entry three days later that reflected her determination: "I need to read all reports. I have to figure out what to do."

Victoria was now focused like a laser beam. She typed 'adverse reactions to breast markers' in a search engine on the internet. Again, she was stunned. A quick read of the postings on one website left her appalled. "I was about as angry as you can get."

Women were describing horrible reactions identical to Victoria's, but they knew about a metal marker that was placed in their breast; Victoria did not know. In fact, Victoria had never heard of a metal clip or marker being placed in a woman's breast for any reason. She joins the ranks of most women and more than two-thirds of American doctors.

By the way, women are not the only creatures being diagnosed with breast cancer. It happens to about 500 men annually, including 71-year-old George Swinson of Mineral, Virginia.

Swinson was referred to the Imaging Center for Women in Fredericksburg, Virginia in January 2012, and endured the same pain as a woman for an ultrasound-guided breast biopsy using a vacuum device and a mammogram which documented the placement of a clip in his left breast.

The clinical findings stated: "A tissue sample marker clip is situated in the biopsy bed. The axillary clip and node are not visualized."

The above statement is Greek to an average person. While the expression dates at least as far back as Shakespeare, it still has the same meaning – completely impossible to understand. Most medical doctors and nurses have never heard about breast biopsy clips. And the average patient would never think that a doctor would place a piece of metal in their body without telling them. If you're wondering how they can get away with it, it's called Standard of Care.

A separate biopsy report used the wording, "A micro clip was inserted into the biopsy cavity." Three specimens were obtained using a vacuum assisted device, the report added.

Conspicuous on the biopsy report were the words, "Informed consent was obtained from the patient."

There's one problem with this report, and this alleged informed consent. George Swinson told me over the phone on December 19, 2012, that he "was not told about a marker."

Swinson had read the words "micro clip" and "marker clip" on his medical reports, but he had no idea what they meant. He wasn't alone.

Chapter 36

A needle by any other name

Two days after hearing about breast biopsy clips for the first time in her life, Victoria consulted Dr. Margaret Colgate, in Asheville, North Carolina. It was June 8, 2010. Dr. Colgate worked with women who have every imaginable health issue, including breast cancer, and never had heard about breast biopsy clips or markers.

Victoria's journal entry on that date: "My gut feeling is this is why I can't get better. Why else do I never get better? After my testing, she said it looked like I had the marker in me."

Victoria had spoken to Dr. Colgate some 11 months earlier, as she was driving to South Carolina for an appointment with Dr. Theodore Rozema, her primary physician. "I want to tell you something, but no one in my family knows," Victoria began. "I've been diagnosed with DCIS."

Victoria was taken back by Dr. Colgate's response. "Victoria, we have that in common, too, because I haven't told anyone in my family and I have been diagnosed with breast cancer." Both women had been through divorces about the same time. "I related with her," said Victoria.

A month later, Dr. Colgate had Victoria stop her weekly intravenous vitamin C. "Having cancer is like walking on a knife," the doctor said. "Unless you've had it, you don't get it." In retrospect, Victoria firmly believes the vitamin C had been holding at bay what was now appearing to be an allergic reaction to a foreign object.

June 8, 2010 was the last time Victoria would see Dr. Colgate. Dr. Meg, as she was affectionately known to her patients, died in her sleep on January 7, 2012 after submitting to low-dose chemotherapy in her own four-year battle with breast cancer. Dr. Colgate had left breast cancer and two root canals on the left side but the extractions apparently came too late to help her recover.

Dr. Colgate moved to Asheville in 2000 to work at Great Smokies Medical Center for several years, and then moved into a part-time private practice. Her work consisted of electro-dermal screening, health psychology, and spiritual and emotional counseling.

"I was so shocked," said Victoria. "With everything she knew about good health, I was shocked that she took chemo. I had no idea that would be the last time we'd meet. I think she was genuinely a nice person."

Not only had Dr. Colgate identified Victoria's problematic root canal tooth in the front of her mouth (#8) in 2007, but she had identified Victoria's excessive accumulation of nickel, most likely coming from constant exposure to stainless steel.

Dr. Colgate had suggested a detox formula for nickel to be used after the foreign object was removed from Victoria's breast.

Victoria wrote in her journal, "Will this breast situation ever end? No doctor will help me."

In December 2009, Victoria became a patient of Dr. Suzanne Hoekstra, MD, who was the medical director at Park Ridge Breast Health Center in Hendersonville, North Carolina. She would see Dr. Hoekstra three times before the doctor resigned and moved to Portland, Maine to become a full-time breast surgeon.

Three days after Christmas, Victoria walked into the Park Ridge breast center and was emotionally turned off by the pink ornaments on a white tree. Pink used in conjunction with breast cancer already had a very different connotation for her, a very negative meaning. After all, she was exhausted from hearing about the Zumba Party in Pink, Pink in the Park, Strides Against Breast Cancer, and a thousand other "pink" campaigns that do nothing to cure breast cancer, and say nothing about the oral pathology connection, "and women keep on suffering needlessly."

Meanwhile, Dr. Hoekstra wanted to do another biopsy. Victoria refused.

Dr. Hoekstra ordered an MRI with contrast of Victoria's breast in January 2010. The radiology report stated that no discrete focal mass was visualized, and the findings may be due to infectious or inflammatory change diffusely. Dr. Hoekstra confirmed that Victoria was dealing with an infection.

"What a relief, I actually hugged her neck I was so happy," said Victoria.

Victoria's breast was still swollen and she was continuing to have a rash and pain when she returned to Dr. Hoekstra in April 2010. The doctor ordered an ultrasound, which again confirmed an infection. Victoria still did not know about breast clips or markers, and continued to have breast swelling and pain and a discharge from the nipple. Dr. Hoekstra confirmed there were no veins feeding a tumor, which would have been typical of cancer. "She felt very comfortable that I did not have cancer, it was scar tissue from the ablation."

Once Victoria found out on June 6, 2010 that metal clips or markers were placed routinely in women's breasts, she knew she needed a doctor's help and therefore returned to Dr. Hoekstra on June 15, 2010.

Dr. Hoekstra confirmed that she routinely placed a titanium clip when she did a biopsy and she offered to order a mammogram for Victoria in order to confirm the presence of a clip, which Victoria declined. Victoria's swollen breast was in no shape to be squeezed between a pair of glass plates. Dr. Hoekstra did agree to request Victoria's records from the Hope Cancer Center.

Victoria had already made a conscious decision; she could not return to the Hope Cancer Center. Why? She was not emotionally prepared for the 'stabbing action' of the stereotactic biopsy which left her completely traumatized. Proper informed consent was not requested by the doctor, nor was it given by Victoria. The doctor-patient trust was permanently broken.

Meanwhile, while Dr. Hoekstra was waiting for medical records from the Hope Cancer Center, a radiologist at Park Ridge said the presence of a clip in an MRI image which Victoria previously had taken could not be determined.

Here's the fine point to remember. A typical radiologist says a foreign object can't be seen, so the interpretation is that it isn't there. In truth, many clips and markers and pieces of plastic that are left in the breast from biopsy procedures 'gone bad' can't be imaged. It doesn't mean they're not there. They're simply not visible to the technology being used by most doctors.

But a woman feels the pain, and it's more than intuition. It's not in her mind and she's not making it up. The pain is real and, in many cases, the foreign object can be felt.

Dr. Hoekstra's office called Hope Cancer Center and was told that Victoria probably had a clip but it would take three or four days to retrieve her records out of the archives. Victoria was informed the morning of June 21, according to her journal entry.

Dr. Hoekstra eventually reviewed the doctor's biopsy dictation from the Hope Cancer Center and, because it said nothing about a marker, the surgeon concluded a marker was not placed.

On June 29, 2010, Dr. Hoekstra emailed Victoria: "I hope you got the message that no marker was used for the biopsy you had performed at the Hope Center. So I suppose it really doesn't explain the troubles you have had, but also should give you peace of mind that surgery is not needed to remove it!"

Victoria's quest to get information from the Hope Cancer Center was a challenge. Even though she had asked for all of her records after the biopsy in 2008, the biopsy dictation was missing.

In July 2010, Victoria returned to Park Ridge for a chest x-ray hoping that it would reveal the object in her breast. By this time, Dr. Hoekstra had moved away. "I feel like I'm in a twilight zone. Why does all this take so long?" she wrote in her journal. The chest x-ray showed nothing.

The biopsy record from Hope Cancer Center did not indicate that Dr. Hetzel inserted a breast marker in 2008. But other of his patients had the same procedure and they received markers. Even the receptionist stated to Victoria that this was a routine procedure when she inquired by phone if she had received a marker.

Victoria's breast pain or discomfort would not go away. She would try a new treatment protocol, and the breast situation would get better for a brief period of time, and then it would flare up again.

Out of desperation and not knowing what else to do, Victoria forced herself to call the Hope Cancer Center in search of any information that might be helpful. "I had no intention of speaking to the doctor. The staff could find the answers in the records, if they were available."

It had been 34 months since the biopsy. She used her journal entries to reconstruct events. Her first call was made on November 30, 2010.

"Had to leave message at nursing station. Lisa called me back in afternoon and told me the Suros vacuum device was used. She asked me to give her a few days to get my records and she will let me know if I got the clip."

Victoria's journal entry on December 3, 2010, stated: "Lisa called and left message. I called her back and she was gone for the day."

Here's the journal entry on December 6, 2010: "Called in morning and asked Lisa on nurse's station voice mail to please call me. Called again about one and left another message. About 3:30 a girl named Willie called me. I asked her if the Mammotome vacuum system was used on my biopsy. She stated yes. It does state on my pathology and cytology report it was a Mammotone biopsy. I asked again if the Suros vacuum device was used. She stated yes. I asked if she knew that because the doctor had circled it on the biopsy dictation. She stated yes."

As for the *biopsy needle*, it was "packaged individually" and sent to the Hope Cancer Center by Suros, and no one knew anything else about the needle, the spokesperson stated.

By this time, Victoria had researched all the stereotactic biopsy equipment and understood that the so called needle was much larger than an ordinary needle. However, she kept asking about a "needle" because that was the terminology being used at the Hope Cancer Center.

A few days later, Victoria asked Dr. Rozema to submit a second nipple discharge culture. But first, she and her doctor enjoyed a hearty laugh. She revealed the June 6, 2010, D-Day phone conversation when she learned about breast biopsy clips. Dr. Rozema knew nothing about the metal clips. "Here we were working and working to detox me of heavy metals," she told the doctor, "and I'm packing my own [metal]."

The request for another nipple discharge culture was being made about six months after the first culture. It was June 22, 2010. Dr. Rozema told Victoria that he thought she would require a lumpectomy. His reasoning is defined in Victoria's journal entry that day: He said the clip and the abnormal (atypical) cells that formed around the clip also had to be removed with the clip. The news left Victoria very depressed. "The last thing I wanted was a portion of my breast cut out."

The nipple discharge was sent to LabCorp and the Aerobic Bacterial Culture was reported to be a corynebacterium infection. This organism, according to medical journals, is typically associated with medical devices.

One source describes a "nondiphtherial corynebacterial bacteremia associated with device infections (venous access catheters, heart valves, neurosurgical shunts, peritoneal catheters)."

Three weeks after first learning about breast clips in a phone conversation, Victoria met a woman at Proven Health Management in North Carolina who had one. In fact, the two women were both seeing the same doctor in South Carolina, Theodore Rozema. Dr. Rozema was already convinced that there was something foreign in Victoria's breast and she was having an adverse reaction, and Dr. Rozema was concerned because his other female patient knew she had markers.

In fact, Brenda Smith, age 68, had two MammoMark clips. In 1963, Smith had a benign tumor removed from her right breast, and in April 2010 she had a core biopsy that was "suspicious." The clips were placed during the 2010 biopsy. Although Smith had given permission, it was done at the last second under duress, moments before the procedure.

Smith was not told about the risks or adverse consequences that women all over America are suffering.

In addition to thermal imaging, the Proven Health Management screening center offered men and women an opportunity to relax in comfortable recliners and socialize while exposed to multiple bio-active life enhancing energy fields, including "scalar waves" which can allow cell regeneration, improve immune function, provide relief from pain, detoxify the body, elevate moods, and assist in balancing right and left hemispheres of the brain to increase energy levels.

"We regularly re-charge our cell phones, don't we? What if we could re-charge the cells of our bodies just as easily?" asks Dr. Sandra Rose Michael, PhD, DNM, who developed Energy Enhancement Systems™.

Celebrities, scientists, doctors, health and beauty professionals, and individuals are already "recharging their cells" and boasting the benefits of coherent unified energy fields generated by this revolutionary technology.

It was in this environment that women began comparing notes about breast cancer and their own breast health experiences. One universal truth kept emerging. All women with breast cancer had oral pathology on the same side of the mouth as their breast issues. No exceptions were found.

Sometimes, the oral pathology is obvious. Other times, it's hard to find. Most of the time, it's painless. Once in a while, the pathology is actually hurting.

Chapter 37

I need a body guard

Victoria made an appointment with Dr. Gayle Blouin in Greenville, South Carolina on July 13, 2010. The Greenville Hospital System consent form that Victoria was asked to sign literally gave the doctor total control over her life. Victoria wisely wrote on the form, "I will discuss each treatment … with the physician before I give my approval."

Dr. Blouin was recommended by an acquaintance at another medical office, a woman who was familiar with the doctor's "breast preserving techniques." The previous week Victoria picked up another copy of the CD of her MRI done January 5, 2010, that stated she had an infection in her breast.

Victoria presented Dr. Blouin with the CD and a complete set of her medical records, including her cryoablation in Toledo, Ohio. She wanted Dr. Blouin to have all the facts.

Victoria's waiting room experience was depressing. She saw a mother with no hair who looked like death warmed over. "I heard her tell her daughter how bad she felt. I knew she had taken chemo because of the hair loss and overall appearance."

"I thought to myself, thank you God that I didn't have to do that to my body!"

While a nurse was recording her weight, Victoria asked if she could consult with the doctor before getting undressed. "It was so important to me that she comprehend all my information and I thought I could have the discussion easier if I could sit across from her and not be on an examination table."

"No, we don't do that here," the nurse replied.

Dr. Blouin immediately started feeling Victoria's right breast. She pressed hard "and it was hurting." Victoria told the doctor about her cryoablation in April 2009 and she was shocked at the doctor's response. "I don't like these cryoablations," Dr. Blouin blurted out. "I asked her how many had she been around and she told me one."

Dr. Blouin left the exam room saying she was calling Dr. Allan Kaufman in Toledo, the interventional radiologist who did Victoria's cryoablation. "He didn't say much," Dr. Blouin told Victoria when she returned.

On July 6, 2010, Dr. Kaufman had responded to my question and gave me his opinion in an email: "My guess is there is a clip. It's almost always placed at time of biopsy. I have no knowledge regarding removal of a clip."

My research had kept me in contact with the interventional radiologist, and with the permission of one of his patients, Dr. Kaufman had allowed me to photograph an ablation procedure and interview his assistants in August 2009.

It was Dr. Blouin's opinion that Victoria should have a mammogram to see if she had a marker and cancer. Victoria adamantly refused and presented Dr. Blouin with copies of recent research on the dangers of mammograms.

Dr. Blouin's demeanor changed abruptly. She defended the breast biopsy markers and mammography, saying they saved lives and there was nothing dangerous about them. And she claimed thermography had been proven not to work. Of course, the studies about thermal imaging published in respected medical journals prove otherwise.

Victoria realized she was in the wrong place. There was no reasoning with this doctor. "She had her way of treating cancer, and if I didn't do it her way, it was wrong." Dr. Blouin instructed Victoria to dress, but when she returned after calling Dr. Kaufman, Victoria was instructed to undress a second time. Dr. Blouin was going to do a cytology report on the liquid from the nipple.

At this point, a foreign object in Victoria's breast could be felt with the fingernail in the lower left quadrant of the right breast. But not for long.

Using her right thumb while holding the breast with the left hand, Dr. Blouin drove the object, which was near the skin's surface, deep into Victoria's breast with a swift and very hard upward and clockwise movement. It was so violent that blood immediately came out of the nipple.

"She hurt my breast so badly. I was traumatized," Victoria recalled. **"She kept yelling at me – loudly and emphatically – that I had cancer. You have cancer! You have cancer! I know you have cancer!"**

Ambushed again, Victoria thought.

On the drive back home, Victoria could not stand for the seatbelt to touch her right breast.

Any possibility of retrieving the foreign object in Victoria's breast probably disappeared in that moment. "I was very angry at myself for putting up with her behavior. I should have walked out of there."

"The next day, I was in shock. Why did I let that (expletive) doctor do that to me? I need a body guard." Victoria's journal entry said, "I'm so tired. I'm just dragging."

When fear grips you – a fear that cancer doctors love to induce – a person can become so desperate in the process of saving their own life that they make poor judgments. Some of Victoria's decisions made over the next 21 months were fear-induced – the direct result of cancer doctors and surgeons whose Hippocratic Oath failed them. Victoria's saga eventually read like a script for a horror movie.

The appointment at Dr. Blouin's was the last time that Victoria would see a doctor in her search for help without being accompanied by her close friend, Brenda Kinder, a certified thermographer, or her "surrogate" husband, Buzz, a retired U.S. Air Force colonel who has a history of medical research on and off the battlefield that spans four decades.

Note: For the remainder of this chapter, Buzz is doing the talking in the first person and Victoria's comments are in quotes.

I examined Victoria's breast a few days before she kept her appointment with Dr. Gayle Blouin. In hindsight, telling Dr. Blouin that Victoria believed a marker or something foreign had been inserted into her breast without her knowledge was a fatal error. The object was just under the skin, and ready to be extracted.

I examined Victoria's breast a few days later and became livid at the bruising and pain that had been inflicted. From this day forward, all issues and symptoms with her breast including pain increased exponentially. What had happened to "Do No Harm?"

Upon leaving Dr. Blouin's, Victoria's pain never stopped and more and more issues began to surface. The doctor's actions reminded me of Nazi arrogance.

From this day forward, I determined that I would accompany Victoria to all doctor visits and never allow such medical abuse to happen again.

Chapter 38

'Clip Angel'

By now, readers should see a theme developing in this book. Not all breast biopsies are the same. Many women have a breast clip or marker that's placed at the time of their biopsy and so far they have no apparent symptoms. However, we must not forget that these breast clips and markers have only been in use since the late 1990s.

Not having a problem after five or 10 years doesn't mean a woman won't have a problem after 15 or 20 years.

Anybody can begin reacting to a foreign object in their body at any time. Just look at young girls who get their ears pierced, and see how many begin having problems after a few years. Even more problematic for causing future health issues are the belly button, nose, lip, and tongue piercing. Many piercings result in infections, excessive bleeding, nerve damage, allergic reactions, and keloids (a thick scarring at the pierced site).

Many women have a biopsy and the clip or marker was inserted at the desired location on the first attempt by the doctor. After full disclosure and informed consent, if a woman chooses to have a biopsy that includes the placement of a clip, she should have the right to make that decision.

At the same time shouldn't this same woman have the right to refuse a clip?

Doctors claim the procedure is safe and assert that there are sufficient medical reasons to place a clip(s). They are quick to voice these claims, but not so quick to reveal the sordid experiences of thousands of women whose lives were made miserable by the clip or a malfunctioning instrument.

Victoria's "clip angel" (Chapter 35), Ronda Lutfey was unusually fortunate when she had her biopsy in April 2010. Her doctor used a localization wire as a guide when placing her clip. "The radiologist got the wire in the correct place on his first attempt." Since the wire sticks out of the breast several inches, she was warned to not stick it in her eye.

Ronda's friend, who chose to have a lumpectomy, wasn't so fortunate during her biopsy. "My friend said the guy (doctor) tried eight times. He wasn't nice to her. He mutilated her." Keep in mind, this is not a surgical procedure intended to cut out diseased breast tissue. It's supposed to be a simple process that removes tiny slices of tissue for laboratory analysis.

In the case of Ronda's friend, "She said it was so painful. It was worse than the surgery (lumpectomy)."

"How bad is that?" Victoria asked.

"He didn't care," Ronda responded. "He just kept poking her." Then they put your breast in the mammography machine, crush it in like a pancake, and you're totally awake."

"I tell you what, women are very smart, very brilliant, and once the complete breast cancer scam is exposed, it's going to be like a tidal wave and women are not going to put up with this crap," says Victoria. "It's one way that they keep women down, because when you're so disoriented and feel so bad, you're not thinking clearly and you're not on top of your game. So, it's just another way to control women, and make a lot of bucks while doing it."

It is rare that a medical doctor admits a surgical mistake and attempts to correct it by personally calling his patient on the phone and inviting them to his office because he has some important information to give them. It's rare, but it happens, especially when the mistake is uncovered by another doctor.

A 60-year-old New Jersey woman with diagnosed breast cancer was having an oral pathology consult at Proven Health Management when she casually mentioned having metal in her breast. She reported symptoms of pain, infection, and general discomfort. When questioned about it, she produced a radiology report from a bilateral breast MRI taken with and without contrast.

Referring to the left breast, the radiologist had written: "There is a large amount of magnetic susceptibility artifact in the upper central aspect of the breast corresponding to the patient's area of surgical biopsy and known cancer site."

The next sentence gets more interesting in light of the fact that this woman was not aware she had metal in her breast. "The large amount of artifact suggests that there is metal in this area which may be from retained portions of the patient's hook wires when correlated with the specimen radiograph."

UNIVERSITY RADIOLOGY

Exam Date: 02/08/2010

LEFT BREAST: The large amount of artifact suggest that there is metal in this area which may be from retained portions of the patient's hook wires when correlated with the specimen radiograph of 1/11/10.

Radiologist found metal in woman's breast image; doctor was forced to apologize.

The woman recounted the phone call and subsequent encounter with her surgeon. After groping for the right words, the doctor informed his patient a week after the MRI report was received that he accidentally left two tiny pieces of wire in her left breast while he was doing a needle biopsy. "He said he was very sorry but he said these markers will do me no harm. I should have known better."

Breast clips, markers or wires can't always be imaged. In this woman's case, there was only a 28-day period between her breast biopsy and the MRI which revealed the presence of metal. The reader should file this fact away in their memory. It becomes important as Victoria's story unfolds.

Victoria has several friends whose cryoablations were done by Dr. Jason Williams at the American Cancer Ablation Center in Gulf Shores, Alabama.

Ronda's cryoablation was done at Mercy St. Anne Hospital in Toledo, Ohio by Dr. Wade Banker, interventional radiologist. She was on the CT scan table a little over two hours, and her tumor was frozen and thawed three times using helium and argon gases, with warm saline poured over the site during the procedure to prevent frostbite on the skin. "I was drenched," she remembered.

Ronda declined the traditional hospital pain killers. "I don't do any of these drugs," she told the doctor. And she's a pharmacist!

274

She agreed to Tylenol Extra Strength, and that was the only time she took it. Afterwards, she used Advil.

"We went out to dinner that night." Ronda, who had gone hours without eating, was so hungry. But food didn't agree with her. "I started to get a little nauseous. I threw up a little bit, not too much," so she stopped eating, at least until she found a Middle Eastern dessert business in Dearborn, Michigan and sampled their Kinafeh, an Arab cheese pastry soaked in sweet syrup.

Because of hospital policy, "they wanted to keep me overnight," said Ronda, but she refused. She did agree to remain under observation until 7 p.m.

"My question to the doctor was, 'Any follow-up?'"

"And he said, 'No follow-up at all.'"

Ronda's new norm is that she exercises a lot, "which I always did, and eat healthier than ever."

"It was a wake-up call," Victoria told Ronda, "so for the rest of our lives we should give our body the respect it deserves. I'm not around toxic people anymore. I avoid negative energy, and that means avoiding negative people, if I can help it."

Ronda lost her sister, a dentist, in 2002. She was murdered by a man she was dating. Little did Ronda know at the time how her immune system was being suppressed by the stress of the family tragedy.

Victoria's procedure was much less invasive than Ronda's. Ronda did not take kindly to the hospital-required mammogram. And she will never have another. "They did do mammography after I had my biopsy. I said, 'My breast is killing me.'"

"Well, we have to do it," the nurse replied.

"I have so many friends that have clips, and they don't have anything wrong with them," says Ronda. One of Ronda's friends recently had her first mammogram, and was told to get a biopsy. The friend had the procedure, no questions asked, and now has the clip and "she can feel it because she has small breasts." Victoria has small breasts, too. Ronda, on the other hand, who wears a 34D bra, so far has not had the same problem.

Victoria and Ronda quickly developed a sisterly bond, and Ronda took Victoria's advice and traveled to Knoxville to have her cavitations fixed and mercury removed from her mouth. There was infection under most of her amalgam fillings and even Ronda's one composite filling had decay under it.

Chapter 39

I was going in circles

It was Independence Day again, July 4, 2010.

"I woke up in the morning exhausted," Victoria wrote in her journal. "I don't know what is wrong with me. I'm sure it has something to do with my breast. Doesn't everything? Depressing day."

But none of this stopped her from scrubbing her 8- by 48-foot wood deck that overlooked the woods behind her house.

Several weeks later, Victoria learned about two doctors in Tennessee who were reportedly having success with hyperbaric medicine, also known as hyperbaric oxygen treatments (HBOT), which is the medical use of oxygen at a level higher than atmospheric pressure.

Although Victoria had never experienced oxygen therapy, hyperbaric treatments are not new.

The prestigious Mayo Clinic reports the successful use of HBOT to treat serious infections. The process was used for years in treating underwater divers that suffered from decompression sickness, hence "a dive" became the slang term for a cycle of pressurization inside the HBOT chamber.

Hyperbaric medicine requires a pressure chamber and a means of delivering 100% pure oxygen. The chamber construction can be rigid or flexible, and can even be portable.

The oxygen treatment has been used for the treatment of problem wounds, thermal burns, autism, Lyme disease, stroke, trauma, pediatric brain disorders, and even migraines.

Victoria would soon pack up and head to Hendersonville, Tennessee, near Nashville, to the S.E.E.D.S. Health and Wellness Center on the grounds of the Gloryland Baptist Church. The wellness center was operated by twin brothers, Dr. Dale Hammond, NMD and Dr. Gale Hammond, NMD, doctors of naturopathic medicine.

Their business card promotes herbs, health consulting, research, and hyperbaric oxygen treatments. Victoria was the first person to introduce the doctors to the dental connection with cancer.

Victoria made phone contact on July 28, 2010, but it was August 2 before she consulted with them in person. Before paying the $8,000 fee in advance and a couple of thousand for lodging, food, and transportation in order to be away from home Monday through Friday for four weeks, she had a list of 10 questions and she was insistent about one in particular. "Is there any additional cost for anything?" She was told no.

Victoria asked nine other pointed questions.

1. Do you think I have a clip?
2. If I have a clip and I get over the infection, will the infection return?
3. If I do have a clip, with every way I have tried to find out and haven't, what is the best way to find out?
4. If I do have a clip, what is the best way to get it out?
5. Will I get a receipt for the total cost of treatment?
6. If you give me a price for 20 days and it doesn't take that long, do I get a refund?
7. How we will know when I don't have the infection?
8. Will an infection show atypical cells in a blood smear test?
9. Would an infection cause my breast to be hard?

Victoria had to know these answers before she was willing to spend an entire week preparing to be away from home for treatment. "I was emphatic that I would not pay them $8,000 if they could not cure my infection."

On her first trip which was to have a preliminary consult, Victoria left in the early morning from Hendersonville, North Carolina and drove six hours, only to see the city limit sign, Hendersonville, Tennessee. The next day, she drove home and arrived in Hendersonville, North Carolina. The city limit signs were symbolic of what was happening. "I was going around in circles going nowhere."

She carried with her an exhaustive list of products and processes that had been used in an attempt to kill the infection in her breast. The list included various antibiotics, herbal tonics, patented Silver

Sol, magnet therapy, nutritional therapy, rebounding, UV (ultraviolet) light blood treatment, Myers Cocktail, and at least two dozen intravenous vitamin C treatments.

There was one other document that Victoria carried with her. It was her personal declaration about a foreign object in her breast. It was akin to the Monroe Doctrine, a policy of the United States, introduced in 1823, that stated further efforts by European nations to colonize land or interfere with states in North or South America would be viewed as acts of aggression, requiring U.S. intervention.

Victoria told the doctors the foreign object "required medical intervention." It had to be found. It must come out. Unless it was removed, she might get better, but she wouldn't stay that way. And she would never be healed. Precedent was on her side. Victoria had already shown improvement from a variety of treatments, but as soon as she stopped using them, the infection would return.

The oxygen therapy was a treatment protocol that her insurance would not cover. The plan included a series of hyperbaric oxygen chamber treatments, and preparation of herbs and enzymes for the infection.

"They promised me they would cure my infection and they were ministers," said Victoria.

Victoria's primary treatment would be hyperbaric dives, twice a day, an hour each time, a total of 40 dives.

Her first pair of dives was on August 9, one in the late morning and the other at mid-afternoon. She had seven more dives by noon Friday before she began the long, lonely six-hour drive back home on Interstate 40 for the weekend. The dives the previous Wednesday left her extremely sleepy and she returned to her hotel room that day and slept for hours, something she attributed to detoxing.

Victoria was constantly asking the question, "How can we find out if I have a marker in my breast?" She wrote on August 23, 2010: "Dr. Gale [Hammond] said he spoke to an HBOT doctor in New Orleans and he said my reports should be taken to a university to be read independent of any doctors. Dr. Gale told me the hyperbaric chamber would probably make the clip come out of me.

For example, it would make the clip come out in the shower and I wouldn't even know it."

"I was desperate. Will this treatment work to excise a clip? I needed to know a percentage. I knew I wouldn't get well unless it did. On August 30, Dr. Gale quoted me 100%."

Before Victoria returned home in early September, she had pain relief, reduced swelling in the right breast, and less rash, but her mind and body were exhausted from the whole ordeal.

On September 6, 2010, Victoria woke up in her own bedroom and wrote in her journal: "My breast is looking and feeling so much better." In the days that followed, she would make regular entries noting the presence of a small bloody pus discharge from the nipple each morning when she got up, apparently the result of the herbal poultices that she was instructed to use. Then her notes indicated the discharges stopped for a few days, and then resumed.

Only four weeks passed before Victoria's breast was totally inflamed again and her temper was red hot. She paid thousands for nothing and the result was exactly as she predicted. "I still think I have a clip. We could never get any medical professional to help me. It finally hit me. I was playing a victim to that clip for so long. I had enough. I knew my body reacts to metal, but couldn't get anybody to listen."

Victoria's journal entry on October 8, 2010: "I feel like I'm fighting an invisible enemy."

Victoria wrote on October 11, 2010: "When I spoke with Dr. Gale and told him how bad my breast was again, he was trying to act like I left too soon and I wasn't finished with the treatment. I told him I'd been there for a month and all he could talk about is he would work with me on how much more I would have to pay for the treatment." Victoria was livid.

Victoria's journal entry on October 14, 2010: "My body and mind are so tired from all the treatments and money I have spent and still my breast hurts, is swollen and has a discharge. I would never pay a doctor $8,000, or been away from home for a month … if that did not cover my complete healing. I am beyond exhausted with all these time consuming, expensive treatments."

Victoria's journal entry on October 15, 2010: "I am burned out, was so tired today I even took an afternoon nap. I never do that. I know my body and mind need rest."

Victoria's desperation continued to grow. "I have to get this clip or foreign object out of my breast to get well, but if I get the wrong doctor to do it, I will be worse off." She needed a doctor and an attorney, and could get neither.

Throughout history, desperate times have called for desperate measures. It was Victoria's time. She began writing an "end of her rope document," that was lengthy, complete, and precise. It was mailed or emailed to dozens of practitioners in late October 2010.

At the same time, she arranged for the use of a bitewing dental x-ray machine to image her right breast. She submitted to three images. That was all the radiation she felt she could afford to absorb. One image showed a faint hairline, possibly V-shaped object.

"I did the dental x-ray out of shear desperation in order to get an image to prove the presence of something foreign in my breast. I didn't know what else to do and I didn't know at that time that many of these clips or markers contained biodegradable material and would not image after a few weeks or a few months." It had been 33 months since Victoria's breast biopsy.

Searching for surgeons who performed "minimally invasive" surgeries, Victoria found Dr. Claudine Siegert in Asheville, North Carolina and saw the doctor on December 8, 2010. Victoria's breast was swollen and almost immediately, she heard the 'broken record syndrome' that had played in her ears so many times previously; it looks and feels like cancer.

"Why do doctors do so much testing if they're all psychics?"

The doctor felt the breast and recommended a mammogram.

Victoria refused the mammogram, knowing her breast could not deal with the trauma. Even a child could look at a swollen and inflamed breast and realize that no woman could endure the pain from having the breast squeezed.

Dr. Siegert called a radiologist who told her he thought the only way to image a breast clip at this point – amid the swelling and scar tissue from an ablation – was with a high-resolution ultrasound. A regular ultrasound would not do it.

Victoria had taken a 10-month break in the hyperbaric treatments. She was refused a refund, so it was either take the remaining six dives or lose the money. She returned to Tennessee for one week in August 2011 to finish up.

Her journal entry on August 25, 2011: "Dr. Dale and Dr. Gale stated when you have 40 dives it changes your DNA. This morning at 9:30 I had my 40th dive." Changing DNA meant getting it back to its original state, Victoria was told.

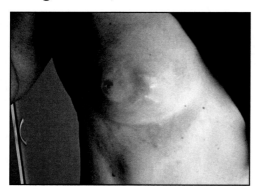

Rash and swelling on breast in August 2011.

Her breast was swollen that afternoon when Dr. Dale examined it and said she needed to continue with the oxygen because the infection was dangerous and could enter her bloodstream. "If that happened, he said I would more than likely die."

"I was working, working, working, spending all of this money, and ending up in the same place every time. I still can't get my energy back from being in Tennessee."

Victoria experienced some pain relief and less soreness for several weeks after her first hyperbaric session, but before too long, "I was back where I started. I always told every doctor that. Until I get to the source, I will get better but I won't stay better."

After the biopsy on January 23, 2008, Victoria always had pain and discomfort that was never there before, and although the level of pain and discomfort varied over the next couple of years, it never went away. It was present prior to and after the cryoablation done April 30, 2009.

Chapter 40

Choose the hornet's nest

Victoria had a new air of excitement about her in December 2010 as she booked airline reservations to Toledo, Ohio. In a December 16 letter to Dr. Wade Banker, an interventional radiologist at Mercy St. Anne Hospital which has 587 physicians on staff, she stated she had experienced continual pain in the location of the biopsy, which was done in January 2008, almost three years earlier.

In addition to biopsies, radiation, and chemotherapy treatments, Dr. Banker was offering cryoablations as an option for women who refused to have toxic treatments.

For Victoria, her breast pain came in unlikely ways, such as "when someone would hug me very tightly or when I moved my arm in certain movements."

Victoria reminded Dr. Banker that she only found out six months earlier about the routine placement of clips or markers during a vacuum-assisted biopsy, and she was exhibiting all the known symptoms of a foreign object in her breast in addition to a hideous infection.

Three days before she mailed the letter, Victoria received a return phone call from the radiologist. It was December 13, 2010, at 12:44 p.m. Her journal entry stated: "He was so nice and made good sense. He told me when he was an intern he would do biopsies and not tell the women he was putting in a marker. It was considered Standard of Care."

Victoria and her close friend and professional thermographer, Brenda Kinder, were headed north on January 4, 2011. Brenda was 44 at the time. "I am so happy Brenda is with me. She is very comforting and she knows how hospitals work. If I was told something really bad about cancer she could read between the lines and could help me get through the mud to see the situation clearly."

Brenda, the mother of three girls, had her own close encounter with a breast cancer diagnosis in her early 30s. During an annual OB-GYN visit, her doctor asked if she knew there was a lump in her left breast. Brenda was not aware of a lump and, in fact, could not feel it.

Her medical history included wearing braces and having wisdom teeth extracted in 1990 at age 24. After the wisdom teeth came out, Brenda began having sinus and ear infections, and allergies reared their ugly head.

The gynecologist ordered a mammogram, Brenda's first. "I was completely unaware of breast issues. That was not for me to worry about, I'm only 35. I'll worry about that when I'm older."

Nothing was apparent on the first set of films except fibrocystic tissue. A second mammogram was also negative.

"I was scared," Brenda admitted. "I was young. I had children, and I was a single mom coming out of a divorce. It was already a stressful situation with an ex, money problems and moving my girls out of their hometown. Could they handle this too, if I had cancer?"

There was no biopsy but following an inconclusive ultrasound, the doctor recommended that she bypass a biopsy and have the lumpectomy. Brenda agreed. If it was cancer it would have to be cut it out anyway, she was told.

It was the fear factor at play. Brenda did not know about other options either, and the general surgeon made it sound like the surgery was her only choice. She had no support from knowledgeable friends or relatives, and she was easy prey for a doctor who was ready to cut.

"And cut, he did," said Brenda. "I had no idea they could do what they want to. When you sign the release statement to have surgery, you are at the doctor's mercy. No questions, just what he feels is right. It was like someone took my innocence and threw me completely into the world of cancer."

Brenda found herself caught in a whirlwind. Things happened faster than she could process them. She didn't get a second opinion. She didn't have time to think. She wasn't allowed to have time to think. She didn't know this is how the cancer system in America works.

She was led to believe the lump would be removed through a "small incision." Following the lumpectomy, she woke up to find a two-inch scar and only then learned that the doctor took the lymph nodes in her breast. A "huge portion of my breast was gone," Brenda explained, leaving an ugly dent in the left breast.

Brenda's surgery was needless. She had a lump, nothing else. It probably would have disappeared on its own as the stress level from her divorce subsided. But there was no hint of an apology when the doctor reported to Brenda that the lump was not cancer, just a mass growing around some lymph nodes.

Why would a male doctor not give any thought to the mutilation of a woman's breast? Why didn't the doctor consider other non-invasive imaging techniques such as thermal imaging, an MRI, or even a CT PET with contrast. The radiation would not have disfigured her breast, and she could have overcome the ionizing radiation exposure.

Brenda said she felt ugly with her breasts in two different sizes and shapes. In order to meet her own emotional needs and feel sexually appealing again, she had little choice but to have implant surgery to make her breasts symmetrical.

Like tens of thousands of women before her, Brenda endured unnecessary pain, suffering, and anxiety because a medical doctor felt the need to act like "he knew what was best for me without regards to what I thought was best, without even giving me a chance to find out what I wanted to do, without even talking to me as an equal instead of someone beneath him." Brenda added, "I never went back to that practice again and never had another mammogram."

At the time, Brenda had never heard about using thermal imaging to monitor breast health. Yet because of her personal experience, she chose to become a certified thermographer so she could help other women avoid the travesty done to her.

The damage was done. It was a wrong that can't be righted. By not respecting Brenda's right to know about other options, the surgeon literally made a mockery of his own profession. She would live in her body for the rest of her life, not him. The decision to mutilate her natural breast should have been Brenda's, not the doctor's.

Brenda and Victoria landed in Detroit, Michigan – Motown if you're musically inclined and Motor City if cars and trucks are your fancy. In spite of the blowing snow, they drove away from the airport in a black Lincoln Continental and arrived in Toledo an hour later.

"I hate cold weather but I was willing to go where a doctor was available that would help me without insisting I have to have my breast cut off," said Victoria.

"Look, Victoria, there's no color," Brenda observed. "The houses are gray. Even in the wintertime, we've got color in North Carolina."

"There was no sun in the sky," said Victoria, "and no hint of the color blue. Everything was brown, everywhere just shades of brown."

"I wanted to get a feel of the place where I was going the next morning, so we drove by the hospital on the evening after our arrival." When Victoria saw the sign in front of the cancer center, she got a knot in her stomach and said to Brenda, "I don't like that it says cancer center." Was this an omen of sorts?

In spite of her excitement, Victoria remained cautiously optimistic because she had been "ambushed" so many times before – her description for a doctor not doing what he or she said they would do over the phone.

The two North Carolinians checked into the same hotel where Victoria stayed in April 2009 when she was there at a different hospital for the cryoablation.

The next morning, Victoria was carrying a large file for the doctor when she was told by the receptionist to sit down. "I will get to you when I can," the lady said.

"I have an 8:30 appointment," Victoria responded. The receptionist apologized and "told me she thought I was there on business. You look too good to be having surgery."

"If you have a choice between a cancer center and a hornet's nest, choose the hornet's nest. You always get ambushed at the cancer center. You know beforehand you are going to get stung by a hornet."

"If I had done exactly what the first doctor told me, I would be sitting here with my breast removed and had radiation. I am so happy I didn't do that because the best thing I have right now is my good health."

"It was supposed to be such a happy occasion. I was finally going to get the foreign object out of my breast and I could get my health back and get my life back on track."

"I just don't like hospitals, but I had to be here to get this object out of my breast." The doctor was advised the month before that it was likely a piece of metal or even plastic could have been deposited in Victoria's breast.

The doctor responded at the time that a CT with "thin cuts" through the right breast "ought to be able to find a small object if it is there. If it is an abscess collection we should be able to see that as well."

Victoria saw Dr. Banker at 10:30 a.m. The first scan was a CT without contrast, and that was followed by a CT with contrast. Banker could not locate the object with the CT. He then tried ultrasound, but he never used a fluoroscope as he previously indicated that he would. That's the technology used by the U.S. military to find metal fragments in wounded soldiers.

Both Dr. Banker and his assistant, Lori, indicated before the CT scan that a fluoroscope would be used in the search for an object in her breast. The fluoroscope can provide active images from almost any angle and thus allow for accurate triangulation of foreign objects.

While Victoria was undergoing the imaging, Brenda was eating a veggie burger in the cafeteria when she eyed Dr. Banker walking toward her. "Oh my God, what's wrong?" she thought.

The radiologist escorted Brenda to a small counseling room where he offered his assessment that Victoria had cancer, a 70% likelihood, and he wanted Brenda to give Victoria support.

Brenda was stunned. For a brief second, she experienced doubt, enforced by the doctor's mannerisms, expressions, and voice tone. Maybe Victoria really is eaten up with cancer. Dr. Banker showed her the "spots" on the scans. Brenda doubted "just for a second," then regained her composure. "He's wrong," she thought. "Victoria does not have cancer."

In the CT room where Victoria was lying on her back, Brenda could sense that Victoria was terrified. Brenda could see it in Victoria's face. "I started to tear up," Brenda remembered. "Then I said, no, I've got to be strong. I can't imagine being on that table."

In Brenda's presence, Dr. Banker then asserted that Victoria has cancer. Victoria felt like her body and his words and movements were moving "in slow motion." Later that day, Victoria wrote Dr. Banker's comments in her journal. "I feel sure you have cancer," he told her. "I am sure it is a 70% to 30% chance. You also have it in your lymph nodes."

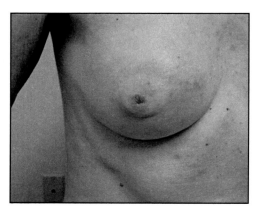

Rash on breast was typical of other adverse reactions to metals that Victoria experienced.

"Would you have a mastectomy?" he asked. "I wanted to scream," Victoria remembers. "He zapped all my energy. That takes a lot to zap me, but he had done it."

Her logical mind kicked in again, and she asked another pointed question. "Let's say you are wrong, then what?" After all, the radiologist had just told her she had a 30% chance of not having cancer, and she had other tests stating she was cancer-free.

We all see this identical analogy each day when we listen to the weather forecast. What does a 70% chance of rain mean? We have a visual image of threatening grey skies with rain. We could just as easily think of partly clear skies and a 30% chance of it not raining. If you're planning an outdoor activity, doesn't a 30% chance of no rain sound better?

Dr. Banker offered to do a culture to see what type of organism is in her breast. "He tells me he needs to do a biopsy of my breast and lymph node."

He did order an anaerobic culture for five days and reported on January 12, 2011 "no growth and no bacteria." Dr. Banker sent Victoria an email on January 26, 2011 affirming the absence of infection: "The cultures came back negative for any bacteria or anything else infective."

At this point in Victoria's journey, and contrary to Dr. Banker's findings, she had four different tests that confirmed an infection.

Victoria's life was literally in shambles because of a biopsy done in 2008, one that she now realizes was totally unnecessary. Another biopsy was simply out of the question, except Dr. Banker was offering a new wrinkle. He said he could use the biopsy procedure as a means of "stirring it up," referring to the infection. Dr. Banker said he had seen the "stirring" process cure infections before.

"I am so overwhelmed and in a state of confusion, and we had come so far, that I look at Brenda and ask her about the biopsy. Out of total desperation, we both decide the breast can be biopsied, but not my lymph node. I don't want anyone messing with my lymph node. I agreed to the biopsy only for the possibility that his actions could cure the infection."

"I was desperate. I made him promise he would not leave anything in my breast. He promised he wouldn't."

Brenda questioned the doctor: "Wouldn't the infection she has in her breast make her lymph nodes swell?"

Dr. Banker admitted it would.

"Are there any extra veins feeding my breast, typical of a cancer tumor?" Banker said no. Using ultrasound, a breast surgeon told Victoria eight months earlier the same thing – no veins were feeding a tumor, there was only scar tissue from the ablation.

The 2008 biopsy was a stereotactic ultrasound-guided procedure where the probe was inserted, and gradually turned as slices of tissue were removed with a vacuum device. In contrast, Dr. Banker inserted a needle nearly 10 times, all through the same incision on the right side of her nipple. "Each time he did it, he would tell me there would be a loud popping noise and then I would have a very bad pain as the tissue was cut."

In the end, the only thing Dr. Banker's biopsy stirred up was the infection; it got worse, not better.

Victoria believes to this day that she contracted a new infection while in the Toledo hospital, and the infection was never identified because no doctor would order an extended culture. In retrospect, a 63-day culture was needed, not the three-day cultures that doctors kept ordering.

This is why Victoria became so angry when she watched CBS News This Morning on Sunday, January 27, 2013. The cover story, reported by Serena Altschul, described superbugs.

"Can anything stop the superbugs that are making people sick and seem to defy the tools of medical science? Researchers are working on the problem, but to no avail so far."

Superbugs are extraordinary resilient bacteria that tend to infect hospital patients, and even kill those who are extremely ill, CBS reported. "The most recent study on health care-associated infections in U.S. hospitals, found that, out of about 1.7 million infections, nearly 99,000 patients died. According to one of the study's authors, the vast majority of the deaths were due to superbugs."

Victoria was carrying a 50-page report that described her ablation at the Toledo Hospital 20 months earlier. She offered, but Dr. Banker did not want to see the report any more than he wanted to order an extended culture for infection. Dr. Banker had done cryoablations for at least two of Victoria's friends.

"I always find it amazing," she says about dealing with doctors. "I have been dealing with this situation for three years and he does not want to see any information I have."

"The worst part was not the pain in my breast; it was the pain in my heart and soul. I know I don't have cancer. But if you are at a cancer center, you automatically are going to have cancer, unless there's unmistakable, 100% proof otherwise. Anything less than 100%, you will be diagnosed with cancer."

If a patient has cancer and the cancer center fails to tell them they have cancer, the cancer center can be sued. If the

patient does not have cancer and the cancer center tells them they do have cancer and treats them with surgery, radiation, and chemotherapy, and they die, nothing happens.

This fact escapes most people because a cancer diagnosis is generally a one-time event. The average person is not experienced in how the cancer industry works.

Victoria had to make one important phone call from the hospital. "My mother and siblings were anxiously waiting to hear that the marker had been removed. I tried to get Brenda to do it because I know how much my mother likes her." Brenda could not bring herself to mislead Victoria's mother, forcing Victoria to regroup. "Mother reads me so well. I knew she'd know I was flipped out."

Being a mother of three, Brenda understood about Southern mothers and she knew Victoria's mom would grill her until she spilled the truth. Looking back on it, Brenda realizes that she would have folded and told the truth.

"How can I be in this state of mind and pull this one off? How could I tell my mother the doctor just told me I had cancer?" Somehow, Victoria kept a straight face and a calm voice and explained that the doctor was unable to image the marker. It worked.

Victoria, who went to great lengths to protect herself from potential germ-infected surfaces, was irritated by an incident that might be all too common in hospital settings.

A nurse brought crackers and juice so Victoria could take her medication. She was lying in a hospital bed in Recovery. Before Victoria could say something, the nurse unwrapped the crackers with her bare hands and laid them on the hospital tray. No hand washing, no napkin, no nothing. Where had the tray been? What had her hands touched? "She would have been fired from a restaurant," mused Victoria.

True to form, she had regained her mental footing and wrapped her mind around the day's discouraging events. She knew more about what was going on in her body than any doctor. Emphatically, she reminded herself that she did not have cancer.

After all, how many times now has she been told she has cancer? Enough to not believe it, for sure. Applying a dab of common sense, she knew she would already be dead, if it was so. It was almost three years to the day since her original biopsy. She was told to make an immediate decision and not wait more than four months or she would die.

She maintained her humor. "I thought, I'm going to die tomorrow, that's what he's telling me. Hell, what's a germ on a cracker?"

Another nurse engages Victoria and Brenda in a conversation about cancer, explaining that her daughter had a lump in one breast and chose to have both breasts removed. "She met a wonderful man who stood by her through the entire process. They were going to get married," the nurse explained.

Then the nurse dropped a bombshell. "Since her cancer is estrogen driven, she is going to have her ovaries and uterus removed just in case, because both her daughter and husband already have children."

"We are thinking, 'oh my God,' what kind of mother is this that could think this is great that her daughter will be stripped of all her womanhood? She works at the cancer center and this is their thinking process? We know we have to get out of this place, the sooner the better. A nurse that thinks all of her daughter's female parts should be taken out is no one I want on my team."

"The ambush of all ambushes has happened to me today."

Victoria quickly gathered her composure. She knew that it was a stressful day for her friend, Brenda, too. "I have learned in life everything is a choice, even your attitude, and you can make a decision to have a good day or not."

"That night, I was worried about you," Brenda told Victoria. "I had never seen you so quiet and reserved. We thought the book was finally done. This is the ending to the story, a happy ending." That wasn't to be the case.

Brenda had one other insightful thought. Reflecting on that traumatic day in Toledo, she said, "I can't imagine any man or woman having to deal with this alone."

The next morning, however, Victoria was vibrant and eager to get going. She was up early and brought Brenda's breakfast to the room from the downstairs lobby. "If it was my last day, I was going to have a good time." Two years and seven months after her cancer diagnosis by Dr. Banker, Victoria is still vibrant and eager to begin each new day, and she has never had chemo or radiation.

"I was very impressed," said Brenda. "Victoria got up the next morning and she was happy and positive, ready to put it behind her."

After Victoria and Brenda had lunch the next day, they decided to stop at Our Lady, Queen of the Most Holy Rosary Cathedral, and the only Spanish plateresque cathedral in North America. Plateresque is an architectural style. Plata means silver in Spanish.

"It is a very beautiful, spiritual place. It's the same cathedral I visited after my ablation in 2009. We drive through the snow to get there. We're the only people there. I give thanks because I believe I'm healthy."

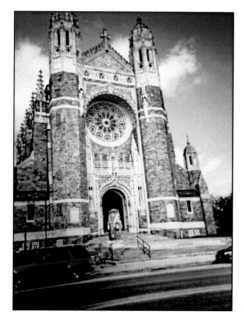

Cathedral in Toledo, Ohio.

After Victoria returned from Toledo, I wrote a letter to a doctor friend in Tennessee, whose medical specialty is prostate cancer. I told him that we were wondering out loud how many cryo-ablated breast tumors have been biopsied three years after the fact? It can't be many. Victoria might be the first.

"As you can see," I wrote on January 14, 2011, "the pathology report gives a diagnosis of cancer."

The original 2008 diagnosis at Hope Cancer Center was stage zero precancerous DCIS. Dr. Banker's diagnosis was a little different – invasive breast carcinoma based on alleged lymph node involvement, although Dr. Banker had no conclusive evidence.

Dr. Banker made two findings:
- Enlarged right axillary lymph nodes, which may be reactive or evidence of metastatic disease.
- Two right lung nodules, both of which are concerning for metastatic disease.

The doctor only used imaging to look at Victoria's nodes and lungs. Victoria is a non-smoker and had no lung issues before or after leaving Toledo, not even a cough.

She continues to exercise and walk at a brisk pace and never gets winded.

"We believe the pathology report was prepared on the basis of testing dead cryo-ablated cancer cells, and the medical test is not designed to do this, thus giving a false positive," I noted in my letter to the Tennessee doctor.

"What do you think about the pathology report?" I asked the doctor. "I value your thoughts."

When he responded, the doctor said he "never" relies on one pathology report. It's just as likely that one path report would say a person has cancer, and the same tissue samples sent to a different lab would return negative.

This wasn't the only surprise. This doctor said, "When there is anything unusual about a patient, the pathologist always comes back with, 'You have cancer.'"

Hours after returning to North Carolina, Victoria was still dazed at Banker's assertions. "He had me so depressed, I thought about killing myself. Where was I to turn?"

Victoria can usually snap out of stressful situations, but the trip to Toledo was almost too much. "He played a head game on me more than any other doctor." To even mention suicide in her journal was an indication of her tenuous mental condition. But relief was only a short drive away. In late January 2011, she had a three-hour biofeedback session with an accomplished practitioner. The results were amazing. Her stress levels plummeted back to normal "and I felt like my old self again."

Twenty days after the shocking report in Toledo, Dr. Banker provided candid responses to questions posed by Victoria in a three-page email. Her letter contained detailed questions which are being summarized, in a question/answer format.

Q – Why was the fluoroscope not used?

A – Much, much less sensitive in picking up small foreign bodies. Would not have seen anything based on the CT images. Would have been additional radiation for no help.

Q – Do you or the labs have a set of textbook color slides that show cryo and heat (RF) breast tissue ablation scar tissues/cell structures and what they look like over time?

A – There is no such book that I know of, but scarring and cancer look very different under a microscope. I thought that right away because the CT scan showed lung nodules and enlarged lymph nodes. In my world that is an indicator of cancer.

Q – What is your conclusion as to the calcium issue?

A – Calcium forms in response to trauma, such as a cryoablation.

Q – Why was the dental x-ray of the breast, which showed a "ghostly" V-shaped image, not used to guide a fluoroscopic investigation of the breast?

A – The wires used for biopsies are much larger than the ones seen on the dental films. The dental films were not detailed enough for me to see much in the first place. The CT is far better.

Q – What methods did you use to check for calcium micro-deposits?

A – Calcium is best picked up by a mammogram or CT.

Q – Just how thoroughly trained and current is the pathologist in observing and identifying the total morphology of cryo-ablated breast tissue, especially ablated tissue that is over two years old?

A – It is not common practice to look at previously ablated tissue. I would say that his experience is low but he is an excellent pathologist. Cancer cells look much different than scarring though.

Q – Do you ever consider the pH of a person when you are reviewing cancer patients?

A – I have never used that in my practice to date.

Q – Potentially, could the small flecks and nodules be just the CT return from fibrin that has been produced by amyloid proteins in response to the amount of very hard scar tissue in the breast?

A – Amyloid (insoluble fibrous protein aggregates) can be contributors. Amyloid is everywhere, just more in some people, especially with certain underlying diseases.

Q – How can you make the broad leap from large and varied thickness induced cryoablation scar tissue and a local recurrence of breast cancer?

A – I would have thought the scarring would have been much improved by then. I see these things a lot and know when I see something not responding as it should.

On the last question, Victoria agrees wholeheartedly. Her breast ablation was not responding as it should, she says, "because I had a foreign object and an infection in my breast."

Nevertheless, Victoria paid $901.80 out of her own pocket for her deductible and her insurance company paid Dr. Banker's hospital $7,860.30, including a $3,123.15 charge for laboratory and $1,846.63 for imaging, a total of $13,731.88.

Chapter 41

Buzz, where is your ring?

By mid-June 2010, the infection in Victoria's breasts was getting out of control. However, she faced an even greater obstacle in the arrogance of oncologists and surgeons who would not consider any diagnosis other than cancer. She found herself getting brow-beaten time after time in the presence of surgeons and cancer doctors, both male and female. She needed a witness and a strong advocate.

The obvious solution was for her to be accompanied by a knowledgeable husband. Since she wasn't married, she enlisted the aid of a mutual friend, a retired U.S. Air Force colonel whose experiences included 40-plus years as a pilot and an Air Commando who worked behind enemy lines in Laos, Cambodia, North Vietnam, and on the China border.

His combat experience wasn't the only thing that made him a valuable addition to the team of volunteers who were trying to help Victoria. Buzz, as he'll be known in this narrative, has a pair of undergrad degrees and two master's degrees. He did doctorate work at George Washington University and earned the equivalent of four additional master's degrees in the course of his largely secretive military career.

He's not a doctor, but his medical education is unique. He received specialized training in emergency surgery in severe field conditions, and he worked at Dorothea Dix Hospital for several years where he assisted a surgeon in nailing broken hips, removing kidneys, setting shattered patella's, and even removing lungs. Another doctor used him during exploratory autopsies.

For the new hospital interns, Buzz became the instructor in doing suctions of lungs and trachea, sub-clavian and ephemeral punctures, male and female bladder cauterizations, inter-cath insertions in geriatrics patients' collapsed veins, and even scalp vein needle insertions in babies. "I did the blood work for the House Officer Lab and dispensed the narcotics and all medicines to include all IM and sub-Q injections on my shift," he said.

For two years Buzz worked in the North Carolina State diagnostics labs doing everything from bacteriology experiments to blood work. He assisted a university professor with genetic experiments, tissue sampling, and cloning.

Buzz worked at the North Carolina State Research Station and also worked with the vets in the animal disease diagnostics labs. His resume includes delivering sheep and cattle caesarean section, and suturing. Intravenous insertions in both animal and human veins were a daily routine in many of his jobs. "In the lab where I worked, we did disease cultures for up to 62 days and kept track of all the changes over time as what was emerging and dying off. Modern medicine thinks they are great if they do a 2.5- to 3-day culture."

Buzz was the perfect surrogate husband to help Victoria, whom he met in January 2010 at a thermal imaging screening center in Western North Carolina. "I heard women talk about the many ways that doctors used fear to get them to have radical mastectomies, chemo, or radiation, and I listened intently. It was beyond belief that a doctor would try to brow-beat a person into submitting to their will, by using fear."

Initially, Buzz was skeptical about Victoria's accounting of her pleas for help. "I did not believe any of this at first, but I was soon to experience a year of horror as I posed as her husband."

"To my great surprise, I found doctors consistently did not want to help, or try to heal, or want to get involved, or even listen to the patient," said Buzz. "It was, 'listen to me lady, it is my way or the highway,' or 'you are stupid and I am smart, so do as I tell you, or you will die.'"

"What ever happened to the oath of Do No Harm?" he asked himself. He found out firsthand how the meaning for many cancer doctors has changed to "do no harm to my precious reputation."

"I am now a firm believer that medicine is all about making money," Buzz declared, "and the Hippocratic Oath is a silly piece of paper for a doctor to put on their waiting room wall to make their patients feel a little better about being used."

Buzz witnessed a distinct and vulgar pattern as doctors would casually glance at Victoria's breast and then immediately declare emphatically the same response – "you have cancer."

"If your mechanic looked at your parked car and by just glancing at the paint job declared the engine was blown, I bet you would immediately find a new mechanic," said Buzz. Ironically, Victoria got a free life lesson from her own mechanic. "If I don't fix your car, you'll keep bringing it back," the mechanic said. "A doctor's treatment can kill someone and the doctor answers to no one."

"People and patients have got to stop making doctors their god and worshipping their every word," said Buzz.

Buzz listened intently, but he did not worship. "My strength is that I have the ability to listen and discern the truth in medicine from the hype and the fear tactics. I research to the max what all doctors say and what procedures they want to perform on the patient. I examine all medicines and research their potential side effects."

With Victoria present, Buzz listened "to their every word, watched their gestures, and mentally recorded their voice inflections. They never stopped trying to induce fear in both Victoria and me. They wanted to get their way and there was no compromise. Why would they do this, you may say? My answer is money!"

The screening center in North Carolina was always full of women with numerous cancer issues. Buzz became good friends with many of them. From the outset, it was clear that Victoria's breast issue stemmed from some form of infection that developed after a biopsy in January 2008.

In the early months of 2010, Buzz could feel the hardness in Victoria's right breast gradually increase until it felt like a hockey puck. The heat in the breast also increased over time as well as a granular hard lumpiness in the breast fat tissue. He described how veins started to become blue in color, swollen, and would "pop-out" in the right breast as well as the top of the chest wall up toward the collar bone. The axillary lymph node (under the arm pit) became more swollen and harder.

"My concern was for an infection that had been introduced deep into the breast at the time of the biopsy. As any student in bacteriology and health science can affirm, there are numerous types of bacteria and some can and do cause just these types of reactions in tissue. There are also even molds and mildews that can cause biotoxins, hemotoxins, and neurotoxins."

"For any readers with a romantic inclination, let me assure you that the relationship between Victoria and me was strictly of the utmost professional and plutonic nature," he said. "This allowed me to be totally rational and not get overwhelmed with the fears that the doctors tried to induce. Yet, in the doctor's office, I would play my role to the max."

In most instances, it was Buzz who would show the doctors all the issues with Victoria's breast and explain all the changes that he had observed over time. "Being truly detached and not being a real husband or 'involved' allowed me to be totally objective," he said. "I did not get caught up in the hype and fear mongering that the medical profession in the cancer/oncology fields are dumping onto their patients."

Buzz not only had extensive medical training, but his background in aerospace engineering led him to work as the chief engineer for six different countries on their military aircraft. "I have also worked on the designs of new and innovative medical devices and procedures and am still doing work in this field at present."

As the chief of the World Wide Corrosion Control and Fracture Mechanics Laboratory for the U.S. military forces, U.S. Coast Guard, U.S. Border Patrol, U.S. Drug Enforcement and BATF, Saudi Arabia, Japan, Korea, and Israel, Buzz dealt with the best in worldwide imaging equipment, electron microscopes, extremely high resolution ultrasound, small area x-ray, magnetic resonance imaging devices, and fluoroscopes "with fantastic abilities for detecting minute objects."

Finding the proverbial needle in a haystack was actually quite simple for Buzz. The technology was readily available in the military. "We could detect foreign objects and abnormalities in anything from high strength steel and alloys to human bones and soft animal and human tissues."

Why couldn't modern medicine do the same thing for Victoria?

Buzz's background includes both organic and inorganic chemistry and the reactive natures with other materials as well as to the human body.

Victoria was asking for help from surgeons who have access to laser equipment that can cut as well as 'zap' (close bleeding veins). They have access to coagulants that can constrict bleeding veins and capillaries. The surgeon also knows where the main arteries are located.

Why would a competent surgeon be afraid of bleeding?

(Note: For the remainder of this chapter, Buzz is doing the talking in the first person and Victoria's comments are in quotes.)

The few doctors who are talking about breast biopsy clips and markers are telling the world that this is a perfectly safe procedure. I know differently, for I have had calls late at night from women and even their husbands because a breast marker has created a tumor that has erupted on the breast and major bleeding was occurring. I have had to calm them and tell them exactly how to stop the profuse bleeding. They do not go to a doctor for they know the only option will be the immediate removal of their breast.

When Victoria commented that she thought she was feeling a sharp metal object, I put my engineering protractor on her breast and diagramed the location on a sheet of copy paper. I could literally catch the protruding tip of this hard object under the skin using my fingernail.

Both Victoria and I could feel the small hard marker protruding from the skin and we could visually see a portion of its outline.

At this point, I could have made a very small incision ($1/16^{th}$ of an inch) with a scalpel and with a fine pair of hemostats withdrawn the object. Closure could have been made with a simple butterfly bandage. I had all the necessary items including all the pre and post op prep, disinfectant, and antibiotic agents. However, both Victoria and I wanted a doctor to remove this device so we would have irrefutable proof that there had been a breast marker or something foreign left in her breast that had caused her issues.

At the time, it was felt that the physical proof was necessary for the credibility of this book (*Saving Victoria's Breasts*). Delaying the extraction was a horrible mistake because it only took one future visit to a cancer doctor and the object was pushed deep into the breast so hard that it never again appeared near the skin's surface.

Totally determined that I would get to know this breast issue better than any doctor could, I did eight hours of round trip driving almost weekly to follow her progress, chart the coloration, breast swelling, hardness of the breast, the swollen and distended veins of the chest wall, any swollen or tenderness in the lymph nodes, and keep track of the crusty brown fluids leaking from the nine mammary duct openings in her right nipple. I read and digested all her many medical records.

"Buzz's medical expertise was always so comforting," says Victoria. "I will always appreciate what he did for me."

Where could she go to get this foreign object removed from the breast?

Perhaps there's a better question: Who would most likely have more empathy for another woman and try to preserve her breast, remove the object, and stop all the pain?

We determined that another woman should best fill that requirement, and so this sad nightmarish saga began.

Chapter 42

Sanity under all this madness

Remember the game we played as kids? Victoria found herself having to choose between "Truth or Dare."

How could Victoria criticize one doctor and still get another doctor to help her? Obviously, she had to change her strategy and look for a doctor with the proper equipment to image the object and the "will and fortitude" to extract it.

A Roman philosopher once said: It is not because things are difficult that we do not dare; it is because we do not dare that they are difficult.

Victoria's search led to a chiropractor in Blowing Rock, North Carolina in May 2011 (callowayclinic.com). Dr. Alex Isaenko had been trained at the Russian Medical Academy and had a chiropractic and applied kinesiology clinic.

(Note: For the remainder of this chapter, Buzz is doing the talking in the first person and Victoria's comments are in quotes.)

Even though most medical doctors want to pooh-pooh these disciplines as non-medical and "quackery," I know better. Plenty of medical doctors go to chiropractors for weekly adjustments. I also have studied the relationship of the body's magnetic field, innate perception ability, and the environment the body lives in, and that relationship to applied kinesiology.

What a breath of fresh air this doctor and his wife were. They listened and they were really concerned about Victoria's health and well-being. We did not feel rushed or part of the great treadmill to generate cash and the next payment for a Mercedes. No fear tactics were used.

After conducting body rejection and allergic reaction tests, it was clear that Victoria was extremely allergic to stainless steel (nickel) and titanium, as well as many other things. This was confirmation for what had already been established about Victoria's extreme sensitivity to metals in her body.

If nothing else, we knew that if a marker were in her breast that it could cause such a reaction as she was experiencing. Any ray of hope and light was welcome at this point in the search for some form of relief from pain.

In Russia, Dr. Isaenko was a surgeon. "He said if I were in Russia, I would do the surgery and remove it, but I don't have a license here and I can't do it," he told Victoria. "He also told me all the women he has seen with diagnosed breast cancer have a dairy allergy that is producing lumps in their breast."

Dr. Isaenko tried to help by referring her to Dr. Kristin Wagner in Charlotte, North Carolina. Victoria's hopes were soon encouraged by a young female surgeon who agreed to see her. This would be the first time that I would accompany her to see a doctor while posing as her surrogate husband, Buzz.

On the afternoon of June 23, 2011, Victoria and I entered the reception area at Surgical Specialists and soon met Dr. Wagner, a tall, beautiful lady with flashing eyes. She appeared to be intently interested in Victoria's breast issue and showed no intimidation as I showed her all the issues with my 'wife's' breast.

I kept trying to impress on Dr. Wagner to do a special long-term culture of the fluid coming from the nipple area. This request of mine always seemed to fall on deaf ears.

I asked if she had the ability to do extremely high resolution fluoroscope imaging and she said no, but the local hospital did and she would give us a referral. Dr. Wagner wanted to do a sonogram or ultrasound imaging as it is called with more precise imaging equipment. She used an ultrasound imaging machine that is used to look at "fuzzy images" of babies inside the womb.

When I started questioning her about the low resolution of her equipment and asked if the facility had a high resolution machine with very small power heads, she seemed to become defensive. When we looked at Victoria's axillary lymph node and she said it looked cancerous and I stated that it was only slightly oval but had none of the inner ragged characteristics of cancer, I realized I had better back off.

I also asked if she would try to get a fluid sample from the breast and do a culture for bacteria or other organisms. She seemed a bit reluctant and seemed to think there was no need for such action.

Dr. Wagner sent us to the x-ray department to see if a chest x-ray would show the marker. Victoria could not afford to have more radiation on her breast, but Dr. Wagner was going to let me place a B-B marker on the exterior of her breast to mark where I thought the internal breast marker had been moved to, by Dr. Blouin's extreme action.

The x-ray did show the paste-on B-B, but no other possible internal breast marker. Due to the large size and distance from the breast that the x-ray was shot, I had no reason to believe that such a small item would be shown. She was requiring the chest x-ray before she would refer Victoria to the hospital for fluoroscope imaging.

When the x-ray report came back, Dr. Wagner's radiologist issued a contradictory report to the information Victoria was given five months earlier in Toledo. "Other than minor biapical scarring, the lungs are clear. The heart and mediastinum are unremarkable. There are no suspicious osseous abnormalities."

To put it in layman's terms, the report used six words in the 'conclusion' to characterize Victoria's chest x-ray: No active disease in the chest.

But we still had the high definition fluoroscope imagery to get done on another day, and we were both so hopeful that would prove to be the correct imaging method.

As we left the office, we both felt that Dr. Wagner was going to go all out and help us to get this marker removed.

The next day, Dr. Wagner called Victoria. She was the same doctor with the same name but a different attitude. It was as though the doctor's superiors had gotten to her and told her to wash her hands of this entire case. Dr. Wagner was intimidating and wanted no more contact and did not want to even give a referral for a fluoroscope exam.

"Ironically, she had wanted me to return to her hospital for the fluoroscopy, but now she told me to find one at a large hospital in Asheville. She wanted no part of it. She had also agreed during my visit that I should not have a mammogram because of the ablation, and during this call she was insisting that I have a mammogram."

How could any doctor refuse to order a fluoroscope exam, knowing it might be the only technology capable of proving the presence of a foreign object in the breast? Was Victoria on a "doctor's watch list, perhaps because of her insurance information?"

We both realized that Victoria's breast pain and suffering was likely to continue. Where does she go from here? Who will help her? Why will no doctor consider that this is an internal breast infection, or an adverse reaction and inflammatory response to a foreign object in the breast? Or both? I knew that Victoria was hyper allergic to certain types of metal, even stainless steel and titanium. Her past history proved this.

Pain, suffering, desperation, depression, and fear can drive people to do just about anything to change their circumstances. Victoria was at the end of her rope, looking for any thread of hope. The swelling, pain, redness, hardness, and bulging of the breast was relentless.

To add insult to injury, Dr. Wagner refused to allow Victoria to get a copy of her chest x-ray on a CD, even though she offered to pay for it. Victoria finally received the radiologist's written report on July 11. She only received the CD of the x-ray after sending Dr. Wagner a certified letter on July 13.

The letter requested a CD image of precise, exact and readable quality of the two x-rays that were performed under the billable diagnostic code 99244. Victoria's letter also cited five of the applicable laws pertaining to a patient's right to obtain full copies of their medical records.

Just like a pin ball machine that has been jiggled too hard by the operator and the bells, sirens, and flashing lights go off, so it was with Victoria's breast. All of a sudden the heat, redness, and swelling started to go wild. A bulbous lump arose on the breast. This was scary. Then more red spots and bulbous areas started to arise on the breast skin.

Based on my work with people and animals, these were infectious sites and possibly pus-filled infections deep in the breast. Victoria used Silver Sol nano particle silver solution on her breast. This solution is made by one of the largest pharmaceutical labs in

America and is surgical grade. In seven minutes it kills over 650 different bacteria, viruses, molds, mildews, and fungi. Desperate times called for desperate measures. Where was the help for Victoria?

She started using a strong "drawing salve" that has been around for years to remove embedded metal fragments as well as to bring pus pockets to the skin's surface in both people and animals. Her hope was to bring the object to the surface. She also used an "old timey treatment" – milk and bread poultice – to also act as a drawing method to move the foreign object.

The pain was getting totally unbearable for Victoria. Her psyche was being challenged as well as her ability to physically stand the pain. The use of over-the-counter pain killers became excessive and no longer worked. Was the marker hiding in that hot bulb? How were we going to get this object removed since no doctor would even discuss it? We even tried two sensitive metal detectors used for finding tiny fragments of nails or wire staples in lumber (before sawing or thickness planing with delicate blades), but to no avail.

On September 4, 2011, the drawing salve and the poultice had to be discontinued because the breast became so red, swollen, and sore. The skin was stretched so tight over the swollen breast that it appeared to be very thin, polished, and shiny red.

Even as a surrogate husband, I become very angry and frustrated. I could not begin to understand how Victoria kept her sanity under all this madness.

Chapter 43

Halloween all over again

It was mid-September 2011 and Victoria's right breast was swollen three times its normal size. On a scale of one to 10, pain was at seven, and one-half of the breast was covered in a red rash.

Nearly a dozen medical doctors, surgeons, and oncologists had refused to concede even a slim possibility that her breast inflammation and infection might be caused by a reaction to a metal marker.

Some of them made their diagnosis simply by looking at her breast. Others pushed on it, to the point of causing excruciating pain and forcing blood from the nipple.

There were exceptions, about a half-dozen of them. These doctors believed Victoria did not have cancer, but rather an adverse reaction and infection, and they had the tests to prove it.

Although strong-willed and determined, Victoria realized that she was in a state of desperation, and it was life-threatening.

A friend who had 40 years experience as a nurse knew Victoria needed medical attention, but the only attention medical doctors were willing to offer came with the demand that she consent to mammograms, additional biopsies, chemo and radical surgery, and that wasn't going to happen.

Victoria's pleas were ignored. Cancer doctors would not even talk about an infection or allergic reaction.

Victoria's friend compassionately suggested that the swollen breast should be lanced to relieve pain and possibly allow an escape path for the marker. The friend, an RN, had personally felt the object, too, before it was apparently embedded deep in the breast by Dr. Blouin.

Her breast pain was pushing her to make a gut-wrenching choice. She remembered seeing the video images of people jumping from the blazing inferno high up in the Twin Towers on September 11, 2001.

"I couldn't keep on with the pain, but I didn't want to lose my breast. There was a possibility that the marker might come out."

"Is this how the jumpers felt on that tragic morning in New York City as they were about to be burned alive?" Victoria wondered. Jumping offered the possibility of survival and a ray of hope. Burning to death was certain if they did not jump. Victoria desperately needed some hope.

Over 200 people who were in the Twin Towers died by jumping, according to *USA Today* – some alone, some in pairs, and others in groups. Firefighters found over 50 bodies on the Marriott Hotel. The first rescue fireman was killed by a jumper. No jumper survived (wiki.answers.com).

If something wasn't done soon, Victoria was probably going to die.

The incision, done on the evening of September 15, 2011, did release some smelly necrotic tissue and fluid. And almost instantly, Victoria experienced pain relief, and it lasted for three blessed days before pain gradually returned.

It seemed to Victoria that the only product that offered any control over the infection was Silver Sol, taken orally and applied topically.

Victoria was living in a non-stop world of desperation. It seemed as though she had only one choice. Nearly 70 years earlier, on October 29, 1941, British Prime Minster Winston Churchill made his famous statement: "Never, never, never give up."

Victoria would do no less. She was a fighter. Like Churchhill, she was determined.

(Note: For the remainder of this chapter, Buzz, her surrogate husband, is doing the talking in the first person and Victoria's comments are in quotes. Buzz recaps the two-month ordeal that took place from mid-September to mid-November, 2011, including the lancing.).

On September 15, 2011, Victoria and two female friends met for an evening meal. One of the women has been a nurse for over 40 years and the other has worked in the health care field for years, too. The nurse decided that the potential pus pocket needed to be immediately evacuated for Victoria's personal safety and health.

"Even though I was desperate for medical attention, I never imagined the lancing would make the situation so much harder to deal with."

An incision was made in the breast and out came a smelly mass of pus. This was all relayed to me by the three women, separately. My past experiences with massive infections in geriatric patients as well as battlefield infection conditions, indicated this was a severe bacterial infection, not cancer.

Closure of the incision was made with a butterfly bandage. The breast experienced some additional swelling after the incision, and then, very quickly, the swelling subsided. The axillary lymph node swelling and hardness disappeared, and the unbearable pain was reduced considerably. This was not a cancer cure; it was a temporary fix for a bacterial infection.

Less than a week after the incision, Victoria called and said it was not healing and knitting shut. The margin lines of the incision had not started to dry and form a scab, but instead looked wet and puffy.

"Exhausted," Victoria wrote in her journal entry on September 19, 2011. "This breast is wearing on me."

When I received a photo of the incision several days later via email, I knew things were not good. The incision could not be held together with a butterfly bandage and the underlying breast tissue was wet and oozing and starting to blossom out through the skin opening. In reality, it should have been drying up and a scab forming, even with the margin lines being apart. This new occurrence was indicative of an infection still in progress and now it was spreading.

Then without any warning, the breast started a new phase of swelling. With more small red bulbs emerging, it looked like a mushroom farm. Growth was slow at first but then went wild. On October 22, 2011, I had a phone consultation with Victoria while looking at a picture sent to me via email. I informed her that this would not heal unless the internal infection or pathogens were stopped and the incision area, which was growing wider, was closed with sutures.

I was now concerned that she had somehow contacted one of a number of pathogens associated with both bird and/or bat droppings, for her home is located in the forest and she works outside so much of the time. These can create all forms of cellular reactions.

With more mushroom-like growth came more pain and more draining from Victoria's breast. I tried and tried to talk to the doctors about the types of bacteria that resemble a fungating "mushroom" mass and, of course, they tuned me out as if I were a stupid civilian.

During this time, a number of medical people promised to find help, but nothing ever panned out – a lot of promises, not much action. Victoria was getting used to the Halloween syndrome – she always got the trick, not the treat.

It was October 25, 2011 when Victoria and I drove to the office of Dr. Amber Passini in Landrum, South Carolina. She had taken over Dr. Rozema's practice upon his retirement. We were both at our wit's end. I had not seen Victoria's breast in almost two months. There was a pumpkin-shaped bulb growing from her breast that had become hard as a piece of burned toast on the outside with large pores that were weeping fluids. It looked black, brown, and red.

This new doctor was not a surgeon but a general practitioner. Our hope was that she had some contacts and they might be able to help Victoria.

Dr. Passini injected Victoria's breast with 2% Lidocaine to kill some of the terrible pain and she attempted a needle aspiration. The only thing that was recovered through the small needle was some blood.

Few things in life scare me, for I have lived through some really bloody and gruesome events in war, but I lost my composure on this day – November 17, 2011 – when Victoria sent me a new picture of her breast. My first thought was, 'How can this woman keep on going and have any hope of recovery with a situation like this and with no help from doctors?'

311

I made no bones about it to Victoria, she had to find a surgeon fast, and get surgery to remove this fungating mass and also kill the infection. I was terrified of the real possibility of septicemia where the bacteria enters the blood stream and kills the patient in 24 hours.

We had been using a Silver Sol gel on the bulb and it seemed to kill the infection and the bubbly cells would just dissolve. Only one problem: when the diseased cells were killed there was nothing left to support the capillaries and Victoria would bleed profusely from the breast.

Again, there was another phone blitz. Victoria started dialing one doctor and surgeon after another trying to make an appointment. No one had the time or inclination to help her. They all wanted her to have a doctor's referral. Finally some help seemed to arrive when a plastic surgeon scheduled her for an appointment.

Chapter 44

Will this ever stop?

On November 21, 2011, Victoria had an appointment at Dr. William A. Young's office in Asheville, North Carolina. She was accompanied by her surrogate husband, Buzz.

(Note: For the remainder of this chapter, Buzz is doing the talking in the first person and Victoria's comments are in quotes.)

I had researched Dr. Young's biography and he had an impressive record from graduating at the U.S. Air Force Academy, then Tulane Medical School, internship at the famous Keesler Medical Center in Biloxi, Mississippi, and then on to USAF Medical Center, Wulford Hall for plastic surgery training.

Being a fellow officer and colonel, I felt sure I could relate to this man for we had common ground. I was hopeful that having worked in a research hospital, he would know the issues associated with the ravages of war and small imbedded items in the human body and understand the potential infections. At least he would be familiar with the latest in imaging equipment that could be used to find and remove very small metal objects.

As Victoria and I looked around the examination room while waiting for the doctor's arrival, we realized he was basically a breast augmentation surgeon. He made money doing breast reconstruction on women who had had either one or both breasts removed during cancer surgery.

These plastic surgeons usually work hand and hand with oncologists who do the chemotherapy and radiation, and operating theatre surgeons who remove breasts. At least we knew he was a board certified plastic surgeon and that he knew his way around breast surgery.

When Dr. Young arrived in the examination room, Victoria already had her paper blouse on ready for her consultation. I introduced us and tried to lay the ground work for some common experiences in the U.S. Air Force. He was all business and virtually tried to ignore the fact that I was in the room.

When I tried to explain the history of the breast issues, my thoughts on a fungating-type breast infection, and a potential marker in the breast, Dr. Young acted as if he did not hear me. I had the feeling that he wanted to make me feel unwelcome.

To show his disdain for me being in the room, Dr. Young pulled his chair up very close to Victoria, who was sitting on the examination table, propped his foot up on the bottom table rail and placed his same-side arm across his knee and leaned forward. This formed a barrier between the two of us and better allowed him to ignore me.

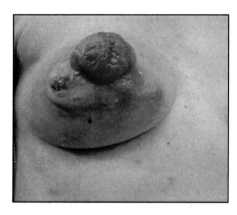

Bulbous growth in November 2011 that formed after September lancing.

Both Victoria and I tried time and again to impress upon Dr. Young about all the allergic reactions she has. These range from numerous aromatic smells, chemicals, and even to metals. She could not wear a stainless steel wrist watch. He did not seem interested. I tried to get this doctor to do an aspiration of fluids from the breast and a long term culture to see what pathogens might possibly grow. I had no luck.

I was constantly 'tuned-out' as if I were just a stupid non-medical person, thus I did not have a brain.

When taking a shower, Victoria protected the growth from soap and water using plastic wrap and tape, upon my suggestion. This was due to the possibility of introducing more biological agents into the mystery growths from her well water. She cleaned the affected area with gauze and a silver liquid and followed this with a coating of silver gel.

Dr. Young actually chuckled at the use of my silver gel. He stated he had a gel that was 1% silver. I wanted to rebuff (but did not) – 1% of what? You cannot use percentages to prove anything. He had no parts-per-million (ppm) count on his product. Being a good husband and wife team, I rubbed the Silver Sulfadiazine 1% white cream onto Victoria's breast.

What a mistake! Was I never going to learn to 'protect my surrogate wife?'

I had allowed a doctor to prescribe something and I had not first researched the product to determine its potential side effects. Silver is used to virtually eliminate scar tissue formation and this of course looks better on a breast augmentation procedure and this was something he routinely used.

Dr. Young quickly cut to the chase and said he would do nothing until Victoria had another MRI and also went to an oncologist for a full evaluation, and of course he had a good one close by. Wow, we were back on the money making merry-go-round, but just through another door. This was the same story, same dance, same song, time and again.

This was just another referral, another big medical bill, and absolutely no action. Would this ever stop? I felt that the doctors were just passing Victoria from one to another. Did no doctor want to heal a patient? Do you understand how frightening this scenario is when it repeats and repeats?

Victoria's journal entry on November 23, 2011: "This breast is so consuming and takes up so much of my time. It is very depressing but I have to accept it if I have to get my breast cut off. I'm going to have to do it. I can't go on living my whole life being so consumed with this breast. The pain is so bad and I can't physically function. I don't want to accept it but I feel I have no choice."

On November 25, an MRI was performed, but with no "contrast" dye shot into her veins. Victoria is hyper allergic to the dye and that has in the past caused almost critical reactions. The possibility of a marker and the fact of altered tissue as a result of the cryoablation were not considered.

The next day, I received a call and Victoria was having a bad bleed-out from the breast. I talked her through the episode. "Research indicates that an MRI with a strong magnetic field can dislodge metal objects within the body. "I believe the MRI moved the marker and caused me to bleed profusely," said Victoria.

Then on November 28 Victoria called, and e-mailed me a picture of her breast. There was a massive allergic reaction underway. I researched the side effects of Silver Sulfadiazine 1% cream, and they are many. Victoria was also having a vision problem. Normally her long-range vision is like eagle vision, but suddenly she could not focus past 20 feet. "Everything was a blur and driving was extremely difficult." When she stopped rubbing the cream on the breast, her long range vision returned, and she has never experienced that problem again.

Why would any doctor prescribe this cream, which has so many potential side effects, to a patient with known hyper allergic reactions?

Based on Victoria's many medical experiences, I now have a new ground rule as part of my belief system. I believe doctors protect each other, no matter what. It is the good-old-boy network.

It's as though most doctors have taken a blood oath to see no medical evil, hear no medical evil, tell no medical evil, and do nothing that could cause another doctor a lawsuit or the loss of their credibility, reputation, integrity, or revenue.

Chapter 45

My way or no way

"My way or no way."

Victoria was getting used to this attitude, but she was still traumatized by the words, especially when they came from a female cancer doctor.

She had an appointment with Dr. Michelle Leblanc at Parkridge Breast Center, at Parkridge Hospital in Hendersonville, North Carolina on December 5, 2011. On the way into the examination office, Victoria and her surrogate husband, Buzz, passed warning signs about "no pregnant women or children beyond this point." In the building, there were people getting chemotherapy in the Cancer Infusion Room.

Victoria would return for a follow-up appointment a week later, on December 14, 2011. At the return appointment, the doctor rejected Victoria having an infection and again declared she had cancer. Dr. Leblanc offered a single solution of total surgical removal including chest wall and all lymph nodes.

Dr. Leblanc's practice includes gynecology and benign and malignant breast conditions, according to the website, vitals.com, where it also states that she provides "a full range of diagnostic and treatment options for breast conditions, including breast ultrasound, minimally invasive stereotactic biopsy, and breast conserving procedures."

Full range of options? Victoria was only given one option.

And Dr. Leblanc demanded chemo. Victoria was seated at the end of an exam table. The doctor was an arm's length away, seated on a stool. "What if I don't want to take the chemo?" Victoria asked. The doctor leaned over and placed her right hand on Victoria's right knee, looked Victoria in the eye, and said, "It's either my way or no way."

Dr. Leblanc was young, slim, stately, and beautiful. Buzz felt in his heart, "Well, here is a woman who will want to heal another woman and do everything possible to find the root cause of the issue." The doctor's conversation was cordial and she wanted to know about Buzz and Victoria. Her father was also a pilot like Buzz.

Here's how the two appointments with Dr. Leblanc unfolded.

(Note: For the remainder of this chapter, Buzz is doing the talking in the first person and Victoria's comments are in quotes. This is the fourth time Buzz accompanied Victoria as her surrogate husband.)

Once we got into the real meat of our visit, she quickly displayed signs that dispelled my previous notion. She was not too interested in listening to any of Victoria's breast history or any of my ideas about infections, breast markers, or allergic reactions.

When either Victoria or I tried to speak and tell her the issues with the breast, she either interrupted us or let us know it was not important. Her eyes would glaze over when we tried to express ideas we thought were pertinent. We soon knew we were again being "tuned-out."

With only a quick glance at the right breast, Dr. Leblanc immediately concluded her diagnosis – cancer. Doctors are not listening. Their automatic response is like a stuck needle on a record album playing on a phonograph, repeating the same word over and over – cancer, cancer, cancer, cancer. Dr. Leblanc seemed to want both Victoria and me to just roll over and accept her quick prognosis.

Time and again I had tried to get doctors to prescribe some form of effective pain killer for Victoria, but none did so. The pain was now so great that Victoria could not sleep. The amount of over-the-counter pain killers she was consuming was excessive and could potentially damage her liver and kidneys. I begged and pleaded with the doctors to extract a needle sample of internal breast fluid and do a long-term culture.

Dr. Leblanc agreed to a needle aspiration, but she let me know that the fluid evacuation and culture were ridiculous. The big question now in my mind was, just how long would she run the culture and try and incubate any pathogens?

Victoria's journal entry on December 11, 2011: "I had really bad pain again this morning with my breast. I'm just trying to hold on until I can get back to the doctor. I could barely hang on when I went to Dr. Young November 21. This crap of just testing and not doing anything for me is getting so old. Thank God for Advil and taking the pain away."

About a week passed and Victoria received a phone call from Dr. Leblanc's office setting up a return appointment. Ignoring me, Dr. Leblanc told Victoria that the cancer was now so bad that she would have to cut down the breast bone and across under the rib cage to the side of the rib cage, and then up under her arm pit and remove all of the lymph nodes and then across under the collar bone to the first incision line on the breast bone.

In other words, this doctor was going to remove one-fourth of Victoria's chest and just throw it away.

She demanded that Victoria immediately start chemotherapy. "She insisted that I must have the chemo or she would not consider doing the surgery."

When I asked for the results of the pathogen test that was incubated, she just stated that cancer was showing. We picked up copies of Victoria's medical records as we departed. To say the least, the doctor's attitude left us feeling really down and out. Victoria and I went to the car and sat quietly for a moment. She was in total shock.

I can only imagine what women who do not know the routine of the doctors and their 'fear-mongering' must really feel like.

I felt like a lost puppy that had followed a stranger's whistle to the front door of their house as though they were offering to feed and care for me. As I panted with expectation, the owner slammed the door crushing my face. Then they opened the door and said in a wicked voice, "Oh, don't worry my cute little puppy for I love you, and I will heal your crushed face with a potato peeler, alcohol, and gasoline."

Later we discovered there were no pathogen incubation/growth test records in the paperwork. When Victoria acquired the missing records, they showed Dr. Leblanc only ordered a 2.5-day incubation period and the lab reported abnormal cells showing. Every lab test since the freezing of her breast lump in April 2009 (cryoablation) has shown "abnormal cells." By now, we all understand the "doctor drill." If it looks abnormal, it must be cancer!

I tried to prevent this conclusion by the lab by having Victoria mail a two-page letter that I wrote and she signed explaining what to expect from the microscopic and growth/culture. Here are three basic points:

1. Please keep in mind that the cells removed will most likely be very irregular looking, but in my particular case this does not mean cancer.

2. The cryoablation uses gaseous Argon ... the gas expands from the pressure cylinder, rapidly cools, and freezes the

tissue in question. This freezing kills the cell structure via little sharp ice crystals in the cytoplasm and the cell is obliterated. This leaves abnormal looking cells which can form a combination of scar tissue or the cells can be absorbed by the body.

3. In my case, there was much scar tissue, and that has become infected and gotten harder/more dense with time. This tissue will most likely appear extremely abnormal in nature.

Later when Victoria and I looked at her breast and the area on the bottom where the doctor placed the clear gel to assist in the ultrasound probe movement and also where I smeared the white gel, there was swelling and an extremely dark red rash. As Victoria has said, "I am allergic to so many things, creams, chemicals, but especially stainless steel."

Victoria began her December 6, 2011 letter by stating: "This morning my breast feels so much better. Even when the nurse lanced the breast and all that horrible smelling pus and heavy corruption came out, there was an immediate better feeling and my axillary lymph node reduced swelling and hardness, and returned to normal."

Victoria was also critical of the Silver Sulfadiazine Cream 1% prescribed by Dr. William Young, saying it caused "extreme allergic reactions to my breast and even seems to be causing me some issues with proper vision. Very dark red spots have formed on my breast, breast swelling has intensified, and increased pain intensity, new areas with no skin have formed, the breast bleeds from areas where it previously did not, the new skin and small veins that had formed over the bulb mass has now died, and the bulbous mass of tissue that has emerged from the point my breast was lanced to remove the large amount of pus has now almost doubled in volume."

A friend of mine who has spent years examining surgically removed breast tissue as a pathologist with the National Institute of Health told Victoria to never again see an oncologist. "No oncologist will ever help you unless you accept the cancer treatment," this medical professional said. Instead, she needed to find a surgeon, one who actually believed in the Hippocratic Oath, to remove the fungating masses.

Chapter 46

It's the right thing to do

Victoria was only seeking a doctor, just one doctor who would help her. One doctor who would save her life! Not finding one was breaking her heart and her spirit.

Her mind drifted back 23 years to a music concert at the famous McCallum Theater in Palm Desert, California where she had driven about 15 minutes from her home to hear country music star Reba McEntire in concert in April 1989. All these years later, Victoria even remembered the dress McEntire was wearing. "It was great color for her because her hair was so red and her dress was so blue. She looked full of life."

It was McEntire, a songwriter and record producer, who was credited with one of the immortal quotes about living. "To succeed in life, you need three things: a wishbone, a backbone, and a funny bone," said the country music singer/actress. Victoria possessed all three. What she was lacking was a doctor with a conscience.

McEntire's concert performance was recorded live over three days. Because of her admiration for the singer, Victoria was heartbroken nearly two years later when eight members of the singer's band, and two pilots, were killed in a plane crash in March 1991 in a mountain area near the Mexican border. McEntire was not on the plane. Victoria found herself even more connected with the singer when McEntire wrote the hit song, "For My Broken Heart," and used it as the title for her 16th album which she dedicated to her deceased band.

The lyrics addressed all measure of suffering and emotional turmoil and gave Victoria a life connection with the song and the singer that was resonating in 2012. In her heart of hearts, Victoria knew her life was on the line. Something had to give.

"Last night I prayed the Lord my soul to keep, then I cried myself to sleep," McEntire wrote. But the lyric that Victoria latched onto was "I guess the world didn't stop for my broken heart." Some people spend their life in a never-ending pursuit of happiness.

Others are always seeking excellence or perfection in everything they do.

Victoria was only seeking a doctor. One doctor!

She was not being picky about her medical practitioner. She did care about his competency. Victoria wanted a true healer. But the name of his college wasn't that important. Victoria didn't care if the doctor was male or female, young or old, single or married. She would have taken an alien if a competent one was available who was truly interested in saving her life.

She resorted to the internet and found the name of a doctor in Ohio, Donna Vecchione, who was listed on an adverse reactions website. The doctor was identified as someone who had removed a breast marker. Victoria called to discuss her situation and spoke with the doctor's assistant who asked her to forward her medical records. She put together an easy-to-read summary and sent a certified correspondence on December 1, 2011 that also contained detailed reports. The package was signed for on December 8, but Victoria never received the courtesy of a return call.

It was like this, over and over again. Victoria met one brick wall after the other. More wasted time and effort, more expense, more exasperation. Could a new year, only weeks away, bring new hope? Or was Victoria running out of both?

(Note: For the remainder of this chapter, Buzz is doing the talking in the first person. Any other comments are in quotes and are attributed to the source.)

I met Victoria at a motel in Morganton, North Carolina on New Year's Day, January 1, 2012. The fungating mass had doubled in size since I last saw it 13 days earlier.

Victoria's journal entry on January 1, 2012: "I wish I could get a break. This thing is so scary. It's like a sponge."

The growths needed to be surgically removed, but not her entire chest. We had to act now to get a surgeon to do some magic or we were going to lose Victoria. I have seen people die from septicemia (bacterial blood poisoning) while we were pumping fresh blood from one person's arm directly into the patient. I have lived in Southeast Asia, the Middle East, and North Africa and have seen people actually eaten alive by unexplained pathogens and fungating bulbous bloody growths.

Now I was seeing the same type of fungating growth on a good friend and no doctor would help. If this had been a stray dog on a street corner, it would have been a different story. Reporters and TV news crews would have shamed any veterinarians who refused to help. The abandoned dog's story would have been plastered above the fold on the front page of newspapers and editorial writers would have taken extreme liberties in blasting the unsympathetic vets. TV cameras would have recorded reactions from angry pet owners.

Victoria is an intelligent woman and productive member of society, yet no doctor would expose themselves professionally to help her. She had monetary means and insurance. Prompt payment was virtually guaranteed. No one can claim that money was a valid reason for refusing to help.

Yet, many doctors who would see her had no problems testing her, doing nothing for her, and taking her money, and then referring her to another doctor who would do more testing, do nothing to help, and take more money. Is this a medical and social travesty of epic proportion?

The bulbous cells were a hyperplasia situation and were dividing in an exponential fashion. I could see there was now no way to stop the situation unless surgery was performed, and fast. I felt that a strong broad spectrum antibiotic must be used directly on the flesh after the infected tissue was totally removed. Who will help?

The pain was beyond description and I could tell that Victoria was also in a state of desperation. She had to deal with this all on an emotional and personal level. I was able to contain myself and deal with the issues objectively. Had I really been her husband, I do not think I could have been so objective and maintained my composure and continued to work with her.

Dr. Amber Passini, at the Biogenesis Wellness Center in Landrum, South Carolina, contacted a surgeon she and her nurse characterized as a "cowboy" because he had a reputation for practicing medicine for the patient's benefit rather than for the

323

medical system's benefit. Dr. Passini sent photos of Victoria's breast and the surgeon immediately declared, by looking at the picture, that Victoria must first see an oncologist. Otherwise, the surgeon said he would not help. "The surgeon and I never had a conversation," Victoria said. "I felt I already knew how that conversation would go."

What was the purpose in seeing another oncologist? In fact, what was the purpose of seeing another surgeon? Victoria believed that another referral would be forthcoming, but no meaningful help would be offered. Victoria needed a long-term culture and a surgeon willing to follow his conscience and practice his trade.

Oncologists deal with cancer. They also create a safety net for other doctors. When a person dies and their medical history includes a cancer diagnosis, it's just too easy for their death certificate to state that they died from cancer. "If you die from cancer, it's never the doctor's fault," said Victoria. "You could die from the cancer treatment and the doctor would still be held faultless."

A biofeedback analysis on January 7, 2012, kept displaying 'foreign object metal with bacterial infection' on the computer monitor. Victoria wrote in her journal: "I needed to hear that. After you go to all these doctors and they brow-beat you, you start to go crazy. I know I have a foreign object."

Another journal entry on the same date: "It's unbelievable that nobody would help me."

Victoria was using a silver gel daily on her breast and it did dissolve the bulb, which equates to the killing of pathogens. In fact, the gel had destroyed enough bulbous tissue so as to leave a hole in the center of the largest masses. The only problem with killing these cells was that it left the myriad of capillaries unsupported, and they bled.

On January 13, 2012, I received a frantic call from Victoria and she was bleeding like a faucet from her breast and nothing would stop it. As she stood over the bathroom sink, I talked her through the exact procedures to get the blood flow under control, and it worked. I also told Victoria to stop drinking 'smoothies' made with beets, for they are a blood thinner.

This was not the only time I have done this procedure over the phone with women bleeding from the breast. A lady who had a marker inserted during a biopsy at Duke University Medical Center in North Carolina was having a severe reaction. The marker had prevented the biopsy incision from properly healing, and she was bleeding profusely. Normally, even husbands of these women are too frantic to listen to my instructions.

Victoria's journal entry on January 16, 2012: "God, please help me."

Victoria did not know where to turn, so she e-mailed Ty Bollinger, the famous author of the cancer book, *Cancer, Step Outside the Box,* and begged again for some help. Bollinger had responded in January 2009 to an email from Victoria and confirmed his own belief that "oral pathology is a major contributor to degenerative diseases."

Victoria's oral infections had been resolved. Now she was facing a life-threatening issue involving an infection in her right breast and she was searching for any doctor with an ounce of compassion to help her, but not with chemo and radiation.

In October 2010, Victoria emailed Bollinger a document that she referred to as her "end of the rope" plea for help. "I can't believe the pathetic treatment of the doctors," Bollinger wrote after reading Victoria's verbal cry. With Victoria's permission, Bollinger forwarded her document to some of his colleagues, but none of them contacted Victoria.

She remains truly grateful for all his help and highly recommends his books. In fact, Bollinger, free of charge, spent more time and put forth more effort to help Victoria than several of the medical doctors who charged her thousands of dollars.

Victoria wasn't surprised that Bollinger responded to a January 2012 email. After all, he had responded twice before.

She was surprised that he sent her the name of someone that should be able to help her; an unconventional doctor reportedly was having marvelous success in many fields from cancer to autism. After researching his website, Victoria was amazed to learn that the doctor was about two hours away in North Carolina. "I felt hopeful for the first time in a long time," she said.

This just had to be the doctor to help for the fungating mass was rapidly consuming Victoria's entire breast.

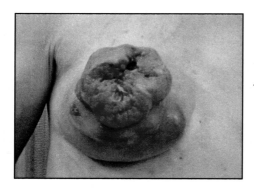

Bulbous growth became a fungating mass by February 2012.

As we waited for our appointment at the Center for Advanced Medicine in Cornelius, North Carolina, on January 24, 2012, with Dr. Rashid A. Buttar (drbuttar.com), I looked at the surgeon's impressive credentials. He had also been a military doctor and worked all over the globe; he was a Brigade Surgeon and Director of Emergency Medicine while serving in the U.S. Army. He's also board certified in Clinical Metal Toxicology. Victoria told Dr. Buttar that I was present as a close friend who knew her situation intimately. Dr. Buttar had no problem with my being present and he treated me with respect. He was gracious and immediately scheduled tests.

He gave each of us an autographed copy of his wonderful book: *The 9 Steps to Keep the Doctor Away.* One quote is very significant: Doctors are just human beings with a license to make life-and-death mistakes as long as they are using an approved method within the 'standard of care.'

On her first visit, Dr. Buttar spent three hours going over Victoria's records. At a later date, a nurse practitioner did a physical and examined Victoria's breasts, but she did not have Dr. Buttar's expertise.

Dr. Buttar looked at all the pictures that had been taken of the breast, but did not physically examine the breast. In fact, Dr. Buttar took a total of $12,040 in payments from Victoria during a seven-week treatment plan and never once physically examined the fungating mass. Victoria found this to be more than odd.

He stated that just from the photos it looked like a possible form of inflammatory breast cancer, but all his tests showed that she had a bacterial infection, fungus, and parasites. This went along with what I had been saying for a long time:

- A bacterial pathogen was introduced at the time of the January 2008 biopsy.
- Victoria developed an allergic reaction and infection as her body tried to reject a foreign object in the breast.
- Additional pathogens were introduced during the second biopsy in January 2011
- Fungi and other issues were introduced after the breast lancing, perhaps while working in the woods around her home.

Soon after Victoria's first consult with Dr. Buttar, he left for a speaking engagement in Australia. Over the course of her treatment, Victoria sent numerous photographs via email to Dr. Buttar's office that chronicled the rapid growth of the mass.

Due to certain tests being performed by Dr. Buttar's associated labs, Victoria stopped taking her Silver Sol liquid and the fungating mass immediately increased in size. The rapid growth caused more bleed-outs. Sometimes she would bleed for 10 minutes. This soon became a daily event, with pain that was beyond comprehension. "It was like having abscessed tooth pain in your breast," stated Victoria. "It was excruciating. I was begging for pain meds to survive. I became afraid to leave my house for fear of bleeding."

She resumed the silver solution after completing Dr. Buttar's lab tests. He realized Victoria could easily be having a reaction to a metal breast marker or a foreign object introduced in the breast at the time of biopsy. His treatments made the growing fungating mass produce a yellow type of globules and pus. The pain increased as the mass of the bulbs on the breast increased.

Dr. Buttar began a treatment technique of injecting her with a liquid synthesized from her urine, a process known as AARSV. He was hoping to get Victoria's body to stop reacting to the allergens in the foreign body or marker.

Other treatment protocols included lymphatic drainage techniques, heavy metal detoxing, raised ozone levels in the blood, and biofeedback treatments.

Victoria made many trips to this doctor over the next two months accompanied by her mother or younger brother. They could see during these bi-weekly trips that Victoria was getting weary, but she could not tell them the breast was getting worse. The list of doctors Victoria had seen by this time was more than she could count on both hands.

By the time Victoria's nightmarish ordeal would end, her insurance company would be hit for more than $108,000 and she would pay over $70,000 out of pocket. The hidden tolls were also adding up. She was physically and mentally drained. Each visit represented additional transportation and other costs such as some lodging, meals, gas, and all auto depreciation.

Victoria had to ask on two separate occasions for additional pain medication. At the beginning of her treatment, she required two over-the-counter pain meds three times a day. Nearing the end of her treatment, she had to take over-the-counter pain meds plus a prescription pain killer every four hours, around the clock, to survive. And that was no quality of life for a woman who tried to maintain a healthy lifestyle.

Dr. Buttar failed to react during the course of Victoria's treatment to the fact that his procedures were not effective. She was progressively getting worse, not better, and the growth on her breast was growing even more rapidly. "It was almost as though the fungating mass liked those treatments," said Victoria.

The fungating bulbs kept consuming her breast, the pain continued to increase, and the bleeding persisted. All the time Dr. Buttar never once examined Victoria's breast, but just looked at the latest picture that she had taken.

I feel that Dr. Buttar is an outstanding doctor but he was so engaged in expanding his practice and helping other doctors that Victoria fell between the cracks, and it happened at the most critical time for her. Victoria was being treated as just another patient. Had he forgotten the unwritten code of the alternative doctor that they should observe each patient as unique and adjust treatments accordingly?

My fear was that Dr. Buttar had found a successful method of treating many patients and nailed himself inside his own self-made box.

"Or was he just too busy? And why had he not done an in-depth long-term culture of the fungating mass on my breast?"

Not one doctor ever conducted an extended culture period to check for an infection. Not one! Not even Dr. Buttar. Why?

Doctors and public health workers are taught that both bacterial and viral culture periods can vary widely. As an example, gonorrhea can take 2-14 days to culture, many other pathogens from 16-18 days, and others up to 61 days. Any college student in Health Sciences can tell you about these pathogens and their incubation periods.

In both animal and plant pathology, we cultured for as long as 62 days and observed the emergence and disappearance of different pathogens and followed their cycles. We varied temperatures and humidity.

You can go to any medical dictionary or pathology book and find "neo plasia." This means abnormal looking cells. Look at warts, moles, scalaria, scar tissue, numerous fungi, and areas infected with yeast. The cells look abnormal, but they are not cancer. We must remember that the big money is in cancer.

On March 1, 2012, I again accompanied Victoria to Dr. Buttar's office and did my best to convince him that he needed to find a surgeon to remove this fungating mass because Victoria was losing so much blood daily that she was very weak, and the pain was so intense she was having a hard time functioning. He finally agreed with my persistence and started calling surgeon friends and sending them pictures of the breast via email. Not one surgeon would touch this case or even see Victoria.

On this same day Dr. Buttar confirmed, based on lab results, that Victoria's overall state of health was higher than most of his other patients. She had no indications of cancer, but did score high in heavy metal toxicity. "After he gave me the test results, he said my results were more normal than most of his patients," said Victoria.

Victoria drove a four-hour round trip to Dr. Buttar's clinic twice a week for seven weeks, while getting worse, not better. All the while, she was forwarding photos of the infectious mass on a regular basis, and even emphasized the frightening blood loss with a picture of a soiled tee shirt. "I believe he had the ability to help me if he had given me the attention I needed. He just never acknowledged that what he was doing wasn't working," said Victoria.

Although Victoria only saw Dr. Buttar personally on two occasions during the seven-weeks of treatment, she continued driving to the clinic because she was desperate. "I was at the end of the road. There was no other place to go, and there was always that hope that he might heal me. I do believe in miracles."

I saw first-hand what women are subjected to in this cancer merry-go-round. I always told doctors, in detail, all the issues about her breast and explained what had been transpiring. I was a type of balancing rod for Victoria as I heard more objectively and was able to see through the fear mongering.

Several doctors 'seemed' to listen and actually examine Victoria's breast. Most examinations, however, were just a mild glance and an immediate proclamation of cancer.

From Victoria's experiences, I have concluded that veterinarians are more competent at diagnostics, and more compassionate, than many medical doctors. The animal cannot tell the vet what is wrong, so the vet must be thorough in an examination and testing if the animal has any hope of getting well.

The medical doctors that saw Victoria pretended that she could not talk and they refused to listen when she did. Their tool kit only included invasive and disfiguring surgery, plus chemo and radiation, all of which make them a bundle of money.

Then exciting news arrived as Dr. Buttar finally found a surgeon who supposedly was willing to help and remove the fungating mass.

Victoria's journal entry on February 23, 2012: "Had a good cry. The pain is so bad in my breast; the growth keeps getting bigger even with all the treatments from Dr. Buttar. I am so overwhelmed."

On March 8, 2012, Dr. Victor Ferrari, a breast surgeon at Premier Plastic Surgery Center in Matthews, North Carolina, listened to Victoria's story and let her guide him through the issues on the breast. He was well aware of the pathogen killing power of both colloidal and nano particle silver.

After his personal examination, he looked Victoria right in the eye and said he would do the surgery because he was such a good friend of Dr. Buttar and that "it was the right thing to do." Those were magic words. It was the right thing to do.

He had Victoria meet his staff to arrange for the payment and stated he would immediately get back to her for a surgical appointment. She was given a statement for $4,978 which she would need to pay out of her pocket because Dr. Ferrari did not accept insurance.

The next day, Victoria waited with anxiety for the phone call that never came. Eventually, she called Dr. Ferrari's office. The doctor returned her call at 5:30 p.m. and bluntly stated he was afraid to do the surgery due to bleeding! It took about 30 hours for him to change his mind.

Victoria's world came crashing down. She was now beyond desperation. Her mental strength was as badly damaged as her physical strength. But Dr. Ferrari held out another ray of hope. He referred her to a surgeon that he thought might possibly help.

Victoria's journal entry on March 8, 2012: "This has just been too much too long."

Chapter 47

Which torture do you want?

Victoria went to see Dr. Marshal Parsons, a surgeon with a specialty in breast diseases at the Carolina Surgical Clinic in Charlotte, North Carolina on March 12, 2012. Buzz did not make this trip. "The first thing out of the doctor's mouth was he did not know if he wanted to get involved with me or not." This statement came after Victoria presented a summary document and a verbal explanation about her breast issue.

The summary was needed because Victoria was "tired of telling it over and over," and her case was complicated.

"He proceeded to tell me I needed surgery and he recommended chemo. He knew it was cancer by looking at it. Another psychic, I thought."

Here's yet another doctor who was giving Victoria a diagnosis based on observation. He emphatically said the mass was cancer and that she needed chemo. He demanded she have another biopsy. And he told Victoria that he would not test for bacteria or fungus.

Victoria took his comments to heart. On March 12, 2012, she wrote in her journal, basically repeating what Dr. Parsons had said: "I got the same cancer merry-go-round. The growth was cancer. I needed chemo. I did agree to a biopsy but, of course, he's just checking for cancer, no bacteria and fungus." Her lapse in judgment during a moment of desperation – agreeing to a biopsy – was quickly reversed.

"I was scared to death and exhausted when I left there," said Victoria. "After I came to my senses, I called and cancelled the biopsy and never went back. It was the same old song and dance. It was déjà vu all over again."

The fungating mass was eating her entire breast. What was she to do? Her mental state was reflected in her journal entry for March 13, 2012.

"Today was one of the most depressing days. I feel like I'm at a crossroads. I need to make a decision whether I should kill myself, go back to Dr. Parsons for the biopsy, or go out of country for treatment. What do I do? I am beyond exhausted, plus this pain and bloody mess doesn't help anything. I know the best thing for me is to try and keep my focus."

Here's the translation. The surgeons who had the expertise to help would not do so because they assumed, based on visual observation, that the mass growing on the breast was cancer. They also refused to culture the breast infection for two months, as was being requested. And no surgeon would verbally acknowledge even a remote possibility that Victoria had a foreign object in her breast. They acted like she was crazy.

Therefore, they insisted that chemotherapy accompany any surgical procedure. On the other hand, Victoria had now seen dozens of patients in her travels that were dying of cancer, although they were being treated with the very latest chemo drugs. Most of them were dreadful sights. It wasn't a quality of life that Victoria was interested in.

It seemed that every test known to man gave her an A-plus on the state of her health; everything except her right breast. She would rather die than knowingly harm her own body – her own healthy body – with chemo poisons. In fact, was there a difference between taking chemo in America and being confined to a Nazi death camp in World War II? "To me, both would have been torture."

Victoria was paying big dollars for doctor visits and no doctor would send her to a specialist to investigate an infection. No specialist would see her without a doctor's referral. "I could do nothing to get any doctor to even consider anything except the big money-making 'c' word – cancer."

"I begged doctors to look for infections and especially the ones related to medical device rejections. Why was the longest culture that had been done or was being offered only three days?"

Why do doctors practice such limited medicine? For one thing, their teaching source is tightly controlled by Big Pharma and government regulations written by people with a vested interest in the pharmaceutical industry as well as the medical and dental schools. The whole system revolves around money, power and control. Sure, mainstream medicine uses a little research to make people think progress is being made. But Victoria discovered it's an illusion.

If everybody was well, there would be little need to spend billions on research. There's no money in an infection; the money is in having cancer. And cancer treatment centers are springing up all over the country like wildflowers.

Meanwhile, the iconic Tasmanian devil, found only in the wild in Australia's southern island state, got more genuine attention from doctors than Victoria. Tasmanian devil numbers are being dramatically reduced due to a contagious tumor with a mortality rate of 100% – the animal dies in a matter of months. Researchers at the University of Cambridge are cautiously optimistic about the potential of their findings to give the devils a chance of survival.

Victoria would have given almost anything to hear a doctor with operating room skills and hospital privileges say to her, "I'm cautiously optimistic, but I think I can help you."

Chapter 48

Culture this damn thing

Victoria's sister, Teri, a long-time resident of New Orleans, knew a surgeon socially in the Big Easy and had actually visited in his family home in India. She encouraged Victoria to consider seeing him. Victoria had nowhere else to go. She didn't want to upset her sister with this horrible condition. But desperation was now ruling Victoria's decisions.

Victoria told her sister, "The only way I will come to New Orleans is for you to accept that I have an infection and an adverse reaction to a foreign object in my breast."

Dr. Surendra Kumar Purohit saw Victoria at his office on March 20, 2012. She had driven 648 miles in less than 10 and a half hours alone two days before, constantly fearing a bleed-out in her breast. If the breast started bleeding, Victoria knew she might not be able to stop it while on the road, but at least she would have a chance of getting to a hospital.

Flying to New Orleans was not an option. Uncontrolled bleeding at 33,000 feet would have been disastrous and without options.

Dr. Purohit performed a visual exam and ordered a biopsy. "He agreed to the surgery without chemo, and he didn't try to scare me." Victoria wanted the doctor to surgically remove the growth, but not totally remove her breast. "Just by looking at it he thought it was cancer."

Victoria's journal entry on March 20, 2012: "When I tried to take my shower, this growth was pouring the blood. I just tried to stay calm and get to the doctor. The doctor is actually going to cut this growth off. Shocking. He still thinks it is cancer. I wish they would get off that kick and culture this damn thing properly."

"How many times have I been told I have cancer, and I don't? It's such an injustice!"

Up to this point, no doctor had agreed to surgically remove the growth unless Victoria agreed to chemo, or had followed up on a promise to do so. "I believed him because of his relationship with my sister."

It was 4 a.m. on Thursday, March 22, 2012, when Victoria and her sister drove from her sister's home in New Orleans through the fog nearly 24 miles across the Lake Ponchartrain Causeway to be at the Lakeview Regional Medical Center in Covington, Louisiana by 7 a.m.

Having lived most of her adult life in California, Victoria was accustomed to hours of boring airport layovers and long airline flights to see her family in North Carolina. This early morning ride was like nothing she had ever experienced before.

Saving her breast and even her life had evolved into her longest journey, nearly 51 months so far. At the end of her rope, radical surgery appeared to be her last hope. The ironies in the final 20 minutes of this journey were staggering. She was crossing the longest continuous bridge over water in the world, two parallel bridges that carry automobile traffic over one of the largest wetlands in the world.

Lake Ponchartrain Causeway

Victoria remembers a gloomy darkness and feelings of sadness and despair that were beyond words. "I knew where I was going and what was about to happen."

The chill settling over Victoria wasn't that far removed from the dungeon-like Death Row scene in "The Green Mile," the 1999 Tom Hanks film set in a Southern prison in the mid-1930s.

At the hospital, she was admitted, and then waited and waited. Her sister sat by her side massaging her feet and her back "and held my hand. She was very comforting." The growth on her breast was biopsied. The breast was about to be cut off the next day; no more worries about ill effects from another biopsy. Her medical records state: "This patient had fungating mass for a long duration, which has been infected and necrotic."

Most of the doctors she had seen before arriving in New Orleans had demanded that Victoria immediately begin chemo. Dr. Purohit did not. "God bless this man, he did help me, and he did so without chemo. He's a surgeon, not an oncologist." Victoria also called him "humane enough to help me. He did save my life. He did not try to scare me."

For years, all Victoria received from most medical doctors was another test, and another claim that an infection or adverse reaction could not possibly be causing her breast inflammation, and no real help. In contrast, says Victoria, "If I'd been a dog, a vet would have helped me. One nutritionist at a health food store in Aiken, South Carolina felt sure her horse doctor would help me."

Removing the growth required what the doctor described as a modified mastectomy. He was insistent that the growth was cancerous. Victoria was equally insistent that she was being eaten alive by an insidious infection made worse by an adverse reaction to something foreign in her breast. Nothing else.

Victoria's surgery was Friday, March 23, 2012. She wasn't worried about cancer. She had a thorough understanding about why the cells in her breast tissue were appearing atypical in a laboratory analysis. Nearly every medical doctor she had seen was completely ignorant about ablations and lab technicians barely had any better understanding than the cancer doctors.

After all, almost three years had passed since the growth in the breast had been frozen during a cryoablation. Unless the pathologist compared her atypical cells with three-year-old ablated cells, he was comparing apples and oranges.

Medical doctors and lab technicians were trained to do one thing and one thing only – stay inside their tight little analysis box, and anything different or out of the ordinary must be categorized as cancer. Victoria presented a unique situation.

Only hours before losing her breast, Victoria was focused on finding and identifying the infection in her breast and the foreign object, something she had physically felt on numerous occasions with her fingernail, and something she could feel cutting and ripping at her breast tissue like a jagged knife.

"I asked the nurse to please have them look for the object. She appeared to write that on my chart. The next thing I remember is I'm awake after the surgery in excruciating pain."

The pain from the radical surgery was way beyond Victoria's pain threshold. The pain in her soul was far worse. "To women who think it's a walk in the park to have a mastectomy, it's not."

Because Dr. Purohit kept mentioning cancer, Victoria's sister, who was present for these doctor-patient exchanges, was about to repeat it on the phone from the hospital to her mother and her brother, Woody. Victoria was not amused. She knew she did not have cancer, and she demanded that her sister refer to her hospitalization as surgery for removal of a foreign object and infection in her breast, and forget the 'c' word. "My sister had promised not to get on the cancer bandwagon."

Before the biopsy procedure, she handed Dr. Purohit a two and one-half page letter written in her own handwriting as she lay in the hospital bed. She was begging one last time … please culture the tissue long enough to identify all the infections, and find the object!

She asked a hospital volunteer to make a photocopy of her request. The doctor was given the original. This is the text of her letter:

"Please culture the tissue. Please have the lab people keep in mind cell blastosis. Hyperplasia and hypertrophy situations (the rapid cell division). Some cells are small and hard-packed and others are big and fat and spongy (like mine).

"There are well over 100 pleomorphic bacteria that can infect any place in the human body from the lungs to the vaginal cavity or in an open wound or the eye. These are simple one-cell organisms without an outer membrane. They penetrate and infect a cell and then spread like wildfire from cell to cell.

"These usually grow in colonies and are unaffected by … penicillin or the beta antibiotics. These pleomorphic bacteria can be parasitic, saprophytic, or saprotrophic.

"The people culturing the large biopsy samples should do numerous cultures of every imaginable thing and do them from several days out to 62 days. Think fungus.

"The culture people should be thinking about the word mycoplasma – a fungus growth that forms a mushroom growth.

"The culture people should be thinking about the word histoplasmosis. This is a pathogen found in the eastern USA that comes from bird and bat droppings. It causes issues like I have and is carried by the wind, even pollen grains and dust particles and can also be carried into open skin wounds via hands or clothing. It is not contagious person to person.

"Please analyze for any foreign object in my breast which I believe is a surgical wire. If it is found, please return to me.

"I am so allergic to so many things. I would never consider breast implants. Since I will not be seeing a plastic surgeon, please keep the job as neat as possible."

Only the last sentence in Victoria's letter had to do with something other than a foreign object and an infection. She wanted to keep her lymph nodes. She was emphatic. She wanted to make that decision, not the doctor. "Please leave my lymph nodes intact and undisturbed," she wrote.

The foreign object was the first thing Victoria asked Dr. Purohit about when she awoke after surgery. "Did you find the marker?" she inquired. "He told me, no."

It would be days later when she realized the doctor had removed at least two lymph nodes, too. In her medical records, the doctor's dictation confirmed removal of a single node. It also stated there "was no other lymph palpable obviously."

However, according to the pathology report, sectioning revealed two possible nodes.

Since women differ on the number of lymph nodes under their arm – typically from as few as 10 to as many as 30 – Victoria doesn't know exactly what she has left to fight infection, illness, and disease. She does know that lymph nodes can become swollen in the armpit because of infection, and there are many sources of infections other than cancer.

Two of the most common causes of lymph node swelling are a fungus infection and an allergic reaction. Independent testing had already confirmed that Victoria was dealing with both of those causes. A website called thelymphnodes.com cites another dozen causes: cat scratch disease, lymphangitis, fatty growths, measles, mumps, chicken pox, reaction to vaccine, AIDS/HIV, mononucleosis, herpes, shingles, and STD's.

With the loss of her nodes, which were surgically removed against her written objection, Victoria is most concerned about developing lymphedema, an abnormal buildup of fluid that could cause swelling under her right arm or on her right side. Such swelling usually results from the loss of normal lymph channel drainage when nodes are surgically removed.

Furthermore, cancer treatments can cause lymphedema, according to an article in the April 12, 2013 edition of *The Advocate*, the daily newspaper in Baton Rouge, Louisiana.

The article quoted the National Cancer Institute and said more than 50% of women who have breast cancer surgery develop lymphedema within two years of the surgery. To a great extent, the risk of lymphedema corresponds to the extent of removal of the lymph nodes in the armpit, the story said.

"I was comfortable enough in my own mind that I had a deadly infection and I needed my lymph nodes to fight it," said Victoria.

When Victoria left the hospital, her discharge papers included a one-page list of "mastectomy post-operative precautions."

"The arm on the involved side may swell and be more prone to infection due to the removal of lymph vessels and nodes," the document stated. "The lymph system is the first line of defense against infection."

Victoria understood this to begin with. From the list of 16 precautions, it's easy to see why she wanted to keep her nodes. Here's a sample:

- Make every attempt to avoid cuts, scratches, pin pricks, hang nails, insect bites, burns, and strong detergents or chemicals.
- Use gloves when gardening, baking, or washing dishes.

- Blood pressure measurements must be taken on the uninvolved arm.
- Do not shave your underarm with a straight razor – try an electric razor.

Sunday, March 25, was Victoria's discharge day. At 8 a.m. there were already signs of a beautiful Louisiana day. There was full sun, but Victoria could not appreciate it, although she did appreciate her sister staying in the room during her entire hospital stay. "I knew it was hard on her to be in a hospital setting because she does not like reality, and this was about as real as you could get."

Again, Victoria was caught off guard – ambushed. She had been led to believe by a nurse the bandages would not be removed until Wednesday. She had specifically asked this question. She was smart enough to know that she needed to make some mental adjustments. In her mind, however, she had not allowed herself to think about the results of the surgery yet. She was avoiding this mental confrontation as long as possible, and she thought she had three more days to prepare herself for a shock.

It was only Sunday morning and suddenly, with no warning so she could prepare emotionally, a nurse entered the room and said the doctor wanted to see how she was healing. That meant exposing the wound.

Minutes later, Dr. Purohit pulled back the bandage. Victoria was not prepared for this humiliating graphic scene. Nobody could have prepared her. "My breast was gone. In its place was a 6-inch scar and what looked like a couple of dozen heavy-duty black stitches. How could I be a sexual creature again, even attractive? I think that was the ugliest thing I'd ever seen in my whole life. I couldn't imagine how ugly it could be. I was in total shock. Life as I knew it was over. I knew that. How could I ever be me again?"

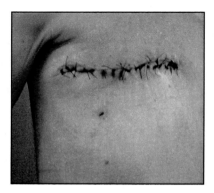

Heavy black stitches replaced Victoria's right breast on March 23, 2012. No explanation is really necessary.

"I felt so dark inside. I just started crying, it was so ugly. It was one of those mornings you'll never forget. As Teri and I started the long drive back over the Causeway, my cousin Denise called, and I just cried and cried to her. I now knew the new reality, how ugly."

Victoria never gave any thought about how mobility of her right arm and shoulder would be a challenge, yet it was. "I never considered you'd have such a movement problem after a mastectomy. It's not like getting a flat tire changed. It's not a walk in the park."

In her surgeon's office where she had a follow-up appointment with Dr. Purohit to have the stitches removed 10 days after the procedure, Victoria again asked about a clip or marker in her breast. "What kind of infection did I have in my breast and if it returns, what will we do?"

"He told me that he did the ultrasound and a mammogram on the breast. I took that to mean it was done on the surgically removed breast. I accepted what he said and was glad that he tried but was surprised that he found nothing."

Victoria had no recollection of having an ultrasound or mammogram immediately prior to surgery. In fact, while she was awake, she was positive these two procedures were never done on her.

Furthermore, it was physically impossible for Victoria to have had a mammogram prior to surgery. She could not have withstood the pain, and the mess would not have been acceptable (profuse bleeding and spreading the infection). "What woman would want to have a mammogram after my infected and contaminated breast had been smashed between the x-ray and plastic plates?"

"I even asked did they go through the tissue looking for it and, not very convincingly, he said, yes."

Victoria also asked the doctor to describe her infection. "He thumbed through my file like he was looking for a report, and he said I didn't have an infection. But, of course, why tell me about infections when you've told me I have cancer."

Victoria was stressed over his answer. Her sister, Teri, was sitting there and listening to the conversation. "How can I convince her I have an infection when the doctor says I don't?"

There's a monumental problem with the doctor's answer.

"The hospital's medical records, a nurse in the hospital, and my insurance records are all saying otherwise. There are no records of any tests being done on the breast tissue to find a foreign object. And there are records that prove I had an infection. Was he just appeasing me?"

"I had two kinds of infections. Why did the doctor think that was of no importance?"

Victoria even went so far as to call her insurance company, Blue Cross and Blue Shield (BCBS), on January 17, 2013, and asked if a claim had been submitted for an ultrasound or mammogram that would have been done March 22 or March 23 on her breast, either before, during, or after surgery. The answer was no.

The culture growth was tested at Tulane University where two organisms were identified: staphylococcus epidermidis and enterococcus faecalis.

Staphylococcus epidermidis is known to live on human skin in hospitals. The University of Connecticut's Department of Molecular and Cell Biology found it to be one of the leading pathogens of nosocomial infections, particularly associated with foreign body infections.

Exactly how would an ultrasound or mammogram be done on a handful of bleeding breast tissue anyway? Use your imagination. But Victoria tried her best to give the doctor the benefit of the doubt.

Victoria's four-year ordeal boiled down to three points and a prayer:

1. A stage zero precancerous DCIS diagnosis.
2. A damaging breast biopsy that led to an almost immediate adverse reaction, followed by an infection.
3. The revelation that the sharp, cutting object she felt in her breast for four years could be a piece of metal (clip or wire) or plastic or both, left in her breast either intentionally or accidentally as part of the biopsy procedure.
4. God, please let this doctor find the foreign object(s), kill the infection, and bring closure to my needless suffering. I never wanted to lose my breast but I want my life back.

Dr. Purohit was no different than most doctors Victoria had sought help from in identifying the physical object she could feel in her breast. The object was too hard and too sharp to be breast tissue. Breast tissue doesn't cut like a knife. Maybe he didn't believe her? Maybe he wasn't going to incriminate another doctor? "Based on the known facts, he made no serious attempt to solve the mystery."

Whatever the truth, I'm indebted to this man because he did what no other doctor would do, but that doesn't change the fact that he ultimately becomes responsible for me not knowing the truth about what was in my breast."

Before leaving the hospital, Victoria signed a document stating that she wanted copies of all medical records to be mailed to her in North Carolina.

When the records arrived, there was no information about an ultrasound and mammogram being done on the breast before or during surgical removal, or on the breast tissue after removal. But there was a digital copy of the chest x-ray which was taken on March 21, the day before she entered the hospital.

Victoria wanted to give the doctor the benefit of the doubt. She called medical records at the hospital on two separate days.

The first call was April 17 when she requested a copy of her EKG and the results of blood work. "I asked if any other tests were done such as an MRI, ultrasound, or mammogram."

A nurse said, "I'm sure that he didn't [do an ultrasound or mammogram] but I will check for you." Victoria was put on hold.

The nurse returned to the phone and said no, there was no record of an ultrasound or mammogram. "She stated the only test I had done was a chest x-ray."

On the second call, Victoria asked specifically about records pertaining to the examination of her surgically removed breast tissue. It was April 18 at 12:28 p.m. when she spoke with Rhonda and was then transferred to Jenny in radiology. "I asked if a test such as an ultrasound or mammogram had been done on my removed breast." The medical records clerk responded, "I'm sure he wouldn't have done that, but I will check for you." Her answer was no.

In fact, when Victoria received the explanation of benefits from her insurance company, there was no record of an ultrasound or mammogram being done during her entire stay at the hospital. "I knew he had not told me the truth."

She went to the BCBS website and looked at her pending claims. The two tests were not there. The hospital and doctor's bill was there, however, a grand total of $75,000.

A few weeks later, the final explanation of benefits arrived in the mail. The ultrasound and mammogram tests were not there.

What kind of mess would a bleeding breast cause in a mammogram machine? "How nice, the doctor just told me this to appease me, but my sister believed the doctor and thought I was out of my mind."

Victoria appreciated the opportunity to recover for several weeks at the home of her sister and brother-in-law, a New Orleans attorney. When her in-home nurse, Mary Catherine, came for the last time on April 5 to change the dressing, she made an insightful comment.

"Since you went to a surgeon, they always solve everything with a breast by cutting it off. If the infection had been on your leg and not your breast, they would have treated it differently." The in-home nurse added, "The doctor had to code infection as cancer so he would get paid much easier."

As she began her recovery from the radical and painful surgery, Victoria allowed her mind to wander a few times to the edge of pity. She would think of herself as a "mutilated freak."

Victoria waited 48 hours after being released from the hospital before she got up the nerve to take a picture of what she described as "this ugly situation" that showed the scars and stitches. She described the drama in an email to me with the words, "Don't throw up," written in the subject line.

"It took all the guts I had to put this on film," she wrote, "but I knew for the documentation of the book I must do it."

Victoria characterized the emotions she was experiencing from the loss of her breast as a cross between an out-of-body experience and the twilight zone. "So I ask myself over and over, how do women line up like cattle to have this done to them? Do women not see how this affects their body, health, soul and entire being?"

On May 18, 2012, Victoria wrote a letter to her sister, Teri, and tried to explain how a foreign object in her breast had prevented her body's immune system from defeating an infection. "Losing my breast should never have happened," Victoria asserted.

Victoria also included details of the culture that was done in New Orleans, although Dr. Purohit, in the presence of Victoria's sister, denied there was an infection. "The reason I am doing this for you," wrote Victoria, "is so you can see the results of the cultures with your own eyes and know because you are my sister does not mean you will get cancer. Fear can make you very sick."

Many women buy into the idea that if a mother or sister has cancer, then they are destined to have cancer too. It's simply not true. "I love my sister dearly and I tried to convince her of the dangers of mammograms and the benefits of thermal imaging. She was convinced having a mammogram was safe and necessary. I went so far as to send her a video via email that described the process and advantages of thermal breasts studies and with her busy life she did not take the time to watch it."

Many women embrace this "safe and necessary" philosophy about mammograms. Victoria is not one of them. In order to save her life, she was forced to become a world-class medical researcher.

"I have never been able to understand how some people make a judgment call about thermal imaging when they have done no research and know nothing about the technology. In life, how can you make a decision about anything when you know nothing about it? Truth be known, you can't."

Victoria knows from experience that areas where body parts have been lost must be stimulated. "We are a magnetic being and the loss of any part interrupts the magnetic balance and thus the electrical pathways in the body. Our brain is a mass of electrical and magnetic currents. The brain knows when any parts are missing, or damaged, or in any way diminished."

The brain is so powerful that it has the ability to shut down and kill the body. "This happened to so many of our military captured and held in North Korean prisons in the 1950s."

"Self love, self stimulation via your eyes and hands, and self approval of what has happened are all essential to the recovery of the body and the healing of the body's electro-magnetic system," Victoria believes.

"We have a genetic system that we are born with, but we also have an epigenetic system that can change based on our environment and massive brain pattern. The epigenetics can control our lives."

Victoria endured fifty-one months of hell. "I want my life back."

Chapter 49

Victim of mind control

Most Americans were thinking about food, family, football, and Black Friday during Thanksgiving week in 2012. No one was expecting a breast mastectomy story to make the national headlines. But that's exactly what happened.

The world was stunned when a Miss America contestant, who lost her mother to breast cancer, announced she would undergo a double mastectomy as a preventative measure to avoid her mother's fate. The most shocking aspect of her story was that she did not have cancer; cancer was not even suspected in her breasts. She has no symptoms.

What she does have is the figure and looks to be crowned Miss Maryland in 2011 and win the title of Miss District of Columbia in June 2012.

Although Allyn Rose graced the stage in an evening gown, displayed her unusual talent for roller figure skating, and flaunted her fit figure in a bikini, she did not win the January 2013 pageant, but plastic surgeons and breast reconstruction doctors were already seeing dollar signs walking up and down the pageant runway.

What if she actually follows through with her promise and has her breasts removed for prevention? How would American women react?

Why is a beauty queen even considering . a preventative mastectomy? It's about a gene, called Wiskott-Aldrich, for which Miss Rose is supposedly a carrier and allegedly the gene runs in her mother's family. The genetic correlation appears to be with cancer, but not specifically breast cancer.

What is there in the human consciousness that could possibly influence a beautiful young woman to choose a disfiguring surgery like a double mastectomy and replace whole body parts with something artificial? How can this be explained?

It's almost as though she is a victim of some sort of mind control. Or is it a lack of information such as not knowing about other options to monitor her breast health? Or did she suffer irreparable emotional damage because of her mother's suffering?

The brain is a strange organ; the mind is even stranger. Many Americans had their first introduction to the mysteries of the mind by Hollywood.

Electroconvulsive therapy, for example, showed up in the movies. The majority of Americans knew little about electrical shock, unless it happened to someone in their family.

That changed in the mid-1970s when the 1962 novel "One Flew Over the Cuckcoo's Nest" by Ken Kesey was released in movie theaters in 1975.

The movie trailers portrayed Jack Nicholson as a brash rebel arriving at a mental institution and rallying patients to take on the oppressive and dictatorial Nurse Ratched, starring Louise Fletcher.

The novel described how different authorities control individuals through subtle and coercive methods. However, the patients never recognized they were being controlled. Even worse, the treatment was ineffective and horribly damaging.

This is exactly how America's cancer industry operates. The cliché that a 'picture is worth a thousand words' is never more true than when comparing 'before and after' photos (before chemotherapy and after chemotherapy) of the late movie actor Patrick Swayze, of "Dirty Dancing" fame. The internet is full of candid photos showing an emaciated man who was dying from his treatment.

Victoria's life in the mid-1970s was defined by computers. Ten days after the movie's release (Dirty Dancing), the name "Microsoft" was used by Bill Gates in a letter. It became a registered trademark a year later. Victoria worked with programmers at National Cash Register Company (NCR) and handled calls from clients involving both computers and cash registers.

When she walked into the downtown Palm Springs, California theater to see "One Flew Over the Cuckcoo's Nest," she was already enamored with Jack Nicholson because of his performance in "Easy Rider" which also starred Peter Fonda.

"I couldn't believe they took a guy who was so full of life and so sane and turned him into a vegetable," remembered Victoria, referring to Nicholson's character in the movie. "He was in a controlled environment, locked up like a common prisoner in a mental institution. His outcome was not voluntary. He was forcibly held down by muscular orderlies in order to be shocked."

People today have the opportunity to make sane choices in life. Miss Rose has an opportunity to do the same.

I'm the first to admit that tens of thousands of Americans have jobs and support their families because of the cancer industry. There's no arguing that fact. Tragically, there are more people living off cancer than dying from it.

But the number of cancer jobs in the marketplace today would be nothing compared to the exploding cancer job market if Miss Rose had been crowned Miss America and then headed to an operating room to have both breasts surgically removed in a process called a preventative mastectomy.

What message would Allyn Rose be sending to impressionable girls and young women who want to gain status, recognition, and praise? The answer is obvious. "Suddenly, popularity, and acclaim are just one surgery away," wrote health activist Mike Adams.

In my opinion, the best technical explanation about Allyn Rose's announcement was written by Sayer Ji, who is the founder and chair of GreenMedInfo.com, a website that claims to be the world's largest evidence-based, open source access, natural medicine database. Ji is a writer, researcher, and nutrition educator who has a unique and effective way with words.

The bulk of his article is reprinted below with permission:

Following closely on the heels of the year's most intensive annual cause-marketing campaign, October's Breast Cancer Awareness Month, two chilling events of grave concern to women and their health were widely (but mostly superficially) reported on in the mainstream media.

First, Allyn Rose, Miss America contestant, announced in early November 2012 that she would be undergoing a double mastectomy to "prevent" breast cancer. Rose, a healthy 24-year old Maryland native who lost her mother to breast cancer when she was 16, has been lauded by certain media outlets as an "awareness raising" role model for having the courage to take this "precautionary step" and for spreading her mastectomy-inspired "message of preventive health care" to the masses.

Many of the reports discussed how her decision was spurned by her awareness of having a genetic predisposition for breast cancer.

Second, on November 22, 2012, the *New England Journal of Medicine* published a review of the past 30 years of mammography finding that not only has the widespread promotion and adoption of breast screenings by millions of women not reduced their mortality (on the contrary, screenings have increased their relative risk of mortality), but that 1.3 million of these women were over-diagnosed and wrongly treated for abnormal findings that were not even cancer.

In other words, these hundreds of thousands of women were being treated for breast abnormalities detected by a screening process, and if left untreated the abnormalities would have caused no harm to the women.

Not surprisingly, this paradigm-challenging finding, in the tradition of embargoed science, was exactly timed to be released to the public on the eve of a major holiday. Subsequently, while folks unplugged from electronic media for a rare family day centered around Thanksgiving dinner, the already watered-down headlines received only lackluster attention considering the true gravity of the study's findings.

How many who did happen to scan headlines released on that day, such as "Study Faults Breast Exams," truly grasped that 70,000 women a year have their breasts either removed or disfigured, irradiated, and then are treated with chemotherapy and/or hormone suppressive therapies for cancers that aren't there?

Rose, of course, is not aware of the disturbing implications within the *New England Journal of Medicine* study, namely, that the women in her family that she believes all died from "inherited" breast cancer, may actually have died not from breast cancer, or breast cancer associated gene mutations, but from the breast cancer treatments themselves.

That is to say, they died as a result of over-diagnosis and subsequent psychological trauma and physical mistreatment by a completely out-of-touch medical system relying on intrinsically carcinogenic diagnostic and treatment technologies to cut, burn, and poison these lesions that would never have progressed to cancer, and may have simply regressed, had they been left undetected and undisturbed.

Nor is she aware that the so-called breast cancer genes, BRCA1/BRCA2, are relevant because they interfere with DNA repair mechanisms related to radiation and chemical exposure, implying that avoiding unnecessary radiation exposure, such as x-ray mammography, and chemicals such as have been found in many pinkwashed consumer products … is of utmost importance in reducing her risk of breast cancer.

In Rose's mind as in the minds of millions of women who participate in the annual 'breast cancer awareness' pinkwashing campaigns, there is no known cause to cancer outside your own genes (i.e. the hundreds of thousands of novel carcinogens modern man has created don't exist), because this has been the quarter of a century long focus of Breast Cancer Awareness Month.

And since there is no known cure either, raising money for future research, promoting mammography at each and every step, and now, removing healthy breasts before a problem occurs, is all you can do.

But Rose's story took an even stranger twist when her genetic tests revealed that she was, in fact, negative for the breast cancer susceptibility genes, BRCA1/BRCA2. The would-be genetic inevitability of cancer implied by her positive family history of the disease, and her disturbing choice to have her breasts removed in order to prevent disease within them, was therefore strictly theoretical, unsubstantiated by empirical evidence.

It turns out that Rose's risk for breast disease may indeed have been inherited through her family in the form of irrational fears passed down by her father. As reported by the *Washington Post:*

Allyn Rose's father first suggested the mastectomy when she was a freshman in college. It was a couple years after her mother had succumbed to breast cancer; genetic testing and a long, sad family history of early deaths indicated that Rose, too, was at a high risk. But she resisted.

'I thought, I just got my breasts! I'm young, I'm beautiful. I didn't want to do this,' said Rose. 'My dad looked me in the face' and said, 'I would end up dead just like my mother.'

The process of grieving can feel like drowning. In our desperate flailing to be saved from the pain of loss, we can unwittingly pull our still remaining loved ones under with us.

Rose's father does not know better. He has not been told the truth about breast cancer, or cancer in general. Cancer does not just "happen to us" because we have inherited "bad genes," or simply the byproduct of a series of chaotic mutational events within our DNA; rather, cancer is something the body does to survive an increasingly toxic environment, diet, and lifestyle.

Prevention is not equivalent to cutting out the organ or organs that 'could' be afflicted. Nor is it equivalent to compressing and irradiating the breasts with highly carcinogenic x-rays to "detect cancer early."

Also, abnormal breast findings, such as ductal carcinoma in situ (DCIS), which is the primary form of "cancer" detected through mammography, do not imply an irrepressible trajectory towards death.

To the contrary, the latest *New England Journal of Medicine* finding indicates that the vast majority of such 'abnormalities' would never progress to cause harm in women. To the contrary, by "treating" such findings as if they are cancer, the treatment itself drives those tissues into greater malignancy, and through the profound psychological and physiological abuse that over-treatment produces, creates the ideal conditions for cancers to proliferate or recur.

Of course, Rose's decision is being upheld by many within the mainstream media as a perfectly sane, if not also a courageous act – one, perhaps, to be emulated by countless other young women in the future who will never be told the truth about the preventable causes of breast cancer, or all that can be done naturally to prevent and treat it.

Chapter 50

Where did I go wrong?

Victoria was a guest at her sister's home in New Orleans during her three-week post surgery recovery, with older sister filling the role of nurse and caregiver. Her diligent battle to save her breast ended after four years and two months.

As she did after every encounter with a medical doctor that refused to help her, Victoria bounced back. Instead of viewing herself as a victim, she became more adamant about becoming an advocate. "I was determined not to let this happen to any other woman." Instead of sulking, she had her sister shampoo her hair (Victoria's right arm was stiff from the surgery, especially because of the loss of lymph nodes in the armpit).

On the first day out of the hospital, Victoria and Teri walked a mile through the neighborhood. It was warm and sunny. "It felt good after being in the hospital."

Teri was shocked at Victoria's high energy level and determination to get out of bed and get on with life. The sisters took advantage of their time together. They drove 20 minutes to a yacht club for lunch in Teri's Mercedes convertible with the top down and their hair blowing in the wind.

How many women walk a mile around the neighborhood the day after they check out of the hospital following major surgery? How many women dine out at multiple restaurants in the 72-hour period following their hospital discharge?

Over the next several days, the sisters shopped the malls, visited the French Quarter for entertainment and famous Louisiana cuisine, and headed to The Fairgrounds, also known as Louisiana Downs.

Victoria's free spirit emerged. She liked the name of a horse, and placed a $5 bet on an animal she knew nothing about. Her sister also placed a $5 bet. It was Friday, March 30, 2012. Victoria won $264 in the 9th race on No. 5, Necessary Luxury. Teri won $250 in the fifth race on No. 8, Sultry Gentlemen.

Victoria drove herself around, did some grocery shopping, straightened the kitchen, washed the dishes, and had bandages changed daily by a home health nurse. "If you had had cancer, you wouldn't be looking like this and doing this well," the nurse told her.

Victoria already knew she was cancer-free. She didn't have cancer when she checked into the hospital near New Orleans. She was certain of it. She had stage zero precancerous DCIS. The biopsy created her fateful health condition.

It was the biopsy on January 23, 2008, that forever changed her life. The biopsy allowed for the infection and the adverse reaction she experienced to get a deadly foothold.

She was sick of looking for a doctor every day to help her. The infection and pain were now gone. Victoria faced two new challenges – a difficult physical recovery due to the radical surgery and the removal of lymph nodes, and a difficult emotional recovery as she stared at an ugly scar where her breast used to be.

There was a full moon on Friday, April 6, 2012, when Victoria began her 13-hour drive back to North Carolina, mostly interstate travel that took her through Montgomery, Alabama, the first capital of the Confederacy and Georgia's capital city, Atlanta, where "Gone with the Wind" premiered. Any mention of the South during the 1800s gets Victoria's attention, and for a moment she thought about her family history.

Her mother's grandfather fought in the Civil War, largely around Richmond as part of the Army of Northern Virginia, and he was at Appomattox when General Lee surrendered. He's buried in the same cemetery as Victoria's maternal grandparents. She has always wanted to join the Daughters of the Confederacy, a women's lineage society and heritage association dedicated to preserving the memory of those family members who served and or died in service to the Confederate States of America.

An avid history buff, Victoria wanted to do her part to collect and preserve the material necessary for a truthful history of the War Between the States.

She was tired but determined. "I want to go home," she told her sister, as they headed east out of New Orleans on Interstate 10.

Make no mistake about it. She was also mad. She tried not to show her anger, but occasionally it boiled over. "After more than four years and 70 grand, the Pope would be pissed off."

Victoria's mother was glad to see her daughters pull into her driveway. Anticipating their arrival, she had the table set with a baked turkey and all the trimmings, even though it was 10:30 p.m. "I was happy to be home and see my mom. I really didn't know if I was going to live or die."

Victoria experienced feelings of jet lag and some disorientation the next morning after driving all day and into the evening. Waking up in her own bed, she faced a new round of depression. "It was worse when I got home and looked in my own mirror."

The depression wore on her throughout the day. By mid-afternoon, all she could think of was how ugly she looked. "After all I went through I ended up looking like this. Will I ever get used to my body?"

It was difficult to raise her right arm, and even more challenging to shampoo her hair. "It's the first time in life I had fought like that and it didn't work." Victoria said she felt "inadequate." She kept asking herself, "Where did I go wrong?"

Easter Sunday was April 8, 2012. Victoria took her mother and sister to eat at the historic Grove Park Inn in Asheville, North Carolina, the century-old resort hotel that houses more than 500 guest rooms and an 18,000 square foot Grand Ballroom. The hotel's illustrious list of famous guests includes Thomas Edison, Henry Ford, Will Rogers, and a succession of U.S. Presidents. One of the most famous guests was magician and escape artist Harry Houdini.

But even Houdini could not unlock the chains of gloom surrounding Victoria's heart and her usual positive outlook and steel will. "I was not the same person, felt like I would never be happy again. This is the pits."

Victoria used her sister's visit for her personal therapy as best she could. They ate out and went places, and spent time with their mother.

However, she could not escape reality. Her journal indicates she spent April 10 crying off and on all day. "And I'm not a crier." Day in and day out Victoria kept her deep pain from her mother and sister.

By early April, most Americans were dreading filing their income tax returns on April 15, but Victoria was finding the preparations to be therapy. "I felt like I was getting something done and thinking about something other than my missing breast."

Victoria was not about to succumb to depression.

On April 12, she took her mother and sister to the Upstate of South Carolina to have lunch at Victoria Valley Vineyards. The dining room with large glass windows overlooks the vineyard and Table Rock, the famous 3,124-foot peak in Table Rock State Park at the edge of the Blue Ridge.

While at the vineyard, Victoria received a message on her phone from her close friend Brenda Kinder that Dr. Meg Colgate had died. "How shocking," she thought. Dr. Colgate's death is significant in this story for several reasons, but the most important one may speak to the subject of fear.

"This lady knew all the right things to do," said Victoria. "Why did she take that chemo?"

This is becoming an age-old question: Why do so many intelligent people choose a toxic treatment with so many known side effects as opposed to proven, but not medically accepted, alternatives that cause no harm?

Victoria raised the same question about mammograms. Why are women so eager to ignore all the new scientific research regarding the danger and ineffectiveness of mammograms? Victoria's own sister had a mammogram five weeks after Victoria's surgery.

Most families in America maintain special traditions. It's Thanksgiving for some, Christmas for others. It's the 4,531-acre Chimney Rock State Park in western North Carolina for Victoria and her sister, Teri. Besides the hiking trails and spectacular views, there's a 404-foot waterfall and the famous 315-foot rock formation accessible with your choice of elevator or stairs.

"If you can walk to the top of the rock, you know you've still got it," says Victoria. "We try to do it once a year."

Areas within the park were featured in the 1984 film "A Breed Apart," and the 1992 movie "The Last of the Mohicans."

On April 13, 2012, the park had opened for the new season but the climbing of the famous rock would not open until the following day and the sisters had to settle for a guided boat tour on nearby Lake Lure's 27 miles of shoreline, where scenes from the 1987 romance film "Dirty Dancing" starring Jennifer Grey and the late Patrick Swayze were filmed.

"I must have seen it 10 times. Patrick Swayze was a fabulous dancer. Every woman loves that movie."

"Weakened by chemotherapy," announced a television news anchor, "Patrick Swayze died September 14, 2009, after a 20-month battle with pancreatic cancer." Like so many Americans, he believed that chemo was the way to fight his disease. In fact, Swayze put more faith in conventional medicine and chemotherapy than perhaps anyone.

Despite continual pronouncements about progress and new cures and treatments being just around the corner, more people are diagnosed with cancer, and more people die every year from cancer. More money is spent every year on cancer treatments as well.

In an on-camera interview with ABC News correspondent Barbara Walters, Swayze said, "I want to last until they find a cure, which means I'd better get a fire under it." The mainstream medical cartel that failed to conquer cancer for half a century clearly had gotten into Swayze's head.

Did no one tell Patrick Swayze the cancer industry isn't looking for a cure? There is no profit in curing people. The money is in the medicine. There's also a lot of money in the research. The only way the cancer industry can maintain and increase its profits is by 'not' finding a cure.

What does Patrick Swayze's cancer have to do with Victoria? Consider this:

Patrick Swayze was allowed by the federal government, the FDA, the American Medical Association, and state medical boards to seek the treatment of his choice. He was given the freedom to place his faith and life in the hands of mainstream medical doctors. Not one of these doctors could be held accountable for the failure of their 'approved' treatments.

Victoria did not have this freedom. Every medical doctor she saw was restricted to the Standard of Care in the medical community, an arbitrary mandate that prevents the use of hundreds of treatments and therapies simply because at least 50% of medical doctors are 'not' using them.

Because of Standard of Care, a doctor can insert a metal clip or marker in a woman's breast during a biopsy and get away without telling the woman she has a foreign object in her breast.

In other words, doctors who attempted to help Victoria outside the approved treatments of mainstream medical doctors could be held accountable, not just for the success or failure of their treatment, but for even attempting it.

Victoria, a private citizen, did not have the same rights as Patrick Swayze, the actor. Isn't this wrong?

Even as Victoria told doctors that she had a massive infection and could actually feel something foreign in her breast, she was told that wasn't possible. "They just ignored me. They ignored the obvious."

Fortunately for Darlene Swayze, the choice to have a non-toxic breast cancer ablation had not been prohibited in 2009. Darlene was diagnosed with cancer in both breasts, and she may be the first woman in history to have had a double cryoablation. The treatments were back to back – first the right breast, then the left. After the procedure, she flew back to her home in Oregon.

Darlene's ablation was done two weeks after Victoria's. The procedure was done May 13, 2009, in Toledo, Ohio by Dr. Allan Kaufman, the same interventional radiologist that ablated Victoria's lump. Darlene's husband, Lew, is a distant cousin of Patrick Swayze.

April 30, 2012, was the third anniversary of Victoria's cryoablation. All day, she experienced sadness and felt remorseful, "a waste that I lost my breast."

The next two months from mid-April to mid-June, 2012 would test Victoria's indomitable spirit in the face of an incredible loss – her breast.

She found her body to be out of sync, missing a body part, searching for balance. She was making smoothies again and taking ozone treatments. She researched exercises that would help alleviate the shoulder and arm stiffness that follows a mastectomy. Out of remorse, she took her mother to a new church. "I was feeling guilty because of neglecting my mother. Besides, I'm mad at God right now. I'm trying to work through that."

"I'm sick of this whole mess. I can't wrap my head around the idea of getting a fake prosthetic breast."

Spring in the mountains didn't come a bit too soon in 2012. Victoria's vegetable and herb garden provided a welcome distraction as she worked in some fresh rotted cow manure in her raised beds and planted organic seeds for basil, Swiss chard, beets, four types of lettuce, in addition to tomato plants. Cilantro was already growing.

Gardening became a daily endeavor with weeding and watering occupying much of her time.

May 2 was a historic day of sorts for Victoria. Four previous biofeedback sessions had each detected a metal allergy to a foreign object. On this day, there was nothing. The first biofeedback session following the surgical removal of her right breast revealed no metal allergy.

As part of her post-surgical trauma, Victoria's hair was falling out. She resumed her iodine supplementation and her hair was soon normal again.

May 5 was another tearful day as she watched the Kentucky Derby. It reminded her of the apparently successful cryoablation three years earlier that would have saved her breast, had she not been attacked by an allergic reaction to a foreign object and a hideous life-threatening infection.

Neither Dr. Kaufman nor Victoria knew at the time about a foreign object in her breast, much less an adverse reaction. Victoria now realizes that she didn't have cancer. The sensations, however, were scary and she "didn't know what else to think." Remember, it would be more than a year after the ablation before Victoria would learn about breast clips and markers.

"It is nice to not have that God-awful pain when I wake up," she said. But living pain-free was little consolation for living without her breast. "It was doctors who allowed my breast to get so bad. They could tell I was in agony."

On May 23, 2012, Victoria wrote in her journal: "I need a break from reality." Three days later she found the distraction she needed so badly. She took her mother to a garden show and picked up flower plants for her own spring planting, including Mexican and pineapple sage plants. "I really love plants. They don't talk back to you. It's very therapeutic. In the spring when all the plants start to bloom, it makes you feel alive again."

Victoria planted Japanese maple, iris, euclyliptus, and dahlias. "The sweating and air felt good. And time heals."

To this day, Victoria has not had chemo or radiation. She is alive and well, and attacked her garden preparation and planting in April 2013 with great vigor and intensity. She's again dragging long water hoses around the yard and works hours in her flower beds and wakes up the next day energized and raring to go.

In June 2012, Victoria declined a dental x-ray when she went for her teeth cleaning and a bridge adjustment. No more infection in her mouth, and she wasn't about to have any more radiation. Two years had passed since the original D-Day, June 6, 2010, when Victoria learned about breast clips and markers for the first time.

"Life is not what I wanted, but at least I have it back. I am alive and I have a purpose, to not let this happen to another woman. Enough is enough! The Standard of Care was a contributing factor in the loss of my breast."

Chapter 51

Wish I'd never had the biopsy

Two years ago, there were only a couple of sites on the internet that even mentioned breast biopsies in the same breath as the metal clips or markers that have been permanently inserted in the biopsy cavity for more than a decade. There are now dozens of sites and thousands of online comments.

It was July 2010 when Victoria discovered the site at healthcentral.com while typing various combinations of words and phrases related to a search for breast biopsy markers.

At the time, this appeared to be the only site that allowed readers to post unedited comments, questions, and complaints on the subject of breast biopsies. It went online in July 2008, but there were few postings until 2009. By January 2013 there were over 160 postings on this one website.

The easiest way to find this site is to type "adverse reactions to breast biopsy markers" into a search engine. On Google, it's usually the first site that appears with the website address, HealthCentral.com.

The breast cancer site is one of dozens of health-oriented websites operated by Remedy Health Media, a health information and technology company, whose published mission is to "empower patients and caregivers." Some companies use the phrase "to empower patients" as a marketing tool. In this case, the phrase became a monumental public service. Without the complaints posted on this website, secrecy could easily have hidden the true gravity of the breast biopsy scandal.

Most of the contributors on the breast cancer site are suffering in some way from the placement of a clip or marker at the time of a biopsy, and some of them get quite testy with their comments because of their pain, rashes, infection, anger, and fear.

These women have good reason to react this way. As you read segments of their stories, you'll understand why.

For the first time, women who were having adverse reactions to a breast biopsy had a place to vent and ask questions at the healthcentral.com website. This site also provides a forum for two female "health guides," who answer questions and offer commentary.

To set the stage for the nature of the complaints that are being posted, we first need to look at an anonymous submission made in August 2011 by a man identified as a radiologist. His doctor's attitude is classic. Describing many of the postings as "misinformation," he asserts that the placement of a clip or marker "far outweighs the risk of any potential adverse effects (which have not been proven in any respected, non-biased, medical journal)."

Herein lies the problem with many doctors. They are so ingrained to demand proof in the form of a published medical journal article that they fail to understand that the proof is in the pudding. A woman who is having pain or a reaction could care less about the publication of a research article. They have an entirely different point of view. Ask Victoria. "I don't need a medical journal to tell me I'm in dire agony with my breast after the biopsy."

Although Victoria has not posted comments on this site, she, too, has a strong opinion about breast clips and what has become a routine procedure in the breast cancer industry. "Why would a woman make this up?"

NOTE: Selected comments made by contributors on the healthcentral.com site, including the concerned radiologist, have been edited and condensed without changing the meaning and are not in quotes. Contributors other than the radiologist are identified as "anonymous." Victoria's comments are in quote marks.

Concerned radiologist: Any breast symptoms, such as pain, after having a breast biopsy are typically the result of the biopsy itself (tissue is being removed and nerves are being disrupted). This is not the clip causing the problem. If you do not want a clip placed, don't have one placed. Your doctor is required to get your consent prior to placing the clip.

Victoria's response: "Then why didn't my doctor fully inform me and get my consent? I know I'm allergic to metal."

The sad truth is, thousands of women have a clip or marker and they never gave their consent.

Concerned radiologist: Those of you contemplating having the clip removed are looking at having another surgical procedure which is sure to cause you more problems than you believe you're having now. It is the standard of care in the breast community to place a marking clip after a breast biopsy.

Victoria's response: "So many times I have suffered hell because I was allergic to metal and no doctor or dentist would believe me. If the patient knows they are allergic to metal, they should be able to make their own decision, but it's a decision they can't make if they are not given a choice."

Regrettably, many women will never recover from the biopsy until they have additional surgery to remove clips, markers, wires, or even pieces of plastic.

Concerned radiologist: Postings on this board by misguided, uninformed individuals are ultimately going to prevent some women from having a necessary medical procedure performed that could cost them their lives.

Victoria's response: "Having the biopsy nearly cost me my life and it did cost me my breast."

One health guide on the site correctly noted that some people are allergic to titanium, as detailed in various small studies, some of which are reported in PubMed, the National Institute of Health's online journal.

Not all women are having reactions to titanium, of course. Stainless steel is also being used, and many women are highly allergic to nickel (a large metal component of stainless steel). Victoria is one of them.

Statistically speaking, only a fraction of women who have been harmed by a breast clip or marker are likely to find healthcentral.com or any other website because they are not looking. They don't even realize that their breast issues could be related to a foreign object in the breast. They were never told. Two out of three medical doctors and nurses have never heard of a biopsy clip.

This, in fact, is the larger part of this story; all women are not being told. "I went two years after a biopsy," said Victoria, "and never heard of a marker." Many of the women who have posted on this site are "as angry as me."

The list of women who are having breast issues because of metal clips is staggering, especially for procedures that were done from 2002 through 2010, and the number of women who are learning about their own fate is growing daily.

In the medical community, doctors are fixated on calling this a 'small problem' with a 'few cases' while there's overwhelming evidence that hundreds of thousands of women are having problems. After all, more than one million women are undergoing a breast biopsy each year in the U.S. This is not a "few" cases and it's not a "small" problem.

"When I complained, most doctors treated me like I was insane, as though I was making it up," Victoria said.

August 31, 2011, anonymous: I am amazed that this clip has apparently been in use for nine years and this is the first time many women reading about biopsy procedures have ever heard of such a thing and I daresay there are thousands of women walking around with this 'item' in their breast and not knowing about it.

August 31, 2011, anonymous: I stumbled on a website of a highly regarded hospital which purported to outline what a patient could expect during a breast biopsy. Lo and behold, not one word on there about a clip (or potential use of a clip). Don't they want patients to know about this clip? Or is it a matter of "what the patient doesn't know can't hurt them?"

August 31, 2011, concerned radiologist: There are many reasons why a clip is placed after a biopsy … all of which benefit the patient with no proven risk.

February 11, 2012, anonymous: Do you have breasts? I would be happy to have these three clips taken out as the pain is 'over the top.'

February 11, 2012, anonymous: I now know that I can't take most metals and that started when I was 13 when I had my ears pierced. I am in pain all the time and I am one tough cookie! I can't wear a bra without paying for it for days and I am talking soft cotton with no underwire. I told the doctor's office that I was going to take a knife and rip them all out myself.

September 3, 2011, concerned radiologist: I, like most physicians, will have to see a nonbiased, reputable study before I will be discussing a potential titanium reaction with any patients. Physicians should be practicing evidence based medicine … anything else is irresponsible and goes against the Hippocratic Oath we all must follow.

"I thought the oath was Do No Harm," says Victoria. "Let me tell you what's irresponsible. When I get a splinter in my finger, my body tries to reject it. It doesn't matter if it's wood or titanium. It's killing me, and you want me to wait for a nonbiased, reputable study on the topic of splinters before you will help me!"

September 3, 2011, concerned radiologist: Clips decrease chance of unnecessary radiation from additional mammographic images obtained to investigate an area in the breast that was previously biopsied (which a clip would be marking if it had been placed).

"What if the clip has moved?" asks Victoria: "You do know that clips have been found to migrate? Some manufacturers have added a mesh covering to prevent migration and others are using hook shapes. Lot of good the clip will do if it moves. One radiologist who uses clips told me she would never put one in a lymph node because she feared migration."

November 19, 2008, anonymous: I had titanium markers in both breasts after a stereotactic biopsy. Since then, I have had some bad reactions with rashes all over and nonstop itching.

November 30, 2010, anonymous: A few weeks after having the clip implanted I had an abnormal period which lasted for weeks. During that time I also developed a rash. I too had fleeting pain in my breast and a crawling sensation under my skin.

February 11, 2012, anonymous: I experienced the fleeting pain and crawling sensation under my skin in the location where the titanium chip was placed. It's been almost two years and it does seem a bit odd that the sensation is increasing rather than decreasing.

May 17, 2009, anonymous: My wife had a stereotactic biopsy in September 2008 with a titanium marker. Since then she has times where she grabs her right breast in extreme pain. During the biopsy

366

they missed the target. They went back in to do it again. She left the hospital and returned about an hour later bleeding profusely. She went to see a breast specialist who dismissed it as typical of a stereotactic biopsy. She continues to have this pain and it has been about eight months.

June 4, 2009, anonymous: I've had similar pain to your wife. It comes up without warning and feels as if something is burning within my breast, about where the marker should be. It goes away quite quickly and seems worse in the morning but does happen randomly throughout the day.

September 2, 2009, anonymous: I had a titanium marker placed in September 2008. My diagnosis was PASH (rare but benign tumor of the breast). For the following three months I experienced extreme breast pain, changes in breast tissue density and I could not roll over in bed at night without waking from the breast pain. The clinic said that it was highly unlikely for it to be from the marker clip. I was told no doctor would remove the clip because it was not 'medically necessary.' Constant burning and periodic stabbing and stinging pains in my breast have been a drain.

May 25, 2012, anonymous: I had a horrible infection set in after my biopsy and I continue to have stabbing pain, burning and itching. Prior to biopsy, I had no pain and felt healthy. Since biopsy, I have endured nothing but trouble. Procedures like this should not be happening to trusting patients.

November 5, 2009, anonymous: It seems like the medical community is not acknowledging that women are being bothered by these clips. I wasn't even informed in advance that they were inserting a clip.

May 5, 2010, anonymous: My burning pain (after titanium marker) didn't begin for a few months after the biopsy. The clinic didn't acknowledge this as a common symptom, but it is very annoying and unnatural.

July 20, 2010, anonymous: I have no clip but will be having a biopsy conducted this month. I will request no marker. I will require this in writing because I don't want to find out later someone thought they could just slip it in.

Victoria's response: "I hope you don't get the same response that I did when I requested in writing for the doctor to not remove my lymph nodes. I personally handed the written request to my doctor. He took them anyway."

May 25, 2012, anonymous: I did have the marker placed in my breast and feel misguided and angry. I have had nothing but trouble ever since. I wish I had never had the biopsy. I had a thermogram and it came back perfect. We trust doctors and that's our first mistake. When in doubt, back out.

November 9, 2009, anonymous: A surgeon removed the infected area. It turned out that when the chip was inserted the needle pushed a piece of my fat under it and my body took it as foreign and attacked it. So the site was not healing and became infected. As for the clip, I don't know if it is still in my breast. I saw four doctors about this. Three had not heard of the clips. You're right, no one believes us! After all, it's just a woman's breast. If it was a male's testicles with this problem, it would be believed, and handled differently. We all seem to have no pain before the clip, and now we do. But it is not the clip, or so they say.

For the record, it does not appear that metal clips or markers are being placed in men's testicles as they are in women's breasts. Internet search engines don't produce any results for the key search words. "Are we surprised," says Victoria.

February 3, 2010, anonymous: I did have my clip removed and the pain went away that day. I just had a general surgeon remove it. Unfortunately, I picked up hospital-born bacteria during the procedure. I went to 11 different doctors before I found a doctor who would remove the clip. One of the nurses I met on the day of my surgery said she had had other patients who suffered severe pain until their clips were removed.

March 24, 2010, anonymous: I had three ultrasound biopsies done and they put three markers in afterwards; however, I was not informed of these markers until they were about to put them in. I protested and questioned if they were necessary; however, being alone in the room and vulnerable on the table, they put them in. Now almost one year later, I am experiencing the sharp pains in my breast.

December 6, 2009, anonymous: I had two biopsies starting in August 2009. The last one was MRI-guided on September 8 and they used titanium clips that I did not want. Since then I have pain in my breast, sometimes it radiates to my arm pit, there are red and raised lumps where the markers are. I do not know what to do but suffer with this pain daily and cannot lay on my stomach or right side.

January 18, 2010, anonymous: I agreed to the clip being placed but instead of one I have three. I began to have pain and eventually an infection track opened and nobody really knows why it started. All along I blamed the clips. I have spent over a year dealing with lots of pain, doctor's visits, time packing the wound, and money to have them drag their feet about taking them out. They want to do another surgery for what they think is a cyst that keeps opening. Not fair! I wish I would have known more instead of being asked to sign a waiver when I am naked and about to have a biopsy, as if I am not scared enough!

February 3, 2010, anonymous: I am so mad right now! I was talked into having the marker during a needle biopsy. Now I have stabbing pain in my left breast and am told it is major surgery to remove it.

June 18, 2010, anonymous: About 10 years ago I had a biopsy and a titanium marker was inserted. I knew this was during the surgery when the doctor said, "Now I'm inserting a titanium marker." I had no knowledge previously. I've been fine until the last few months when I feel a sharp pain where the marker was placed. It's worse when I'm stressed or have had too much caffeine or if I'm in front of a computer or microwave for a long time. It is disappointing how this entire procedure seems to be handled, especially by male MD's.

December 16, 2009, anonymous: I believe there are many more problems with stereotactic biopsies and their markers than we have been told. There are certainly no long-term studies on what a titanium marker in your breast for 30 or 40 years is going to do to you. And I think it's egregiously insulting to tell us that they need that marker for subsequent scans: this is for their convenience, not necessarily for our health. I felt coerced into having that biopsy. There was actual pressure, specifically designed to frighten me into having this procedure.

February 23, 2010, anonymous: I had an ultrasound needle biopsy in February 2009 after an abnormality on my mammogram. While on the table, after the tissue was pulled, the female surgeon springs on me that she was going to put in a titanium clip. I have massive allergies to anything from dust mites, cats, foods, chemicals, to medications. One year later, the pain in my ribs is worse. There is pain along my left side of the breast area (ribcage) as well.

February 24, 2012, anonymous: Let's get wise here, it's a foreign object and it's happening after her markers were put in. They are killing us.

March 21, 2012, anonymous: Last year I had saline breast implants removed. Over the past 12 months, I've had unexplained sensations in my left breast. A few weeks ago, while traveling, the TSA body scan machine showed I had "something imbedded" in my left breast. TSA told me I will always get the agent 'hand pat down' because of this. I was shocked! Markers and clips were never explained to me, nor was I informed prior to or after surgery that I would get one.

Victoria: "It may not be a breast clip that's setting off the TSA body scan machine, although the culprit was put in your body during the biopsy. You might be shocked to learn the truth (in the next chapter)."

March 9, 2010, anonymous: I was in excruciating pain after a biopsy where a clip had been inserted and I was told by the doctor that my pain "couldn't be related" to the biopsy.

March 19, 2010, anonymous: I did not want the marker either, but they basically said they wouldn't do the biopsy without putting it in. I am convinced that the stinging and constant irritation is being caused by the marker. Frankly, no one is taking me serious.

March 19, 2010, anonymous: The day the clip was removed the pain in my breast was gone. I did have a 2.5-inch incision and had to have a wire localization so the surgeon could locate the clip. To be honest the whole experience was quite traumatic. The doctor who put the clip in me acted like there was no way it could be bothering me. Sure enough it was. I was so ill from the clip, losing weight, unable to work, vomiting from the pain that I could not have continued to live a productive life with it in me.

March 19, 2010, anonymous: I originally asked this question almost three years ago. It amazes me that so many are having the same reactions. It's true; no one thinks it's possible. We'll all have to wait until this happens to someone famous to have this brought out into the open.

Victoria: "I'm not famous but hopefully that won't stop women from uniting and putting an end to this insanity. If a woman wants a breast marker, let her have one. Don't force it on all women, but disclose everything you're going to do before you do it, and tell women every possible adverse reaction. After full disclosure, a woman should be allowed to say no. It is her life, her body, her breast."

May 19, 2010, anonymous: I was not informed until the woman surgeon was ready to insert it, that a clip would be used. I "consented" at the time, but of course had been given no advance notification to allow me to consider or research it.

June 23, 2010, anonymous: I get reactions from both the areas where they inserted the stereotactic needles (both breasts) and where the clip is located. These procedures were done eight months ago. It started getting worse after I had an MRI on my knee (the magnetic fields pulled on it and it may have cut the tissue).

August 6, 2010, anonymous: For over a year I have complained about shooting pain in my breast but never thought to ask or even research if it could be a result from a marker left after last year's core biopsy. My GYN, GP and breast surgeon all said that it wasn't possible. They totally ignored the fact that I was in pain.

November 10, 2010, anonymous: I'm only 19. I had this biopsy done about a week ago. I am feeling similar pain in my left breast. I'm so shocked that they wouldn't give me any warnings concerning allergies to the clip. Ugh, I just want this nightmare over with.

November 11, 2010, anonymous: It may not even be the titanium you are responding to, but a contaminant that happened to the titanium in the factory. The titanium produced in the USA is not as pure as we would like to think. It is like a person who has peanut allergies eating a Milky Way that was made in a Snicker's factory.

February 22, 2011, anonymous: I had a biopsy a year ago. They would not do the biopsy if I refused the titanium clip. I was told this literally minutes before the procedure that I could not refuse the clip. Feeling the pressure and not knowing any better I went against my better judgment and had the biopsy.

June 8, 2011, anonymous: I had a breast biopsy last fall and a titanium marker was put in at the time. The nurse said it was so small, I wouldn't even know it was there. So not true! It hurt from the time I got it in there until I had it removed. I felt the burning, aching, and sometimes shooting pain. When I talked to my surgeon about it, her first reaction was that it was "impossible" to have a problem with the marker.

June 11, 2011, anonymous: I had a needle core biopsy about two years ago and a marker was inserted without explanation or my permission. I was surprised they would insert a permanent marker into my body without my permission but trusted them. I was breast cancer free but I began experiencing sharp brief stabbing pains at the site of the marker. Then I began to experience pain in my shoulders and upper arms.

June 13, 2011, anonymous: Same thing happened to me. I had no idea the procedure would be so invasive, painful, bled a lot, bruised for a month, and now itching pain lasting two years for a negative biopsy which I believe is from the titanium clip.

June 15, 2011, anonymous: I am so mad! I had a titanium clip put in my left breast about a year and half ago. I thought nothing of it at the time (as they told me about it as they were doing it). But I am increasingly having issues with it. It is extremely tender and hurts. I am basically aware of that breast all the time. It is such a shame that the medical community is in complete denial about this. The other day a client, who is a breast augmentation surgeon, was furious when I told him they left a clip in my breast. He said that was horrible and that finding a good doctor to do 'foreign object' removal might be difficult. I asked him why he didn't educate, and write about these kinds of issues in the breast health community. He said "because his colleagues would be furious." So it is basically known, but taboo to talk about.

August 7, 2011, anonymous: It's been a month since my stereotactic biopsy and a few weeks ago I noticed a burning feeling on my breast. I am sick with a cold now and when I cough, sneeze or blow my nose, I feel the burning exactly where the marker is.

August 31, 2011, anonymous: I called the office today to ask if they use a marker, telling them that I was curious if it was part of their process. The facilitator, who is my contact, said, "Yes, that it is a standard part of the procedure."

December 11, 2011, anonymous: The first I heard of the procedure was when I was disrobed, consent forms signed and dated, and on the table about to undergo bilateral biopsies. The ultrasound tech stated, "Oh yeah, I forgot to tell you that we are going to place titanium markers where we biopsy ..." Certainly not best medical practice, as well as ethically and legally questionable. My reaction is that this information was intentionally and off-handedly mentioned at the last moment. Shame on them.

March 19, 2012, anonymous: The doctor didn't explain anything to me about putting a clip into my breast. I was lying on the table and in severe pain and scared out of my mind. Afterward I was told that a clip had been put into my breast. This was four years ago, and I haven't had peace of mind since. I feel like I have been taken advantage of and used as a guinea pig.

August 9, 2011, anonymous: I had scheduled a stereotactic biopsy after they found a cluster of micro calcifications. They did tell me about the markers, and even showed me a sample of them. Each one had at least two pointed wires sticking out. I'm concerned about those pointed wires landing on a nerve ending. I have very small breasts and sleep on my stomach.

Chapter 52

Where's marker for men's testicles?

The final mutilation of Victoria's right breast is over.

The biopsy procedure that started her downward spiral occurred January 23, 2008. After 1,521 days, she succumbed to her weariness and total exhaustion and agreed to have an ugly, radical surgical procedure to remove her breast in order to excise an infection because no medical doctor took the infection seriously or admitted that she could be experiencing an allergic reaction to a foreign object.

Victoria's mother used to tell her, "You have the patience of Job," the biblical prophet known for his perseverance in suffering.

As for an infection, "it's all in your head," Victoria was told. "You have cancer," doctors would say, although 95% of the medical evidence confirmed the obvious – infection. But the obvious wasn't Standard of Care, and not one doctor who had the skills to address the infection would do it. No doctor would step outside their comfort zone and surgically excise the infectious growth.

Only one surgeon admitted that the swollen breast was an infection and he could surgically remove the infected tissue while saving as much of the breast as possible. He went so far as to quote how much the procedure would cost and said he would do it because it was the "right thing to do."

For whatever reasons, within 30 hours, he changed his mind.

The mutilation was done. The statement serves as the best introduction to this chapter, an expose on a medical practice that gradually, by default, has become the Standard of Care for diagnosing almost any issue with a woman's breasts.

Never mind that a biopsy procedure is fraught with dozens of dangers, all of which have been thoroughly identified and published for the world to see on a medically and publicly accessible government website.

However, the routine placement of metal clips or markers during breast biopsies has been such a closely guarded secret for nearly 15 years that only doctors and nurses, whose work directly focuses on women's breasts, know about it.

For certain, Victoria knows the secret.

I have two daughters-in-law and one sister that are Registered Nurses, and they work in two different states, and they knew nothing about the markers, or the potential immediate and long-term dangers of the biopsy procedure.

If there's a problem with food, drugs, or medical devices, you're supposed to be able to find out about it on your Smart phone or with a couple of clicks on your computer's mouse. It's an internet site called MAUDE, not to be confused with the six-season run of the American television sitcom by the same name starring Bea Arthur that was broadcast from 1972-78.

From this day forward, all anyone need remember is the sitcom. Enter the name on a search engine and you'll be directed to the U.S. Food and Drug Administration's (FDA) database known as MAUDE (Manufacturer and User Facility Device Experience).

As important as public access is to this information, it's equally important to have a central site where physicians and patients can report malfunctioning equipment, even if the reporting is voluntary. The majority of the reports about breast biopsies and clips or markers have been posted by physicians, not patients.

I find this very strange. Is it because the women really don't know what happened to them?

This is a site where researchers, journalists, and the public can search for information on food, drugs, biologics (including vaccines and blood), animal and veterinary, cosmetics, radiation-emitting products, tobacco products, and medical devices.

The website allows searches for recalls and product shortages as well as providing an access portal for private citizens and professionals to submit reports of problems.

But the site is based on key words, and we've searched it dozens of times in the past two years looking for reports on clips and markers, only to come up empty handed. It was there; we just didn't find it until after months of searching.

"MAUDE may not include reports made according to exemptions, variances, or alternative reporting requirements granted under 21 CFR 803.19," the FDA said, and allows database searches on medical devices which may have malfunctioned or caused a death or serious injury.

The mayhem being caused by breast biopsies has been happening under the radar.

The FDA says that MAUDE data is not intended to be used either to evaluate rates of adverse events or to compare adverse event occurrence rates across devices. "Please be aware that reports regarding device trade names may have been submitted under different manufacturer names. Searches only retrieve records that contain the search term(s) provided by the requester."

Eventually, we found the combination of key words and phrases that exposed the real history of metal clips and markers, and it's as ugly as the deception itself.

Maude website

In the medical world, any adverse event is classified as serious or non-serious; expected or unexpected; and study-related, possibly study-related, or not-study-related.

"Serious" adverse events would result in death or be life-threatening, require hospitalization, or lead to disability or incapacity, or other significant medical condition, and must be reported immediately.

"Non-serious" adverse events are generally 'bundled' and reported later.

Since 2002, more than 250 reports of "adverse events" involving breast biopsy clips or markers were posted on the FDA site. These voluntary "adverse event" reports are archived from the late-1990s.

How many hundreds or thousands of adverse events were not voluntarily reported?

Victoria learned about breast biopsy markers in 2010, almost two and one-half years after her biopsy. Even then, there were only a couple of websites reporting the complaints of a few women who claimed they were having a reaction to the metal in the marker.

Today, the number of sites has mushroomed. There are now thousands of mentions of breast biopsy clips or markers.

Google: Adverse reaction to a stainless steel breast biopsy clip or marker. You get 99,300 results.

Google: Adverse reactions to titanium breast biopsy clip or marker. You get 86,800 results.

Google: Adverse reaction to a breast biopsy clip or marker. You get 331,000 results.

The most reports in the FDA database for a single year – 98 – were posted in 2009, followed by 35 in 2010 and 31 in 2008. Many reports described events that occurred a year earlier, and some even two years earlier. So much for the intent of voluntary reporting!

The pattern was an increasing number of adverse events being posted each year until 2009, and then a decline in the numbers through 2012. But who was paying attention? Who was looking for information about breast clips or markers? Most women weren't even being told about them.

Why are there dramatically fewer "adverse event" reports in the past two years – two in 2011 and six in 2012? This is an open question, but it needs to be answered. There has to be a reason for the decline. Here are some of the possibilities.

- What are the medical, moral, and ethical reporting criteria being used today and have they changed?
- Have manufacturers resolved the 'bugs' in the entire process so, after 10 years, there are no malfunctions and no "adverse events" to report?
- Are doctors simply cutting off more breasts, and therefore the reporting of a malfunction during a biopsy procedure seems meaningless?

- Are doctors better trained and becoming more proficient, thereby reducing or eliminating human error?
- Is there an attempt to cover up a scandal?
- Are medical sales people taking the 'load' off doctors and offering to report and track all the problems, and then failing to follow through?

There was no mention of a biopsy marker at the Hope Cancer Center in 2008 when Victoria arrived for her procedure. She was not told about the possible use of a clip or marker, and she was not asked to sign a waiver or permission form to have a marker placed. Most importantly, she was not told that the biopsy process itself has a disturbing history where pieces of plastic or metal are purposely or accidentally left in a woman's breast.

Even without considering a foreign object accidentally left in a woman's breast, women all over the country are carrying metal clips and markers in a biopsied breast and they don't know it. The metal clip or marker was inserted during a biopsy procedure and they were never asked for permission, and never told.

The trend appears to have changed in 2012. As recently as 2011, it was easy to find a woman who did not know. Today, most women who have a biopsy clip or marker from a biopsy in 2012 or 2013 know it's there. They might not like the deceptive way they were told, but they were told, in some manner, even if under awkward circumstances.

They might know of the clip or marker's presence, but very few women even in 2013 know of its potential consequences. In fact, I haven't found a single woman who knew that the U.S. government operated a website that describes the history of faulty breast biopsy equipment and even tells how plastic is being sheared off in a woman's breast.

Some doctors have informed their patients that a metal clip or marker will be placed, but even when 'informed,' it's almost impossible to find a woman who was fully informed about the potential dangers. Without knowing about the history of malfunctions, how could any woman make an informed decision?

A distinction needs to be drawn at this point. Most women who agreed to accept the marker did so under duress. They were scared out of their wits, naked, and often partially anesthetized, or all three, when they were asked to sign a consent form.

One patient, who was blindsided during a biopsy, posted her reaction on the FDA's website, December 4, 2006: At no time did a doctor physically examine or discuss with me the procedure or the implantation of a bovine collagen radiopaque to which I had an adverse reaction. I never consented to be injected and was in no way informed of adverse reactions. I experienced incredible pain and anguish.

Even if a woman was given notice beforehand that a tiny clip or marker would be placed in her breast, why would that set off any alarm bells? I mean, what could possibly go wrong when inserting a 'tiny' needle in a woman's breast and leaving behind a 'tiny' metallic clip or marker?

Most women are shocked by their misconception of the needle's size. Victoria felt like a "stuck pig." She also felt violated. It's not your grandma's sewing needle, and your grandmother is not gently holding the needle.

The pieces needed for this procedure seem simple enough – biopsy gun, plastic tips, metal tissue markers (mostly titanium but some stainless steel), collagen plug, probe, stereotatic catheter, introducer tube, vacuum power, and pre-packaged components (some erroneously labeled), to mention a few. The potential human intervention of the doctor and staff must not be ignored, nor the human intervention of the patient, manufacturering defects, packaging and shipping errors, faulty raw materials, or poor quality controls.

Let's consult Murphy's Law: If anything can go wrong, it usually will.

FDA website, February 10, 2012: While taking post mammogram images they noticed two clips and the tip of the marker was in the biopsy site. They checked the marker and noticed that the tip had sheared off in the breast. The physician attempted to retrieve the tip, however, was unsuccessful.

One further note about the previous incident: The mammography manager was contacted for additional information. She stated the tip remains in the patient.

Leaving a part of a biopsy tool in a woman's breast is not a rare occurrence. Many doctors who are doing biopsies are being intellectually dishonest on this point.

FDA website, March 1, 2010: Doctor reported placing clip "but the instrument could not be removed properly from the probe, the most anterior part seemed to be broken." Using ultrasound, the doctor "was able to identify a hyperechoic structure that may correspond to the broken tip of the insertion tool. The patient claims about pain. I will try to remove the part again."

Whether it was her metal watch or metal earrings, Victoria has a long and established history of adverse reactions. One of her most memorable adverse events occurred on the morning of February 1, 1998. "I was walking my brother's dog and an aggressive five-year-old German shepherd escaped from his fenced yard and attacked the Lab, an old and sweet dog named Ben."

"I got in the middle of the fight to break it up." Victoria was bitten on the inside right inner thigh. After getting a tetanus shot at an urgent care, she couldn't go to work the next day, and by the third day the swelling had her immobile – the leg was three times larger than normal.

Her oldest brother, Woody, picked her up in his arms and carried her to the doctor. In 30 years of treating dog bites, the physician said, he had never seen a reaction like Victoria's. He even wondered out loud if the dog had something on his tooth that Victoria was allergic to. She missed 10 days of work during a year-end audit and needed six weeks of recuperation, and most of that time she had to walk with a cane.

A nearby Cathedral City, California maintenance worker heard the commotion and ran to her aid carrying a shovel. The city employee was later presented a commendation for "saving a life."

The shepherd was quarantined for 10 days to rule out rabies, before being returned to its owner. When all was said and done, Ben fared much better than Victoria.

If Murphy's Law is still a force to be reckoned with, why aren't patients fully informed about breast biopsy procedures? If a doctor took the time to tell the patient everything that has already happened – not what might happen in the future – what would he say? Here's a sample list:

- Doctors historically have failed to explain to patients the history of known defects and malfunctions in the breast biopsy procedure. Doctors typically rely on the concept of Standard of Care to substitute for their negligence.
- Many women have experienced reactions to a foreign body in the breast such as pain, rash or infection.
- Clips have disappeared in some patients.
- Clips have migrated in some patients.
- Clips or markers were deployed but not in the correct location.
- There are instances when a tissue marker would not deploy, or more than one marker was deployed.
- At times, doctors could not remove the sheath after the clip was deployed.
- Tips have sheared off in the breast on numerous occasions, and many tips are never found.
- The introducer tube has detached during procedures.
- Metal fragments have been left in the breast.
- Tips of the clips were found to be broken.
- Introducer tubes have been found broken, torn or missing.
- A stereotactic catheter with a post procedural clip was found still inside the catheter.
- Doctors have failed to align the applicator as specified, which can result in improper deployment of the collagen plug and possible tip shear.
- Some patients have had the adverse effect of granuloma formation mistaken for malignancy of the breast. This is a condition where the body attempts to wall off a substance, such as a marker, that it perceives as foreign.

"Gee, doc, these procedures are extraordinarily safe and necessary. I can't wait to get started." Excuse the sarcasm! This is nothing to laugh at. But I can't help wondering, where is the outrage from women?

Historically, women became outraged when they were denied the right to vote, and their outrage changed the law. The

same thing happened with equal pay for women. Why aren't women outraged that markers are being placed in women's breasts and not in men's testicles? Why aren't men outraged that there's no Pinkwashing Campaign (or Bluewashing) for their testicles?

Please recognize the sarcasm. There's nothing funny about the horrors being imposed on women without their knowledge or consent.

There might be more outrage among pet owners, whose dogs and cats are being implanted, than among women who are submitting to breast biopsies, clips and markers at the mere suggestion or insistence of a doctor.

In 2010, three months after Victoria first learned about breast biopsy clips and markers, pharmaceutical giant Merck & Co. was served a lawsuit over claims its HomeAgain® pet ID microchip induced cancer in a cat. The complaint named implant maker Digital Angel Corporation as a co-defendant.

"Based on the alarming number of microchip-linked cancers we're discovering, I predict this lawsuit will be just the tip of the iceberg," said Dr. Katherine Albrecht, a consumer advocate and expert on adverse reactions associated with implantable microchips. Her website is chipmenot.org.

Have women been used by the manufacturer of the biopsy devices as human guinea pigs to work out the 'bugs' in the breast instrument? That's what the numbers are suggesting, and that's what the posted reports on the FDA website are telling us.

FDA website, December 18, 2009: Two devices were placed in a patient's right breast. She later saw a primary care physician for a skin reaction/infection at the biopsy sites. "This has progressed to some tissue necrosis at the biopsy sites, which are very close together." The patient saw a dermatologist as the area was not getting better, then suffered an allergic reaction and rash to an antibiotic. The doctor who performed the biopsy indicated that "there is no evidence this is from the clips."

No evidence the allergic reaction is associated with the breast markers, really?

FDA website, February 2, 2009: Patient who had biopsy four months earlier was "possibly having a contact dermatitis by the metal of the device. The marker is going to be removed."

Thirteen years earlier, Victoria was struggling with a similar allergic reaction, and the diagnosis was referred to as contact dermatitis. In that instance, it was the dental wire being used in her adult braces that triggered the reaction.

FDA website, February 27, 2009: Following a breast biopsy, "the patient had an allergic reaction to the clip within a few days after it was placed: burning, itching and pain." Symptoms have worsened. Patient has hives and itching and a rash that is "coming and going all over the body now, no longer just on the breast area."

As is often the case, the physician posted the adverse reaction but did not return the biopsy device for analysis.

Crunching the numbers on the FDA website reveals that dozens of times, the biopsy devices were received by physicians from the manufacturer and they were already damaged or defective – packages arrived mislabeled, parts broken or jammed, and pieces missing.

FDA website, November 24, 2005: Device was received with the introducer tip broken off and missing.

Dozens of times the devices failed to deploy the markers, even after repeated attempts, and the physicians gave up.

FDA website, August 31, 2009: "During a breast biopsy, their tissue marker would not deploy. They tried four more markers from the same lot number and had the same issue. They switched to another lot number and that marker would not deploy. They then switched to another device and that tissue marker did not deploy. They switched back to the original code from a different box and finished the case. No patient data available."

Do you wonder what the woman was doing all this time? Seriously! I hope she was listening to some loud rock 'n roll on her iPod, perhaps Led Zeppelin and his English rock band, and was totally oblivious to this procedure. If not, she was probably freaking out. I'm sure the doctor was telling her to be patient; just because the first six attempts failed, the seventh one surely will be a charm.

Patients are seldom if ever told, depending on the manufacturer, that there may be a narrow window for imaging some of the clips and markers.

A report in 2002 by doctors in the Department of Radiology at Mayo Clinic in Rochester, Minnesota on a Sonographically Guided Needle Localization After Stereotactic Breast Biopsy stated: "Over several months, this material degrades so that it is no longer visible on sonography; however, the metal marker is permanent, as with other wire marking devices."

Also found in the same report is this revealing tidbit: The option to perform needle localization procedures with sonography and mammography equipment "adds needed flexibility and increases patient flow in a radiology department." Of course, that's medical speak for making more money.

Not everything that's implanted or accidentally left behind in a woman's breast is metal. Plastic is a real and present danger.

The FDA was notified on November 24, 2005, when a breast biopsy procedure went bad. The surgeon noticed that the "white flexible applier broke into two parts, and the distal one remained in the probe cannula. The radiologist has not been able to find the missing plastic part. The patient underwent echography and mammography, but the plastic is not radiopaque and not even visible at echography."

FDA website, February 3, 2009: "During a breast biopsy, the plastic applier tube sheared off inside the patient's breast. They plan on using ultrasound to identify the location of the plastic piece and attempt to remove from the patient."

FDA website, April 2, 2009: When attempting to deploy the marker, encountered some resistance but managed to push the marker forward to deploy into the breast … waited a few minutes, pulled the complete set out of the breast and noticed the marker and part of the applicator had sheared off in the breast. The doctor removed the patient from the table, made a three and one half inch incision in the breast and excised the marker and sheared applicator out of the breast. The incision was closed with sutures.

"Why did this doctor know that leaving a foreign object in his patient's breast would be harmful?" asked Victoria. "What

384

prompted him to do the right thing and so many other doctors won't? Good for him. He must have a conscience."

FDA website, September 21, 2009: A piece of the plastic from the introducer sheared off when deploying the clip and went into the patient's breast. "The plastic is still in the patient's breast."

Doctors are consistent on one point. They tell patients that the plastic and the metal clips and markers are perfectly safe, and they emphasize that the patient cannot have an allergic reaction. This, of course, is total nonsense.

What's the real reason the sheared off plastic tips are not removed from the patient's breast? Is it possibly because the plastic can't be found or imaged?

FDA website, March 23, 2010: After withdrawing the probe, surgeon realized that the collagen plug was "seated" in the aperture of the probe and that the tip of the applicator was sheared off. It was unknown if the tip was left in the patient's breast.

Why is it unknown? Is it because doctors can't reliably image the plastic tip? And what happens if they go digging for it? Of course, the woman stands to lose a chunk of her breast.

FDA website, May 3, 2010: After application of the clip, the tip of the clip broke off and remained in the patient's breast. "Introducer tip will not be removed from the patient's breast." (Apparently, it was the introducer tip that broke off, not the clip.)

There is no follow-up information on the FDA website, but the question begs to be asked anyway: How many women have a piece of plastic in their breast and don't know it?

There's also a follow-up question: Will the embedded plastic cause a health issue in the future? The introducer 'tip shearing problem' started about 10 years ago. What if the plastic must remain in the breast longer than a decade before causing a health issue? What if the plastic migrates and gets in the bloodstream?

FDA website, November 11, 2009: While removing the marker from the probe on the second site, the physician noticed that the plastic tip sheared off. Physician checked the probe, tubing and canister and was unable to locate the tip.

FDA website, January 4, 2008: Physician noticed the tip of the probe was sheared off. He then closed the probe and removed it from the breast. "The physician was unable to locate the plastic tip."

FDA website, April 24, 2012: Two images were taken post deployment to see the clip placement. A foreign body was seen at this site on the post images with no biopsy clip present. The end of the biopsy site identifier was examined ... the plastic tip was sheared or broken off.

FDA website, March 8, 2010: Doctor realized that the plastic tip of the marker was missing. "It must be inside the breast, cut off by retraction. Another device was used to complete the procedure. There were no adverse consequences for the patient."

So they say? "I'd like to ask the woman," said Victoria, "and I'd really like to know if she still has her breast." Here's a case where a doctor knew an equipment malfunction had occurred. Rather than stop the procedure and attempt to locate the plastic tip, he completed the biopsy with "another device" and assumed there were no adverse consequences for the patient.

It was the popular London playwright of the late 1800s, Oscar Wilde, who said, "When you assume, you make an ass of u and me."

If there is a follow-up procedure that doctors are required to follow, it is not explained on the FDA website. How exactly can doctors be so sure there are no adverse consequences? How many women will step forward and confirm that their doctor is monitoring a foreign object in their breast?

That brings us full circle to one nagging question: How can a woman report about a foreign object in her breast if she doesn't know it's there?

FDA website, January 22, 2010: After deploying the marker, it was noticed that the tip had sheared off. "Physician was unable to locate the tip." It was not located on the post mammogram.

Chapter 53

The infection was real and deadly

Over a 28-month period, 10 attempts were made to identify an infection in Victoria's right breast using either laboratory or medical imaging results. Seven results were positive for an infection, which Victoria instinctively knew was true. Two results were not positive, and Victoria strongly questioned both of them.

The two negative tests – reporting no infection – were ordered by medical doctors in major hospitals where their primary jobs involved radical surgery.

Four tests were negative for cancer.

Two tests were positive for cancer.

Is this not insane? Who was Victoria to believe? Who is anybody to believe?

In fact, the real estate developer she worked for in Palm Springs 34 years ago was a former hospital administrator in Chicago. He told Victoria that he wouldn't have any surgery before getting at least seven opinions. This was 1979. Has anything changed?

If the doctors that worked at this hospital didn't order tests and surgeries, they were fired. The hospital was run as a business, her former boss said.

On March 16, 2007, National Public Radio's Morning Edition reported on a new book, *How Doctors Think,* by Jerome Groopman, MD. Groopman is a "doctor who discovered that he needed a doctor," NPR announced.

"When his hand was hurt, he went to six prominent surgeons and got four different opinions about what was wrong. Groopman was advised to have unnecessary surgery and got a seemingly made-up diagnosis for a nonexistent condition.

Victoria and Ronda have more in common than a metal breast marker. They were both diagnosed with DCIS, and they both had cryoablations in Toledo, Ohio, although by different doctors.

DCIS was rarely diagnosed 30 years ago, according to an article written by Tiffany O'Callaghan published in the November 2012 edition of *Reader's Digest.* O'Callaghan's full story was published in the June 27, 2012, issue of NewScientist (newscientist.com) under the headline, "Cancer cuts: Is all breast cancer surgery necessary?"

DCIS could be regarded as a creation of modern medicine, as most cases are found through breast screening, wrote O'Callaghan. The fear is that screening may be leading us to cut out lumps that, left alone, would never have caused a problem. DCIS now makes up about a quarter of breast cancer cases found through screening, she reported. "In the United States, the incidence has grown more than sixfold since the 1980s."

When Jerome Groopman was interviewed by NPR, he said, "Usually doctors are right, but conservatively about 15% of all people are misdiagnosed. Some experts think it's as high as 20 to 25%. And in half of those cases, there is serious injury or even death to the patient."

In his book, Groopman talks about how so-called evidence-based medicine is rapidly becoming the canon in hospitals. "Treatments outside the statistically proven are considered taboo," he stated.

Groopman said today's rigid reliance on evidence-based medicine risks having the doctor choose care passively, solely by the numbers; statistics embody averages, not individuals. He noted that statistics cannot substitute for the human being before you.

The *Reader's Digest* article tells the story about a 28-year-old photographer who was diagnosed with DCIS. The woman found it bizarre that a mastectomy was recommended. "How can they cut off one of your boobs for something that's not going to kill you?" she asked.

That was Victoria's position in January 2008 when the biopsy was done. However, she never anticipated contracting a seemingly incurable infection in which all evidence leads back to the biopsy. It wasn't the cancer diagnosis that dogged her; it was the infection and a foreign object in her breast – the apparent source of the infection.

Victoria needed a medical doctor with hospital privileges to help her. The only doctors who wanted to help her did not have hospital privileges or surgical expertise. Those who did turned their backs. They dropped her like a hot potato.

But the infection was real. Here is the case-by-case summary:

- Positive for infection, negative for cancer – 2009: A fluid sample from Victoria's right breast discharge was submitted December 1, 2009 to LabCorp by Dr. Theodore Rozema. The culture confirmed staphylococcus. Dr. Rozema's testing and examinations indicated Victoria was cancer-free.
- Positive for infection, negative for cancer – 2010: A radiology report on a breast MRI bilateral from January 5, 2010, ordered by Dr. Suzanne Hoekstra at Park Ridge Hospital in Hendersonville, North Carolina reported that "findings may be due to infectious or inflammatory change," and that diffuse abnormal enhancement of the right breast is "most compatible with active infectious or inflammatory process."
- Negative for cancer – 2010: Dr. Hoekstra advised Victoria on April 2, 2010 that there were no blood vessels feeding the scar tissue, based on an ultrasound, and therefore no cancer – only scar tissue from the cryoablation.
- Positive for infection – 2010: A second fluid sample from Victoria's right breast was submitted July 2, 2010 to LabCorp by Dr. Theodore Rozema. The culture confirmed corynebacterium, typically associated with medical device infections such as a heart value that contains metal.
- A cytology report (examination of cells) on July 15, 2010 from Pathology Consultants, Inc., in Greenville, South Carolina, ordered by Dr. Gayle Blouin on discharge fluid from Victoria's right breast did not confirm cancer, but rather "atypical ductal cells and foam cells present" and the probability of infection.

("Atypical cells are cells that appear abnormal under a microscope, but they aren't necessarily cancerous. The presence of atypical cells is sometimes referred to as 'dysplasia.' Many factors can make normal cells appear atypical, including inflammation and infection. Even normal aging can make cells appear abnormal," according to the website, mayoclinic.com. This is also an expected result when breast tissue has experienced cryoablation.)

(In Victoria's mind, she was going to see Dr. Gayle Blouin at her private office in Greenville, South Carolina with high hopes that the physician would image the breast, find the marker, and remove it. "That was my plan.")

- Negative for infection – 2011: Using a tissue sample from a needle biopsy, a 5-day culture ordered by Dr. Wade Banker at Mercy St. Anne Hospital in Toledo, Ohio, was negative for bacteria on a January 12, 2011 report.
- Positive for cancer – 2011: When looking at the right breast, Dr. Banker (Toledo, Ohio) said Victoria had a 70% chance of having cancer. Asked if he saw veins feeding the ablated site, he said no. Out of a sense of desperation, Victoria agreed to a second biopsy, with the doctor's promise that no marker would be placed. If it is an infection, the doctor said sometimes tissue being "stirred up" during a biopsy will allow healing. Based upon breast tissue that had been altered by cryoablation, the hospital's lab reported the cells were cancer.
- Negative for infection – 2011: The laboratory at Park Ridge Hospital in Hendersonville, North Carolina reported "no growth" on a culture, ordered by Dr. Michelle Leblanc grown over three days using an aspiration sample taken from Victoria's right breast. The culture was done December 6-8, 2011.
- Positive for infection – 2012: A biofeedback practitioner in Haywood County, North Carolina, identified the presence of mycoplasma bacteria on two separate occasions, January 10, and February 18, 2012, as well as metal allergy from a foreign object.
- Positive for infection – 2012: Medical diagnosis on Victoria's right breast by Dr. Rashid Buttar, in Cornelius, North Carolina reported on January 24, 2012 – breast fungating mass.
- Positive for infection – 2012: Dr. Rashid Buttar, in Cornelius, North Carolina, submitted blood work to LabCorp on March 3, 2012 that the physician said revealed a chromium deficiency and research connected the deficiency to an infection.

- Positive for infection – 2012: Lab tests performed March 22-26, 2012 on Victoria's right breast tissue at Tulane University Hospital in New Orleans, ordered by Dr. Surendra K. Purohit, confirmed presence of two organisms; staphylococcus epidermidis (University of Connecticut, Department of Molecular and Cell Biology, describes this as a "true opportunistic pathogen" particularly associated with foreign body infections; and enterococcus faecalis (can cause life-threatening infections in humans and is frequently found in root canal-treated teeth).
- Positive for cancer – 2012: Dr. Surendra K. Purohit insisted Victoria had cancer, after he performed a third biopsy. Dr. Purohit also wrote: "This patient had fungating mass for a long duration, which has been infected and necrotic." The fungating mass was the same conclusion reached by Dr. Rashid Buttar two months earlier.

The various tests confirmed that Victoria's infection was associated with a medical device, foreign body infection, an infection found in root canal-treated teeth, or all three.

Was Victoria a victim of snap judgments made by doctors with preconceived notions about what cancer must look like? Was the refusal to consider the presence of a metal marker actually a passive way of protecting a new cash cow in breast diagnostics, or was it ignorance?

Dr. Groopman suggested to NPR that doctors do make errors in thinking. "We use shortcuts. Most doctors, within the first 18 seconds of seeing a patient, will interrupt him telling his story and also generate an idea in his mind [of] what's wrong. And too often, we make what's called an anchoring mistake – we fix on that snap judgment."

Each time Victoria began telling her story, she was interrupted. "That's cancer," the doctors would say. "They acted like I was crazy."

Dr. Groopman's comments suggest that each time Victoria began telling her story, the doctor formed an opinion within the first 18 seconds. That is exactly what happened to Victoria, time and time again. There is no logical reason to believe otherwise.

Chapter 54

I don't need a leg

It was no secret that Victoria had no intention of giving another surgeon an opportunity to carve into her chest wall and reconstruct an artificial breast using her own skin or synthetic products, or silicone or saline implants.

"I don't know how my body would react to that, and I was not about to chance any more torture, pain or allergic reactions. Besides, my breast and my nipple were part of my womanhood and produced sexual feelings. An artificial breast can't bring that back."

Victoria waited seven months following the mastectomy before she was emotionally prepared to deal with the purchase of a breast prosthesis.

It was October 2012. Several factors were at play. Her annual insurance deductible was about to expire. She had met the deductible after the hospital surgery. If she didn't make the purchase soon, she'd be paying out of her pocket to reach her $1,000 deductible.

Her wardrobe was somewhat limited, especially when she wanted to wear a tight-fitting top. And she was scheduled to drive her mother to meet her sister at Navarre Beach, Florida for their annual November rendezvous.

"I might as well get it behind me," she thought.

Over the previous five years, Victoria had received a college-equivalent education in the areas of filing insurance claims, oral pathology related to breast cancer, cryoablation, and non-invasive cancer treatment protocols. She was about to get another education, one she was not expecting.

The first breast fitter Victoria visited was a breast-only business. However, the owner's business was so small that Victoria's insurance company, Blue Cross and Blue Shield, would not allow the business into the insurance network.

Victoria inquired about the cost, and was shocked at the $300 price tag for the prosthesis, and she was even more horrified when told that she must have a doctor's script in order to make the purchase and have it paid by insurance.

"Why? My insurance company had on record that they paid for a mastectomy. You can't look and see that you don't have a breast? I have to pay a doctor to write something that is obvious? This doesn't make sense, unless it's all about money."

Victoria's new education was beginning.

As she turned into a parking lot in front of a second breast prosthesis business, Victoria was confronted with a huge pink ribbon display, the folded pink ribbon that signifies October as Breast Cancer Awareness Month. The ribbon must have been three feet high and one foot wide. There was no way to miss seeing it hanging under the sign next to the entrance.

Victoria about gagged as she was overwhelmed with all the pink paraphernalia being used to brainwash women.

She walked in the door at the mastectomy services business, and soon learned that it was a full-service orthotic and prosthetic facility. Victoria wasn't exactly prepared for what she was about to see as she waited. She noticed a man sitting in a chair, and then she watched as he reached down and removed his artificial leg below his knee and then handed the prosthetic to the fitter for an adjustment.

She realized for the first time that she had walked into a business setting that dealt with people who have missing body parts. "I've got an imperfection. I'm handicapped, that's what I was thinking. I knew from this point on I'd have to order a part to look whole in my clothes."

Victoria was informed that the breast fitter is "so busy, you'll have to make an appointment" for four days later.

If you find yourself laughing at any point in this chapter, you're in good company. Victoria and I laughed out loud many times as we compiled the sequence of events. At times, we wanted to cry. Imagine! So many women are losing their breasts that she had to wait for four days to be "fitted." But much of this tragedy is pure comedy. Since laughter is good for the soul, you might as well sit back and have an old fashion horse laugh as you read.

As Victoria gazed in a wall-mounted display case containing breast forms and bras, she asked if the prosthetic came with a bra.

"Did your doctor give you a script for a bra?" the receptionist asked.

Victoria handed the receptionist a script for a prosthesis only. "Would you like a bra? We'll call your doctor," the receptionist said. A script for the bra is also required.

"Why is this so complicated?" Victoria thought. "I'm already irritated." The prosthesis would not work with a bra that could be purchased at a department store without the doctor's script. The specialty bra has a built-in pocket that holds the artificial breast form. "If you didn't have that, it would fall out."

When Victoria returned, the receptionist spoke warmly of the fitter Victoria was about to meet. "She's very nice and you'll feel comfortable with her." Even so, Victoria was apprehensive. "I certainly would not have wanted a man to do this."

On the return visit, Victoria waited in the reception area until it was her turn. The fitter pointed down the hallway. "We will be going to the last door on the left," she said. Victoria was about to be shocked, again.

As her eyes peered down the hallway, she was greeted by a hot looking, full-size female mannequin dressed in all pink and wearing a pink feather boa, a fashion accessory usually worn around a woman's neck. Instantly, Victoria thought of Gypsy Rose Lee, the American burlesque entertainer famous for her striptease act. "Let me entertain you."

Not to be outdone by the humor of the moment, Victoria observed that the mannequin was exhibiting a perfect physique, a low-cut dress that exposed both of her voluptuous breasts. "I didn't think I'd be going in that room for a new leg," Victoria quipped. The fitter did not respond to her humor with much emotion. "Maybe that's part of her training," Victoria thought. "Since I didn't do the chemo and radiation, I was feeling and looking a little perkier than most of the fitter's clients."

She wasn't expecting the extent of the next pink shock. But that's what she got as she walked through the door. "It was absurd." Pink couch. Adult-sized tea party table with two chairs, all yellow and pink. The whole room was a combination of yellow and pink. It was an adult-sized dollhouse effect.

"We're in fantasy land with this pink crap, it doesn't matter that I lost my breast. They treat women like fools. It's

presentation instead of substance. I really wanted to throw up. I'll act like I'm at a tea party in lah lah land. I wish they put French imported champagne in those cups. I might be able to take this a little easier."

Victoria sat on the pink couch. The fitter asked for her bra size. Victoria said her sister had always wanted her to go to Victoria's Secret and be professionally measured for a bra. Finally, this was Victoria's chance to be professionally measured, or was it?

"Do you have to measure me?" Victoria asked. "No, I can tell by looking," the fitter replied, but the fitter asked for the bra size anyway.

The fitter returned from an adjacent room that was loaded with bras carrying a 34-A and a silicone breast form. Victoria informed the fitter that she was highly allergic to many things and she was concerned about the gel-type material in some prosthetics that were designed to adhere to the skin.

"Another lady had the same problem," the fitter said. "If it happens, we can exchange yours for one that doesn't have the adhesive gel."

Victoria was given a few minutes in a private setting to try on the bra. The fitter said, "Yes, this works for you."

Victoria's insurance pays for one prosthesis every two years and four bras annually.

The fitter shared that her mother had breast cancer and a mastectomy. Victoria immediately wanted to share what she knew about the trigger for breast cancer. "I thought to myself, I know that woman's got dental issues." When Victoria returned several days later to pick up three bras that were on back order, she saw the fitter in the parking lot and used the occasion to privately hand her a copy of the book that changed her own life (*Am I Dead?*).

"I told her, your mother has dental issues. You must read this book and get them corrected."

"I couldn't in good conscience fail to tell her about the oral pathology connection to breast cancer. Besides, she could help a lot of women, most of whom will be purchasing prostheses and still have the trigger for their breast cancer in their mouth." No amount of chemo or radiation will take that away.

Victoria also wondered about the emotional toll on the attractive young lady that was helping her. Surely, seeing women all day with scarred chest walls would have to affect your psyche. "Looking at scars on women with missing breasts all day, I would be stressed out."

"When I was her age, the last thing on my mind was losing a breast. But this girl is seeing it daily. The horrors of mastectomies are hitting her in the face constantly. To make matters worse, most women have had chemo and lost their hair and look like death warmed over."

Then there's the propaganda the young breast fitter must hear. If your mother had breast cancer, then you're probably going to have breast cancer too, which is not true. There is a genetic connection and it's the mouth. "I watched my sister fall for that," said Victoria.

Before leaving the store, Victoria was presented with a box that resembled a miniature hat case – pink, of course. It was a carrying case designed specifically to hold and protect the prosthesis. Victoria didn't know whether to laugh or cry. After all, it didn't even match her black American Tourister luggage.

Victoria's purchases included a round box that resembled a miniature hat case – pink, of course. It was a carrying case designed specifically to hold and protect the breast prosthesis.

It was a round case with a zipper. When placed in the carrying case, the prosthesis is nestled in white netting, something similar to hair netting used by restaurant employees. To clean the prosthesis, it's washed in biodegradable dishwashing liquid and air dried. "To my surprise, it dried fairly quickly."

Becoming a Certified Mastectomy Fitter is more than joining an organization. Applicants must pass a training course mandated by the American Board for Certification in Orthotics, Prosthetics & Pedorthics, an organization established in 1948.

What does the training course require?

According to the ABC website (abcop.org), an applicant must possess a high school diploma, GED, or college education, document 500 hours of mastectomy fitting experience, and finish the Fitter Educational Course.

What does the fitter course require?

The applicant pays a $300 fee and must complete eight hours of training, most of which can be done by home study or the internet. A minimum of two hours is required for lab work that includes measuring techniques, product choices, and practicing patient etiquette, in other words kindness, compassion and sensitivity training.

Fitters with 1-4 years experience can expect a salary ranging from $26,400 to $38,710, according to a national salary schedule in 2012.

Most fitters get into this business with the sincere intention of helping women who have lost a breast. "They don't realize that their business is part of a larger equation that is feeding the cancer industry's bottom line."

There are no reliable numbers that reflect the number of women who actually have a mastectomy each year. Nor are there any reliable figures that tell us how many woman proceed with breast reconstruction. However, Victoria had to wait four days after requesting an appointment before she could see the breast fitter. That should tell you something.

"I'll bet the larger percentages of women are getting the plastic surgery," says Victoria. One plastic surgery website says, "There's nothing wrong with wanting to self-improve."

Victoria's question is basic: "Why does society make women feel like they must have breast surgery to feel like they have improved their body? I think it makes it much easier for an oncologist to sell a woman on getting both breasts reconstructed."

No business can survive unless it has a market in which to sell its wares. It's supply and demand. If a breast fitting business can survive in a 2013 economy, imagine how huge the business of cutting off women's breasts must be. The business was so busy there was a waiting period to see the fitter. Victoria found this very surprising.

Add the obvious absurdities such as special training to ask bra size with proper patient etiquette, getting a medical doctor to write a script so you can buy a prosthesis, and a separate script to buy the special bra that holds the prosthesis in place. No woman in a post-mastectomy state should be without a pink miniature carrying case, either.

In all seriousness, certified mastectomy fitters do serve a purpose for women who are dealing with emotional issues like their self-image. The fitters do no harm; the mutilation was done by oncologists, breast cancer doctors, and surgeons, the same professionals that prescribe chemotherapy and radiation treatments that leave women hairless.

And what's the fix for no hair? Another business model has sprung up to grab some of the cancer industry's ripe profits – hats, head wraps, scarves, wigs, and turbans – all shapes, sizes, colors, styles and materials. There's nothing wrong with chemo survivors covering their bald heads for their self esteem. There is a crime involved here, however.

The crime is with medical doctors who will rarely tell a woman that she has other viable options, including not losing her hair, and therefore not needing the wigs, wraps and scarves. In fact, women have options that can keep them from losing their breasts, too. They just don't know about them.

There's another crime, and the FDA is to blame. Unlike Victoria, hundreds of thousands of women choose plastic surgery and breast implants.

Reconstruction for Victoria was not prohibited. It was a choice because of her known reactions to foreign substances and her knowledge about the untruthfulness of medical doctors when it comes to safety issues. She personally knew two women in California who had health issues because of their implants.

However, even Victoria was shocked to discover the level of fraud being perpetrated on women with breast implants where doctors insist they are "safe" and there's "minimal risks."

One of the country's leading authorities on breast implants is Ilena Rosenthal, author of the book, *Breast Implants: The Myths, the Facts, the Women.* She is the director of The Humantics Foundation for Women, and she heads the largest Breast Implant Support Group in the world (HumanticsFoundation.com).

Rosenthal tells how manufacturers and plastic surgeons flew around 400 women some years ago to lobby legislators in Washington, DC to pressure the FDA into reversing the ban on the use of silicone gel implants. In November 2006, Fox News reported that "the government ended a 14-year virtual ban on silicone-gel breast implants ... despite lingering safety concerns, making the devices available to tens of thousands of women who have clamored for them."

There appears to be no end in sight to the rising demand for breast implants.

Probably because I do so much research using the key word "breast," I received an email last November with a special offer: "Make this the breast Christmas ever. Breast augmentation special, $3,499."

This increasing demand has happened although early studies, which had been long hidden by manufacturers, were resurrected, explained Rosenthal in a commentary in which she referred to breast implants as "America's silent epidemic." The studies proved manufacturers knew that their implants would break, immune reactions would occur, the gel would migrate, and "even more disturbing, could cross the placenta and affect unborn fetuses," she said.

Women who complain about their implants are labeled as crazies, fear mongers and whackos. "This is exactly how I felt every time I went to a doctor complaining about my breast pain, infection, and a foreign object that I could feel in my breast," said Victoria.

If a doctor would not acknowledge the possibility of an adverse reaction in the breast caused by a foreign object placed during a biopsy, they certainly will resist admitting that a breast implant could be causing bad reactions and serious health issues in women.

Yet, according to Rosenthal, indisputable evidence was released in October 2000, when the FDA published a landmark study of implanted women, many still without symptoms. The study revealed that 69% of these women had at least one ruptured implant, most without any knowledge of it.

"When it happens to you, the rupture rate is 100%," said Dr. David Feigal, director of the Center for Devices and Radiological Health at the FDA.

According to Rosenthal, by January 2000, over 127,000 women had written the FDA about the serious complications they were experiencing from their silicone gel implants. Yet the implants are still legal.

Dogs get better treatment. An FDA investigation in 2007 prompted a limited dog food recall but continued investigation and monitoring expanded the recall effort. In spite of intense lobbying, the FDA refused to buckle to the pet food industry.

But they wasted little time in buckling to the breast implant lobby. Women should be ecstatic that their dogs garnered more concern from the FDA than problems with silicone implants.

"The tragedy is that still today," said Rosenthal, women who are having problems with silicone breast implants "are unable to get good medical care as the majority of doctors refuse to believe the connection."

And silicone implants alone are causing women serious health issues. In spite of 50,000 reports of serious adverse reactions from water-filled implants, the FDA still gave their safety approval.

Nearly 40% of post-mastectomy patients who had reconstructive surgery with implants must have additional surgeries within three years, according to the manufacturers' own studies.

If you are a woman with silicone or saline breast implants, and you have never had a health issue related to the breast enhancement surgery, you simply haven't lived long enough yet. The statistics are stacked against you. One study says there's a 90% chance that implants will rupture within 20 years.

Perhaps more disconcerting is the question, how many women are having health problems because of their breast implants, but they have not connected the dots and established the connection?

The same question applies to clips or markers being placed in a woman's breast as Standard of Care during a biopsy.

The cancer machine continues to be about money. It's a racket from start to finish.

Chapter 55

Mercury: Less hazardous in mouth?

"By any measure, the average American is not scientifically literate, even with a college degree." That's the conclusion of Robert M. Hazen writing for Action Bioscience (ActionBioscience.org). Hazen builds a strong case for understanding scientific issues in order to make informed personal choices. That's especially true when dealing with cancer and oral infections.

For example, consider the attitudes of many doctors that won't even engage in a rational discussion about the importance of healthy nutrition for whole-body wellness. Or the dentists who can't bring themselves to admit even a remote possibility that mercury in silver amalgam fillings is dangerous when placed in the mouth although they're required by the EPA to dispose of removed amalgams as hazardous wastes.

In an article credited to the Paracelsus Biological Medicine Network, Kathleen Muto wrote: "When they come to pick up already removed amalgam fillings in our separators for disposal they are dressed as if they are in a nuclear power plant. There it is, toxic hazardous waste, and we have had this in our mouths and bodies."

Even Dr. Mehmet Oz, whose March 28, 2013 TV show featured the subject "toxic teeth," could not get two dentists to address the real danger of silver amalgam fillings, which are more accurately defined as mercury fillings. While one dentist spoke of "growing evidence" that mercury fillings can be hazardous to a person's health, a second dentist claimed there was insufficient evidence to reach that conclusion.

Of course, the official position of the American Dental Association (ADA) is that dental amalgam (lots of mercury and a little silver) is harmless in the mouth. The ADA is a trade guild whose members are its main interest, not patients.

The Dr. Oz Show set off international fireworks. Five days after the show's broadcast, Freya Koss, publicist for the International

Academy of Oral Medicine and Toxicology (IAOMT), issued a press release accusing the American Dental Association of "lying through their teeth about mercury fillings."

Freya Koss is the same woman who literally begged Victoria nine years earlier to not have a root canal done on tooth #14.

Koss can speak with authority about mercury toxicity from personal experience. She was confined to a wheelchair because of the dangerous heavy metal. Koss previously worked with Consumers for Dental Choice (ToxicTeeth.org) and that's where Victoria first saw 'before and after' photos of Koss in 2004. "She looked like a completely different person after the mercury detoxification. She was walking and she looked 30 years younger."

The IAOMT took a hard line stance against allegations made by the ADA that there is no scientific evidence validating the harmful health effects of dental mercury fillings. The organization's legal counsel, James M. Love, said, "The ADA continues to support its self-serving view by denying that mercury fillings are dangerous. Clearly, public health is not an ADA priority."

Silver-colored dental amalgam fillings contain 50% mercury, a known neurotoxin, and the ADA's latest defense of these fillings came as a retort to Dr. Oz's broadcast entitled "Are Your Silver Fillings Making You Sick?"

The day following Dr. Oz's program, the ADA issued a press release accusing Dr. Oz of "sensationalism" and declaring that "not one credible scientific study" shows dental mercury is a health risk.

Contrary to the ADA's position, the IAOMT, in its press release, said hundreds of scientific studies were catalogued dating back over a century demonstrating that mercury in dental fillings is hazardous to human health. In fact, in 1845, the American Society of Dental Surgeons, the ADA's predecessor, required its members to pledge not to use amalgam because mercury was known to be extremely toxic, yet in 1859 the ADA was founded based on its endorsement of these controversial fillings.

In more recent years, Norway, Sweden, and Denmark have banned the use of mercury fillings, and other countries have restricted their use for pregnant women, children, and patients with kidney problems, the IAOMT reported.

In 1991 and 2003, the World Health Organization (WHO) confirmed that dental amalgam is the greatest source of human exposure to mercury in the general population, and in 2005, a WHO report listed adverse health effects caused by mercury exposure, cautioning, "Recent studies suggest that mercury may have no threshold below which some adverse effects do not occur."

The U.S. Food and Drug Administration (FDA) warned about dental mercury's potential neurotoxic effects on children and fetuses five years ago, but later removed the warning without explanation.

At a 2010 FDA Dental Products Panel meeting to discuss the health impacts of mercury amalgam fillings, Dr. Suresh Kotagal, a pediatric neurologist at the Mayo Clinic, concluded, "...I think that there is really no place for mercury in children."

The same FDA Panel encouraged consideration for limiting dental mercury for pregnant women and children, as well as labeling to warn consumers of the mercury risks. The public was told that FDA's ruling on the issue would be made by December 31, 2011. However, no action has been taken to date, according to the IAOMT.

IAOMT was founded upon the belief that "science" should be the basis upon which all diagnostic and treatment modalities be based. Amalgam risk assessments conducted in 1995, 2010, and 2012 by Dr. G. Mark Richardson, an expert to the European Union's Scientific Committee on Health and Environmental Risks (SCHER), revealed that toxic levels of mercury were released from dental fillings. Other risk assessments confirm these findings.

The IAOMT also stated: Additional "credible" scientific research released in 2012 includes a Yale University study substantiating occupational dental mercury exposure, two studies corroborating the harmful impacts of mercury fillings on children and adolescents, and a study demonstrating that maternal amalgam fillings release mercury into breast milk.

While dental schools continue to teach the 'safety' of silver amalgam (with mercury), the ADA continues to distance itself from responsibility for the harm being done to patients. "The ADA owes no legal duty of care to protect the public from allegedly dangerous products used by dentists. The ADA did not manufacture, design, supply or install the mercury-containing amalgams." That statement comes from a 1995 legal brief filed by ADA attorneys.

The IAOMT also confronted the ADA on its lobbying efforts. Last year, the ADA lobbied the U.S. Department of State to oppose a ban or limit on the use of amalgam fillings in connection with the United Nations Environment Programme's legally-binding mercury treaty. However, the treaty text agreed upon in January includes the global phase-down of dental mercury fillings.

"While worldwide action is being taken to protect humans and the environment from mercury, the ADA continues to mislead the public into believing that one of the most toxic elements on this planet somehow becomes less poisonous when it is placed in their mouths," said Dr. William Virtue, DDS, president of the IAOMT.

During the Dr. Oz Show broadcast, Dr. Oz participated in a live science experiment that measured the amount of mercury vapor being released while brushing teeth – and the amount was alarming – but no mention was made of the danger posed by simply entering the office of a dentist that places or removes mercury without taking special precautions.

Like it or not, a patient arriving for a composite filling in an office where mercury vapor is prevalent, is going to breathe the dangerous mercury vapor in the office air, whether it's released from the mouths of other patients that are having amalgams placed or removed, or from the patient's own mouth.

Neither was any mention made that the American Dental Association Health Foundation holds two patents on a so-called "improved" high-copper dental amalgam which critics claim releases much more mercury vapor than older dental amalgam. The United States Patent numbers are 4,018,600 (April 19, 1977) and 4,078,921 (March 14, 1978).

"I would gather that part of this debate is about money," Dr. Oz commented.

Historically, dentists have charged patients less for silver amalgam fillings than white fillings, but they are not doing their patients any favors by pushing a less expensive and dangerous material. The number of Americans that have mercury in their fillings is estimated at 100 million.

For at least four years, most knowledgeable insiders have reported that more than half of America's dentists are now mercury-free. Why did so many dentists really stop using mercury?

Twenty-five percent of mercury-free dentists responded to the realization that mercury in the mouth is dangerous and harmful. These dentists voluntarily stopped using mercury, received proper training to remove mercury, and outfitted their offices to provide a clean air environment in which to work and protect themselves, their staff, and their patients.

The other 25% stopped using mercury alright, but the reason had nothing to do with the health or safety of their patients. It had to do with the health of their pocketbooks. It was an economic necessity. Patients well versed in the dangers of mercury were not returning; they were looking for a mercury-free dentist.

A word for the wise: Beware of a so-called mercury-free dentist who does not believe mercury is harmful and beware of a dentist who offers a choice of silver amalgams or white fillings. In either case, you are in a lose-lose situation.

Many in the dental industry claim that new dental materials preclude the need to use silver amalgams containing mercury. It's true, there are new materials, but the major reason for the switch to non-mercury dental material is patient driven. That's the reality.

Chapter 56

Blindly follow advice of dentists

"Surprisingly, intense study of a particular field does not necessarily make one scientifically literate." Robert M. Hazen made this statement in an article posted at Action Bioscience (ActionBioscience.org). In other words, doctors and dentists don't necessarily have an edge over private citizens who are willing to read and research. Victoria discovered this truth the hard way. Her story has the potential to save millions of women from the fear and oppression she was forced to endure.

It's a good thing we have private citizen researchers like Victoria, and people like George Meyers and his wife, Janet, friends of mine from Jacksonville, Florida, who are also willing to share the fruits of their research labor. They publish an 'occasional paper' named The Cascade Commentary (6045 University Club Blvd. N, Jacksonville, Florida 32277), and they are not a bit shy about telling their readers straight out what they discover. George, who has a PhD, is the commentator in the family and Janet is the contributing editor.

In their July 2012 newsletter, they posed this question: Do you have a family member or friend with cancer?

As with anyone who writes about cancer treatments, they included the obligatory disclaimer in their newsletter, where they make mention of the numerous references cited and many quotations used from other documents. "The remarks made are the views, opinions and the result of the research of the commentator and contributing editor. No organization has contributed to it unless specifically referenced."

Because they are not medical doctors, their newsletter has an authentic feel about it that anyone who is already reading this book will appreciate. Their information has been edited and condensed with permission. By the way, George and Janet always encourage their readers to conduct their own research.

What follows is condensed material from their newsletter:

A Personal Testimony

In October 2011 we lost a dear Ethiopian friend, Woineshet Feyissa, age 40, to breast cancer. She had lived in the U.S. 10 years and we had become close friends.

We spent a lot of time doing research in the two-plus years following her diagnosis helping her explore alternative possibilities to the usual treatment prescribed by her physician: surgery, chemotherapy and radiation (cut, poison and burn), which she rejected outright.

We helped her pursue some alternative possibilities that may have helped to prolong her life. However, because her insurance would not cover any of her medical expenses if she did not comply, during the last year of her life she reluctantly submitted to the chemo and radiation treatments prescribed by the oncologist. Her quality of life was absolutely horrible that last year and she regretted having had the treatments.

In her home country of Ethiopia, cancer is rare! We wonder why our dear friend and so many American women got breast cancer.

Root Canal Dangers

George and Janet proceed to quote from Lee Euler's *Cancer Defeated* Newsletter #189 (CancerDefeated.com).

"You need a root canal" is now nearly as common as hearing you need a filling. Certainly dentists are aware that people don't want to lose their teeth. There may be a lot more at risk than simply loss of a tooth.

In the early 1900s, Weston A. Price, DDS, and Dr. Charles Mayo (founder of the Mayo Clinic) conducted research on 1,000 extracted teeth in which root canals had been done.

Dr. Price's work was deliberately buried for 70 years, and continues to be derided and suppressed by medical and dental professionals alike.

Now the founder of the association of root canal specialists, Dr. George E. Meinig, DDS, FACD has joined Drs. Price and Mayo in speaking out about its risks.

We covered the whole root canal story years ago in a Special Report called, *The Secret Poison in Your Mouth.* Observing patients in his dental practice, Dr. Price became suspicious that teeth with root canals always remained infected despite treatment.

Root Canals and Breast Cancer

The cancer connection has also been studied by Dr. Robert Jones, clinical senior lecturer, Institute of Cancer Sciences. He found an extremely high correlation between root canals and breast cancer. His five-year study of 300 breast cancer cases showed:

- 93% of women with breast cancer had root canals.
- 7% show other oral pathology (disease issues).
- Usually these tumors occurred on the same side of the body as the root canal or other oral pathology.

Dr. Jones found that toxins from the bacteria in an infected tooth or jawbone can inhibit the specific proteins that suppress tumor development. His findings were confirmed by a University of Michigan study about protein suppression (meaning that the bacteria interfere with the natural cancer fighting process).

The German physician Dr. Josef Issels found that 97% of his terminal cancer patients had root canals.

Incidentally, no cancer cure can kill the microbes inside a root canal. That may explain the reason some people effectively treat cancer with alternative treatments, then later regress and die anyway. It's also a reason many alternative doctors won't even start a treatment regimen until all root canals are removed.

Root Canal Cover-Up

In the early '90s, Dr. George Meinig, an endodontist (root canal surgeon) practiced root canal therapy and taught the subject to others. He spent 18 months of intensive study of the meticulous 25-year root canal research found in Dr. Price's *Dental Infections*, and in 1993, Dr. Meinig published, *Root Canal Cover-Up.*

The author of the article quoted throughout this commentary, Lee Euler, doesn't believe anyone should ever get a root canal.

Personal Testimony Found Online

Wow, where do I start? wrote Tracy Parish, CPRW (TrendSettingResumes.com). This book saved my life (*Am I Dead? ... or do I just feel like it).*

I had a root canal (a back left molar) bothering me and also had a constant headache on the back left side of my head. I was living on pain meds and noticed when my root canal was re-done by an endodontist that the headache went away for a few weeks. So I knew it was related to the root canal.

My thermal imaging showed hot spots in the left side of my mouth where all four of my root canals reside. I also had a streak coming down from the left jaw, down the left side of my neck, and into the left breast! He tells in the book how breast cancer (and many other cancers and diseases) start in the teeth and jaw and then spread to the breast or body but always stay on the same side of the body as the problem in the mouth. He was right and this was a very visual picture of that happening!

A biological dentist identified which root canal was the biggest problem and worked on that tooth and from that moment on I've had no headaches.

I'm a believer! The author was wonderful and gave me lots of tips and advice on what to do for my health – much of it is low-cost or no-cost and is working miracles in my life so far! I feel they saved my life.

Medical Doctor's Personal Testimony

For years, environmental physicians have been taught by dentists that "disease begins in the mouth or in the dentist's office," wrote Allan Lieberman, MD, FAAEM, medical director, Center for Occupational and Environmental Medicine (Charleston, South Carolina).

We have heard over and over again that silver mercury amalgams, root canals and cavitations were making us all sick. Although indoctrinated with this information I am not sure we truly believed it. But something recently happened that is changing my opinion.

One of my patients brought me the book, *Am I Dead? ... or do I just feel like it*, which she asked me to read. She has Parkinson's disease and literally left no stone unturned to find help in reversing her disease.

The research thesis is that cancer always occurs on the side of the body where oral pathology occurs. This observation was based on using thermography of the breasts and face.

If this observation is not enough to awe you, the book reports that most neurodegenerative diseases such as Parkinson's, ALS, Alzheimer's and MS are associated with the right-sided oral disease. There is also the corollary – for prevention, do not inflict any of these oral diseases by using root canals, silver-mercury amalgams and causing cavitations at sites of dental extractions, especially wisdom teeth.

We are doing breast, thyroid and peripheral artery thermography, but up until now, have not looked for oral disease even though it is so easy to do. This has now changed and we are adding thermography of the mouth to every breast exam we do and will certainly look for oral disease on every patient presenting with neurodegenerative disease.

The question we are all asking: Is this data real?

I have personally heard Hal Huggins, author of several books on dangers of mercury amalgams and root canals (one title is *It's All In Your Head*), tell a woman with breast cancer that if she wanted to live, she needed to pull out every root canal in her mouth. I know she survived.

The new research suggests that unless you correct the oral pathology you will never be free of a reoccurrence.

It is important for my readers to understand how the oral pathology influences or causes cancer. Genetics loads the gun but the environment pulls the trigger. There are chemical triggers like the P53 gene that induces a cell to die a natural death rather than undergo a malignant transformation. The toxicity that comes from root canals and other oral pathology suppresses the good P53 gene thus promoting cancer. Other good genes are also down regulated or suppressed while up regulating bad genes resulting in cancerous cellular changes.

As it is so easy to do thermography of the mouth, I am asking all of our patients who have undergone breast thermography to add testing of their mouth to see if oral pathology from root canals, amalgams and cavitations exist. If present, we will strongly recommend consultation with a biological dentist. This recommendation also applies to any patient with a neurodegenerative disease.

Using our present treatment protocols, we have been able to reverse abnormal breast pathology. If we correct any oral pathology, would we be able to reverse breast and neurodegenerative diseases even more effectively? This is a challenge we can't afford to not try.

George and Janet Ask a Question

If you have enough interest to have read this far, what will you do with the information you have just read? Will you blindly follow the advice of your dentist? Will you do further research on your own to make a well-informed, long-term decision?

Chapter 57

Firing near chest wall scares me

Many women who know for a fact that they have clips or markers in one or both breasts may not have been too concerned about the health implications until they read Victoria's story. After all, their doctors assured them the metal was harmless. For some women, the metal may be harmless, at least today.

Finally there's a dialogue about clips and markers. Many women have a track record with breast clips and markers; they've had the devices in their bodies for five, seven, even nine years without apparent problems. But what about 15 or 20 years from now? Will all be well then? What about women who have a breast marker and don't know it. Could their health issues be related?

If you are a woman who has a marker and is concerned, how will you get rid of this foreign object?

That question raises a whole round of new questions:

- Is there any place in the U.S. that a woman can go to have a breast biopsy clip or marker safely removed?
- Can the tiny pieces of metal be located without relying on large doses of radiation?
- Can the metal be safely removed without mutilating remaining breast tissue?
- What is the procedure if the foreign object is not metal?
- Is there a doctor who will perform this surgery while treating the patient with respect?

The research for this book yielded one possible answer, a radiologist in South Carolina with a 21-year track record. "She was the first doctor with enough compassion to try and remove a marker from a woman's breast that I had met."

The doctor's compassion comes naturally. It's who she is. The doctor's extensive knowledge comes, in part, from her association with one of the major suppliers of breast biopsy devices.

Three-quarters of the doctors in the U.S. know absolutely nothing about metal clips or markers being routinely placed in a woman's breast.

411

The quarter of the doctors who do know about the Standard of Care procedure firmly deny that a breast clip or marker can pose a potential danger to a woman's health, much less be the source of pain and discomfort or even a trigger for infection.

You can't fix a problem if you don't know or refuse to admit that you have one.

Because of this denial, women face another difficult challenge. The doctors who are willing to remove a clip or marker from a breast are few and far between, and those who have experience doing this without causing further damage to the delicate tissue in a woman's breast are even more scarce.

Victoria located a customer care website for the Suros breast biopsy system in November 2010 that led her to a female board certified radiologist in Anderson, South Carolina, who graduated from the Medical University of South Carolina in Charleston. The doctor worked with Suros Surgical Systems in customer service. A Suros system was used on Victoria's breast in 2008, according to her biopsy dictation report.

Suros is a subsidiary of Hologic, Inc., which develops and manufactures imaging technology.

Dr. Paige Huber's office wasn't far from Greenville, South Carolina and was close enough that Victoria could make the drive from her North Carolina home in less than 90 minutes. The office is a few miles off Interstate 85. Victoria's first appointment was several years ago on November 23, 2010.

Victoria was already accustomed to doctors talking down to her. She was disarmed by Dr. Huber's warm smile and greeting. Instinctively, Victoria knew she had found a doctor that was following her professional training, but had not abandoned her compassion for her patients.

When Dr. Huber looked at Victoria's breast for the first time, she said, "Bless your heart. That must be painful." Dr. Huber did something else that Victoria deeply appreciated. After visually looking at Victoria's breast, the radiologist did not declare that she had cancer, as so many doctors had done.

It was also apparent that Dr. Huber connected with her patients by listening, and she did not attempt to malign breast ablations as

412

other doctors had done. She readily admitted she knew nothing about them, and had no opinion on them.

Dr. Huber's demeanor was "delightful," according to Victoria, and the radiologist appeared to be filled with zest and energy.

Until meeting Dr. Huber, Victoria had no idea that the radiologist had removed breast markers before. During Victoria's consult, the radiologist said she had recently removed a breast marker, but the procedure failed on the next lady who asked to have hers taken out. Why did it fail? Dr. Huber discovered that the marker was encased in a biodegradable mesh, which must dissolve and 'release' the marker before any surgery could take place.

Why was a breast clip being embedded with mesh? Victoria was told by Dr. Huber, "Without the mesh, the markers were migrating." This is the tale of two "don'ts."

"I wonder how many women don't know they have a breast clip or marker and they don't know it's moving around," said Victoria. "Do they have sharp pains in the breast and don't know why? Are they wondering why there's a strange sensation in their breast?"

In Dr. Huber's practice, the radiologist requires a mammogram to pinpoint a marker, and the doctor fully understood Victoria's refusal to have one because of the swelling and an understanding of the pain that would have been involved. "She knew I was in pain. It would have killed me."

"But she was nice about it all," Victoria said. It was an independent imaging center and women were marching in and out in droves to have their mammograms.

The office was being remodeled during Victoria's first visit. "To my surprise, Dr. Huber did not charge for the consultation." Dr. Huber is the only doctor in Victoria's five-year ordeal that was not paid out-of-pocket or by her insurance company.

Victoria's second visit came 27 months later on February 20, 2013. She was still trying to prove the presence of a foreign object in her breast. Everything in her life turned upside down after her ultrasound-guided stereotactic breast biopsy in January 2008.

In regards to breast biopsy technology, "You are the smartest doctor I've been to," Victoria told the radiologist. "She was the first doctor who spoke of a marker like it existed; it was not just a figment of my imagination."

Victoria had acquired copies of more medical records from the Hope Cancer Center in Asheville, and this included a mammogram and ultrasound images taken at the time of the biopsy. The mammogram was taken before the stabbing in Victoria's breast and wasn't expected to reveal any foreign object.

But Victoria believed there was an outside chance the ultrasound images might solve the mystery. However, they were only images used to guide the biopsy probe, and they were of no value in identifying a foreign object(s) in her breast.

Many biopsy devices have been marketed in the past 15 years, and there are dozens of metal clips, markers or wires in every imaginable shape and size, some of which are embedded in a biodegradable mesh, and others are coated with a material that dissolves over a few weeks or months and becomes 'invisible' with typical imaging applications. For many women, there is a narrow window of opportunity to image the device in order to have it removed without excessive mutilation of breast tissue.

As she sat within an arm's length of Dr. Huber, Victoria kept her composure although she realized that Dr. Surendra Purohit in New Orleans had sealed the fate of ever retrieving any physical proof.

Whether there was a piece of metal or even plastic left in her breast, either purposely (Standard of Care) or accidentally, Dr. Purohit had destroyed the evidence. Although he identified two infections, he failed to order an extended culture on the tissue, perhaps a 60-day growing time that might have finally identified one or more additional deadly infections.

The real tragedy is that Dr. Purohit probably did not destroy the evidence with malicious intent. He simply didn't believe his patient's claims or respect her wishes, and the easiest way for him to be paid by the insurance company was for Victoria to have cancer, not an infection.

Meanwhile, Dr. Huber continues to work with Suros in a testing capacity, and stated that she does not hesitate to tell the engineers from the manufacturer when a product is not working properly or might have design flaws.

Although Dr. Huber routinely places a clip during all breast biopsies, she declines to place a marker in a lymph node on the outside chance the metal might migrate and enter the lymphatic system.

In April 2007, Suros Surgical Systems issued a news release describing clinical findings with the company's first vacuum assisted, spring loaded core biopsy device, the Suros Celero™. Dr. Huber was instrumental in testing the company's product.

"Only two to three samples are needed for a diagnosis and DCIS staging with only two samples," wrote Dr. Huber. "While many physicians are accustomed to 6-10 needle insertions for spring loaded core biopsies, Celero needs only 2-3 insertions to gain the same results."

One benefit to firing and collecting tissue in two separate steps, the news release stated, is that it allows for confirmation. "I can place and confirm the aperture is where desired before firing the outer cannula and taking the sample," Dr. Huber reported.

According to the Suros company, more than 550,000 ultrasound guided core needle biopsy procedures are performed annually, primarily with spring loaded core devices. "The number of diagnostic breast biopsies is increasing every year," the Suros news release said. That statement was issued in April 2007.

In March 2008, Dr. Brian S. Englander, who held several positions including director of imaging at the Integrated Breast Center of Pennsylvania Hospital, prepared a 'white paper' on advanced technologies in women's healthcare. "Over one million women undergo surgical procedures each year to diagnose an abnormality found during mammography," he said.

While reviewing a new device manufactured by Suros, Dr. Englander wrote: Until a decade ago, the only alternative to a surgical biopsy was the use of fine-needle aspiration, but the procedure could "not distinguish between ductal carcinoma in situ (DCIS) and infiltrating carcinoma."

Dr. Englander said many physicians found vacuum-assisted techniques rather cumbersome, making them "difficult to use in the handheld biopsy arena where ultrasound technology is employed." As a handheld, disposable device, the Suros Celero overcame these difficulties, he explained.

Dr. Huber wrote a paper in which she described looking for a breast biopsy device "to use in those challenging lesions such as those located in the axilla, near the chest wall, nipple, or near implants." She found it in the Suros device, she said.

She also wrote that "firing near the chest wall scares me to death with the currently available 14-gauge spring loaded core device because it dives, and must be fired within the breast. The pre-fire option is nice because it allows sampling of the lymph nodes deep in the axilla without risk to adjacent structures."

Dr. Huber was unaware of the thousands of complaints that have been posted in recent years on internet websites and in the official database of the U.S. Food and Drug Administration. Dr. Huber works with one manufacturer's customer service and she was never clued in about equipment defects or patient complaints.

Chapter 58

Yes, even doctors get sick!

Dr. Connie Theisen, DC, lived "a fairly decent and healthy lifestyle" before suddenly experiencing a "rapid and progressive downward spiral." After several health professionals suggested a diagnosis of MS (multiple sclerosis) and offered a gloomy future, Dr. Theisen had a decision to make.

The chiropractor observed MS patients being prescribed drugs to suppress the condition and treat the discomfort but no one was ever healed, she said. "I chose to figure out the why. Why would I get this and what can I do to cure it?"

"A friend recommended I read the book, *Am I Dead? ... or do I just feel like it,* and that was the beginning of my life changing forever in the right direction." Dr. Theisen proceeded to have full-body thermal imaging that included scans of her mouth plus a digital panoramic dental x-ray and a tooth-by-tooth evaluation by Dr. Gary McCown. It was the same wellness path that Victoria followed.

Dr. Theisen's oral pathology included eight large silver amalgam fillings (50% mercury) and four jawbone infections at the site of her wisdom teeth extractions. Four mercury fillings were hidden under crowns.

The chiropractor was shocked at the outcome of her first dental visit. Two amalgam fillings were removed and two jawbone infections were cleaned up. "Before I was even out of the dental chair," she declared, "my double vision, slurred speech, and right arm pain was instantly gone."

Although she had a rubber dam in her mouth and was quite numb, she excitedly tried to tell the dentist her symptoms had suddenly vanished. "He couldn't understand me. He probably thought I was some crazy but he told me I could just relax and share the exciting news when we were all done. It is quite comical when I think back about it today."

Dr. Theisen's personal experience changed the way she conducts patient evaluations at her DC Wellness Center in

Minnesota. "I began to study what I was never taught in school about the health of our mouth and the connection with the rest of the body."

Chiropractors receive years of doctoral level training to discover the causes of disease in both children and adults; they don't just treat symptoms.

Dr. Theisen, 40, is no longer surprised when she finds an oral pathology connection with patients who have chronic disease and health challenges that haven't improved under the care of their primary physician or other health providers. "I know that we have saved hundreds of people from trouble down the road by evaluating their mouth."

The chiropractor admits to making an "amazing" observation. "Most of them will say, 'You know that tooth never really felt right but it didn't hurt.'"

"People need to understand that an absence of pain is not equivalent to meaning that you are healthy," says Dr. Theisen. "It simply means your body has not given you a signal that something is wrong, yet. With that being said we ask our patients about their oral health even if they are coming in for a wellness checkup, because we are a profession that promotes prevention of disease."

Not everyone readily accepts the oral pathology connection. "Some people just don't want to hear it, or it is outside of what they have been told for so many years. They look at me like I am just a chiropractor, for heaven sakes, and not a dentist."

One woman came to see Dr. Theisen with chronic mid-back pain and chest pain. "During the history I discovered not only does she have chronic pain but she also has anxiety, depression, sinus congestion, and adult onset acne. She is young and has 24 crowns in her mouth. Not one health practitioner has ever considered the health of her mouth."

Dr. Theisen is also fighting another battle that directly impacts her patients. It's an insurance battle where insurance companies attempt to limit their benefits. Victoria fought this battle too.

Practitioners that accept insurance, whether MD's, DO's, DC's or any other health professional, frequently are forced to offer certain treatments and not offer other services, she says. "Rarely is the decision based on what the patient really needs [in the way of treatment]."

"Even in our profession, some chiropractors are offered bonuses for staying under a payout quota from the insurance companies. These bonuses can be thousands of dollars," says Dr. Theisen. In such situations, are doctors and other health professionals tempted to refrain from care so they can get their bonus?

We can also rephrase the question: Do doctors get bonuses from insurance companies when they limit certain screenings, or when they administer certain drugs?

Dr. Theisen is so angry at the practices of Blue Cross and Blue Shield of Minnesota, especially as the practices apply to chiropractors, that she has converted her practice to cash only. She notified her patients that she was no longer willing to be "bullied and blackmailed ... and risk the health of our patients by not being able to provide them what they deserve."

Chapter 59

Outrage: Good for flush, not steady diet

By now, readers should understand that the real terror behind a breast cancer diagnosis is not the tumor.

- The terror is not the mental trauma that plagues the mind and triggers thoughts of death or bodily disfigurement.
- The terror is not about the staggering and life-altering financial burden that accompanies a cancer diagnosis.
- The real terror comes from a group of highly regarded professionals that Western civilization holds in god-like regard – the cancer doctors who push the drugs and radiation for the pharmaceutical industry, and do so using fear and intimidation.

In spite of numerous adverse reports appearing on the official database of the U.S. Food and Drug Administration and thousands of complaints posted on internet websites, the cancer industry has successfully kept breast biopsy clips or markers a 'dirty little secret' for nearly 15 years.

There are no long-term studies on what a breast biopsy marker is going to do to a woman after 10 or 20 years, much less 30 or 40 years, but it's already known how thousands of women are having negative reactions. For some women, a reaction occurs within hours or days. It is also insulting to tell women that a marker is necessary for subsequent scans; this is more for the doctor's convenience and continued treatment, not necessarily for a woman's health.

Even if a doctor could present a credible case for having a breast clip placed during a biopsy, what level of arrogance is necessary for the doctor to insert the marker and not tell each patient that the biopsy devices have a history of malfunctions and complications? How would the doctor know if the patient would not have an adverse reaction? There is no informed consent without providing details of the risks.

Why do women allow this to happen? Does this suggest a massive cover-up, or the voluntary surrender of the individual's health care responsibilities?

We might get some insight from comedian Jeff Foxworthy, who appeared on FOX television April 26, 2013, and noted that we only need visit a county fair to realize that all of us think our families are a little crazy. But they're really clueless in California.

Petitions were being passed around on the streets, asking signers to support the abolishment of the Bill of Rights. People young and old couldn't wait to sign, even after being told, "We want to take guns out of the hands of law-abiding citizens and be sure they're only in the hands of criminals."

Women could wield a lot of control over the breast cancer treatments that are available in this country, but they appear to have abdicated their power and responsibility.

In truth, it's both a failure on the part of women to unite on a single front, and the failure of doctors to inform patients about all the dangers associated with breast biopsy clips and the biopsy itself. One danger is that the biopsy needle can spread cancer cells as it's removed from a cancerous tumor. A doctor says the procedure is necessary, and women accept the doctor's claim without question.

Trey Gowdy, a South Carolina congressman, spoke about recent events in Benghazi where four Americans were killed in a terror attack and his analogies apply to women who have failed to come to their own party and demand the truth about options for both breast cancer diagnosis and treatment. It's the reason we don't let students grade their own papers, and we don't allow defendants to sentence themselves, said Gowdy.

Yet, women allow a doctor to put a foreign object in their breast and think nothing about it. Is this the new normal: Lie, stab, and place? There's quite a similarity with an archaic dental attitude: Drill, fill, and bill. It's all a set-up for additional treatment.

"Doctors get away with this for several reasons," Victoria believes.

- Women blindly allow it.
- Women are ambushed – told at the last possible moment about a clip – and sign a consent form under duress (their clothing is off, they have been anesthetized, and they're scared and intimidated).

- Doctors frequently don't tell the patient and proceed to place a clip without informed consent because they consider the markers Standard of Care. Too many doctors take the position that women don't need to know.

Grandmothers, mothers, daughters and granddaughters have been the breast cancer industry's guinea pigs. Breast markers obviously can't be tested for safety unless a living, breathing woman agrees to test them in the flesh of her own breast. They certainly can't be tested in a rat's breast.

Will women ever become outraged enough to put a stop to this? Someone once said: Outrage is good for a flush, but not a steady diet.

Having read this book, what should women be doing? Victoria has some ideas:

Women who want to be proactive with prevention should observe the proper precautions and preparations, and have full-body Digital Infrared Thermal Imaging that includes a breast study and face scans (a minimum of face, both profiles and both front obliques).

Who's going to interpret the scans for oral pathology? Many health practitioners will need to get trained to do this correctly. Some will be medical doctors. I suspect chiropractors will become heavily involved in thermal imaging. Their specialized training has prepared them to comprehend the connection between oral pathology and degenerative diseases.

An accurate evaluation of the thermal face scan is a great asset to a dentist. The images frequently identify inflammation in the jawbone that is not apparent on a dental x-ray. Very few dentists have been trained to read a thermal image, however.

First, get full-body thermal imaging, and follow this with a breast study in 90 days to establish a thermal breast baseline. Afterwards, most women can rely on annual thermography to monitor breast health. Always ask for face scans whether getting full-body imaging or a breast study.

Learn the truth about mammograms. Study the research. In addition to thermal imaging, consider other non-invasive technologies such as ultrasound and, when necessary, use MRI before using technologies that expose you to radiation. Avoid a biopsy. Deal with oral pathology. Use only a dentist who is mercury-free because he knows mercury is harmful to humans. Avoid dentists who use and endorse fluoride treatments.

In fact, care for your teeth like your life depends on it.

This is not a new concept. Nearly 400 years ago, Miguel de Cervantes stated: "Every tooth in a man's head is more valuable than a diamond."

Make every attempt to eliminate or manage stress. Make lifestyle, nutritional and supplement changes. Begin a detoxing plan. Be hydrated and alkaline. Ignore the Pinkwashing Campaign.

If you already have a breast clip, gather as much information about your biopsy procedure as you can. Request copies of all records from the doctor or hospital and demand that a copy of your biopsy dictation report is included.

If you decide you want to have the marker removed, remember that time may be against you. Some types of markers are difficult to image after a few weeks, and you may have a marker that will migrate.

If diagnosed with cancer, don't allow insurance to dictate your treatment. Become familiar with every option. Get your mental attitude right. Be your own person. Seek counsel and guidance but make your own decisions. Avoid unnecessary family pressure.

Information in this book will empower and guide you to healing. The websites and books mentioned only scratch the surface of the information that's available. They happen to be the ones that Victoria found in her search. There are hundreds of sites, dozens of credible books, and many medical doctors and dentists that are not mentioned.

Do not expect just any doctor to have the ability or the will to guide you. When it comes to cancer, the medical system is stacked against doctors who are not oncologists, although many of them are perfectly capable of administering a successful treatment protocol. But if they were to attempt to help a patient 'cure' their cancer, they could end up in prison.

Remember, not every cancer diagnosis is accurate. Just ask Bill Irwin (author of this book's Prologue). It's better to do nothing than to rush into conventional medical treatment.

Search for doctors who operate under the radar. They exist. Never go to a cancer doctor alone, and never go with someone whose only experience is with surgery, radiation and chemo. If you are accompanied by someone who rejects alternative therapies, then slash, burn, and poison are the only options you will hear about from them or the doctor. Take someone who is calm, knowledgeable and isn't easily intimidated. Take someone who has your best interest at heart. Do not agree to any testing or treatment until you have done your own research.

If given more than one approved cancer treatment option, which one do you think will be recommended by most oncologists? If you guessed the more expensive one, you get a gold star. And you might even get free valet parking at the hospital, too.

The hardest part of dealing with a cancer diagnosis is listening to all the negative medical hype as you continue to believe your doctor's advice is not the answer, says Victoria. "It will be hard to keep your focus, but that's what you must do. It is not easy because doctors have already scared you to death, and no one wants to die."

You will be scared. Be prepared for it. But you have time to read all the references in this book. Only you can prevent self-destruction after you hear an oncologist explain your options in their view.

On January 31, 2008, an oncologist told Victoria that she must have her breast removed, "but not to worry as he would set me up for plastic surgery for both breasts, and some radiation. If I did this I would stay alive."

Victoria was determined to not surrender her treatment to a third party. She elected to play an active role in getting well, and it started with research plus changes in lifestyle and nutrition. "I had the attitude that I was going to get well." Victoria's attitude is vital if you wish to survive.

Almost immediately she was hit with predictions of urgency and doom. Here are three examples:

- "On February 5, 2008, a medical laboratory worker said I should definitely have a certain blood test to see if I have cancer in the rest of my body. His mother had died of breast cancer and she had tried to cure it naturally and nothing had worked. He said I should have my breast removed and not fool around with this."
- "On February 6, 2008, a doctor with a supposedly integrative medical group called at 8 o'clock in the morning and said after discussing my situation with two doctors I should have the surgery because a doctor in Germany had confirmed it was the best way to survive."
- "In January 2009, a misinformed thermographer told me to get the surgery ASAP or I would end up having chemo. She had seen lots of women with breast cancer and never had seen anyone heal themselves."

"It's now the summer of 2013," says Victoria, "and I know that all these scary comments are hogwash, but I did not know it in 2008. At the time, the comments caused me a great deal of stress and took a toll on my good health, my well being, and my spirit. It takes your spirit."

On the day of her biopsy, Victoria's life was about to change, "not as much from diagnosed cancer but the way doctors wanted to treat their diagnosis. I wanted to keep all my body parts, including my breast and my lymph nodes, and my ability to move my arm. In the process of surviving, I was not willing to ruin my overall good health."

Allow your mind to drift back to January 31, 2008, the day of Victoria's return visit to the Hope Cancer Center. "When I was sitting in my car crying after the oncologist told me I had to have my breast removed and be bombarded with radiation, I would have given anything if someone would have told me to read this book *(Saving Victoria's Breasts).*"

"That is why I have taken so much time and energy to compile this story," she says. "Women must know the reality of the breast cancer industry, and they should have this knowledge before a doctor tells them they have a lump in their breast and badgers them with fear and intimidation. Women have the power to stop taking the abuse but are not using it. I lived through pure hell. No woman should be forced to endure this pain and suffering."

How did Victoria save her life?

"I had to go on my blind faith and gut feeling to know there was a better answer for me. I spent so much of my time, energy and money to find the answer to save my life. Thank God there is another way. This book is a gift for women and the families who love them."

Is there a woman who will take the mantel and run with it, leading women all over America to put a stop to the breast cancer insanity?

One woman can make a difference. Mothers Against Drunk Driving (MADD) was founded in 1980 in California by Candice Lightner after her 13-year-old daughter was killed by a drunk driver. Fourteen years later, the *Chronicle of Philanthropy,* an industry publication, reported that MADD was ranked the "most popular charity/non-profit in America of over 100 charities researched."

The original cover for this book was designed in the spring of 2010 with a subhead, "New Approach to Cancer Cure." The cover and the book's subhead were eventually changed in the spring of 2013 because of the discovery of the breast biopsy clip scandal.

The original book cover was published on the website of Proven Health Management and was shown to at least a thousand women, plus hundreds of men. Maybe a half-dozen people rolled their eyes as if being offended or actually stated that the cover was offensive. Those who took that position were judging a book by its cover, and not substance. Virtually everyone else understood the cover's remarkable significance to women.

In late April 2013 I received a message from a natural doctor who characterized the book's cover as tacky, saying it was inappropriate and it wasn't even a medical image. Without realizing it, he said a mouthful in a few words. His message arrived as Victoria and I were struggling with how to end the book. The message was a blessing. What *should* the last few paragraphs say?

The answer came instantly. The image on the cover is not a medical image, and wasn't intended to be. On the contrary, it's a very private and personal image.

"A doctor views a woman's breasts from a medical perspective and sees them *only* as part of her anatomy, and I believe this is a serious problem for women," says Victoria. "A doctor needs to understand that a woman's breasts are part of her very soul and are essential for her to feel complete with herself."

For the record, the book cover represents the consensus of dozens of breast cancer survivors, all of whom agree the naked image is their message. The cover represents their femininity, their sexuality, their inner sense of beauty. It captures their anxiety when breast issues surface, and their apprehension and fear when a doctor talks about surgically removing the breast and offering an artificial substitute.

Male doctors don't get it. Neither do most female cancer doctors or most male and female surgeons.

Victoria's message to women is simple and pure: "They are your breasts, not the cancer doctor's. A woman's breasts are beautiful and give her insight into her feelings and emotions. Without her breasts, she is not gathering all the information the universe has to offer her. Your breasts are a vital part of who you are. Don't let a doctor take your breasts just because the doctor says so. Remain calm. Get other opinions. Consider alternative treatments. Be fully informed. Have no regrets.

Disclaimer

Peering deep into the cancer culture

The logical starting place for this book was to print a disclaimer that, theoretically, would keep everyone associated with this five-year project out of legal hot water. This was no easy task given that reputable organizations frequently make ignorant statements.

Here's a classic example published in January 2003 by the AARP, which operates as a non-profit advocate for about 38 million senior citizens and is one of the most powerful lobbying groups in the United States. By the way, one of its affiliate organizations is managed wholly for profit.

According to AARP's 2008 consolidated financials, it was paid $652 million on royalties from insurance companies that sold products referred by AARP, and the organization received an additional $120 million for the ads placed in its publications.

AARP published a 'scam alert' in its bulletin and the headline was Cancer and Snake Oil. The practical result was an indictment against every cancer treatment plan that does not follow the dictates of America's powerful cancer industry. If power is the ability to get what you want, wrote Robert J. Samuelson, op-ed columnist in *The Washington Post* on February 21, 2011, then the AARP "runs government budgetary policy, not presidents or congressional leaders."

The first paragraph of the 'scam alert' mentioned surfing the internet for a few minutes, "and you're likely to stumble across something that so far has eluded the world's leading medical researchers: a cure for cancer." At the bottom of the alert, AARP readers are directed to the National Institute of Health for "authoritative information," and readers are told to visit a different site that exposes cancer quackery.

What a disservice to America's senior citizens.

Being listed on a quackery site is akin to wearing The Red Badge of Courage, because that's where you'll find the closest thing there is to a cancer cure. Technically, we should make it plural, because there are many ways to cure cancer. But the government has declared the methods illegal, and driven 'outside the box' researchers and practitioners underground, or spent millions of taxpayer funds trying to imprison them.

Take the case of Dr. Stanislaw Burzynski, a Polish immigrant, who was trained as both a biochemist and a physician. He spent the last 35 years at his clinic in Houston, Texas developing and successfully treating patients suffering with some of the most lethal forms of cancer. The treatment he developed involves a gene-targeted approach using non-toxic peptides and amino acids, known as Antineoplastons.

After a grueling 15-year long battle, the Texas Medical Board on November 19, 2012 officially ended its crusade to revoke Dr. Burzynski's medical license in an effort to end his use of Antineoplastons.

After it was revealed that the U.S. Food and Drug Administration had pressured the Texas medical board to revoke Dr. Burzynski's medical license – despite the fact that no laws were broken, and his treatment was proven safe and effective – the obvious question was "why?"

The answer to this has to do with money. Dr. Burzynski owns the patent for this treatment, and should it actually gain FDA approval, not only would it threaten conventional chemotherapy and radiation, it would also result in billions of dollars of cancer research funds being funneled over to the one single scientist who has exclusive patent rights – Dr. Burzynski.

Two years ago, the doctor's story was chronicled in a documentary, "Burzynski: The Movie," that detailed how he won the largest and possibly the most convoluted and intriguing legal battle against the FDA in American history. Soon afterward, the Texas Medical Board sued him again – without success.

A second film is in production. Every American should read about Dr. Bursynski and see video footage (ForbiddenKnowledgeTV.com).

Meanwhile, Dr. Burzynski is now doing the unthinkable. He is the first and only scientist in United States history to enter the federal drug approval process for a proprietary cancer therapy without any financial support from the American government, the pharmaceutical industry, or the cancer establishment.

As a journalist (radio broadcaster and newspaper publisher), I have lived and breathed the First Amendment for a half-century as a staunch advocate for freedom of speech and freedom of the press. As a radio broadcaster in Florida, I was privileged to contribute to the thought process that led to passage of that state's Government-in-the-Sunshine Law. And I worked to preserve the First Amendment while publishing newspapers in Florida and North Carolina.

I am telling Victoria's story while relying on the protections afforded to everyone by the First Amendment. Unfortunately, too many Americans have never read the Constitution, much less the Declaration of Independence, so they might not grasp the true meaning of free speech.

In the early days of my career as an editor and publisher, I found great pleasure in asking political candidates a simple question: When was the last time you read the Constitution of the United States?

There were a few jaw-dropping moments. Too many political candidates, in my experience, have *never* read the Constitution or the Declaration. That's absurd, when you think about it; a person is asking for your vote and their only knowledge of the nation's heritage is what someone else told them.

The absurdity spills over into our modern "fix all ills with a pill" culture. Seriously, how many members of state medical and dental licensing boards, regulators at the FDA, or officials at the AMA or ADA could finish this sentence from the Declaration of Independence: We hold these truths ...

The correct response, of course, is: "We hold these truths to be self-evident, that all men are created equal, that they are endowed by their Creator with certain unalienable rights, that among these are life, liberty and the pursuit of happiness."

How many people that are literally controlling healthcare could finish this sentence, also from the Declaration: That to secure these rights ...

The correct response is: "That to secure these rights, governments are instituted among men, deriving their just powers from the consent of the governed."

My assertion that this book is distributed under the First Amendment of the U.S. Constitution is probably not worded strongly or thoroughly enough to keep me out of hot water with all the legal beagles in the healthcare industry, much less the physicians and dentists and other healthcare professionals who are named in this book.

To give this book's disclaimer more authority, I added six additional sentences.

1. Do not use information in this document without consulting with your doctor or health care provider.
2. Information in this document is for educational purposes only.
3. References to products, technology, claims and/or statements are not intended to diagnose, treat, cure or prevent any disease or illness.
4. The FDA has not evaluated any statements contained herein.
5. No medical claims are made or implied.
6. Please consult a qualified physician for any medical conditions.

I felt pretty good about my disclaimer until I read the book, *Cancer Research Secrets, Therapies which work and those which don't,* by Keith Scott-Mumby, MD, PhD. His disclaimer is an entire page.

He mentioned that all content in his book was "commentary or opinion and is protected under Free Speech laws in all the civilized world." In addition to using the phrase "educational purposes," he added "entertainment" purposes.

The author also stated that in his book, no warranty of any kind, whether expressed or implied, is given. He also claims a "comprehensive limitation of liability that applies to all damages of any kind."

It seemed like a good idea to add Dr. Scott-Mumby's additional claims to my own disclaimer, which I have done. But I then found the book, *Take Control of Your Health and escape the sickness industry,* by best-selling author Elaine Hollingsworth. Her disclaimer beats anything I have ever read.

"It is customary for writers and publishers to have their work scrutinized by lawyers prior to publication in order to preclude the possibility of lawsuits from companies who feel affronted by statements and evidence presented which are critical of their products, commercial practices and ethics. I have chosen not to do so," she wrote.

Hollingsworth said she went to "extreme lengths" to ensure the accuracy of her statements and the veracity of her evidence.

Hollingsworth castigated doctors and drug companies for "disgraceful, self-interested conduct" on behalf of millions of their victims.

Before she became a successful businesswoman and director of the Hippocrates Health Centre in Australia, Elaine Hollingsworth was a movie actress and far better known by the men she associated with under her acting name of Sara Shane.

In the 1950s and '60s, she was frequently paired on the silver screen or in a television series with some of Hollywood's leading men, including Clark Gable, Sean Connery, James Mason, Raymond Burr, Rock Hudson, Carroll O'Connor and Fred Astaire.

When she moved Down Under in 1980, Hollingsworth became well known for her health lectures and her research into natural ways of maintaining health.

She developed a habit of putting her money where her mouth is. Just read the last paragraph of her disclaimer. "Should any of those I have singled out for dishonourable mention feel that my attack is unwarranted in their case, I would welcome the opportunity to debate the issue with them in court and in public."

She spoke of a "massive, growing worldwide audience of victims and their families" who would be eager to hear their defense.

Victoria's true story involves many people, mostly medical doctors, dentists, and a variety of healthcare professionals. Institutions are also involved – hospitals, cancer centers and clinics.

Every effort has been made to tell Victoria's story in a truthful, straight-forward manner. Her story is supported by stacks of written documents and graphics including newspapers and magazines, books, personal journals, oral and written testimonies, notes from interviews, photographs (prints and original digital images), x-rays, thermograms with medical interpretations, thousands of research documents, hundreds of articles and research data posted on websites, medical reports, lab reports, radiology reports, insurance claims, receipts and travel logs. All of these sources have been utilized in the preparation of this book.

The decision to use real names, real dates and real places was not taken lightly. While there is no intent to malign anyone's character or reputation, sometimes the truth hurts. Questions about money, motives, fear, ignorance, lying, deceit, character, honesty and integrity are brought into play as Victoria's search for help unfolds. The questions are unavoidable.

Telling Victoria's true story also required that we peer deep into our culture and our traditions, and what we observed is frightening, especially in the culture of the cancer industry.

There are many doctors and health practitioners who will have to answer to Almighty God because of what this woman was forced to endure. They can't hide behind their self-defined Standard of Care. Some will answer for the sin of omission and others for the sin of commission.

But they will answer.

About The Epilogue

By Fred Hughes

Robert Palmer is the author of the 400-page paperback, *In Search of Honor,* the fictitious Huckleberry Finn and Tom Sawyer-type adventure of two childhood friends, Clint and Ezekiel, who grow up in the mid-1800s on a Charleston, South Carolina plantation.

Robert's intent was to give children and parents a vision and understanding of the virtues and ethics that make a civilized world.

A lifelong tennis instructor, Robert has used the sport he loves to teach thousands of young people how to face the challenges in the game of life.

Few people can relate the principles found in the Declaration of Independence or the Constitution of the United States to daily living the way that Robert does.

Although the words "truth and honor" were not part of everyday conversation as I was growing up, they were principles that my grandparents and parents lived by. As a longtime personal friend, Robert managed to inspire and challenge me as I followed by own journey in life. By example, he never let me forget where I came from.

His book is dedicated to "those hearty souls who have been undaunted by environment and circumstances in their search for truth and honor."

Saving Victoria's Breasts is the true story of an undaunted North Carolina woman who was diagnosed with breast cancer and it brought her face-to-face with the enemy, and it wasn't her tumor.

Read between the lines in Robert's Epilogue and you will understand what's happening in America's cancer industry. Robert's use of a thistle under the skin to tell this story is uncanny, because Victoria did not learn about breast clips inserted during a biopsy until June 2010. Robert's story was written months earlier.

Epilogue

By Robert Palmer

Once upon a time, an Indian tribe lived in harmony with nature in the land of the Big Sky, sparkling streams, rugged rock walls and snow-capped mountains. White Owl, the chief of the tribe, had ruled wisely with input from the elders whenever a major decision was to be made.

Seldom were controversial decisions needed because Chief White Owl had no desire to dominate, but rather to encourage his people to be free. Chief White Owl not only had the support of the elders, but also the loyalty of the witch doctor, One Who Takes Care Of.

It seemed the only possibility of opposition could come from Fierce Warrior, who on two occasions had organized the young braves into a formidable force and defended the tribe from attacks by a neighboring tribe.

Fierce Warrior had saved his tribe from annihilation and slavery but lost three-fourths of the horses in the process. With the tribe vulnerable for another attack, Chief White Owl called for a tribal council. Attending the council would be the elders, One Who Takes Care Of, Fierce Warrior, and, of course, Chief White Owl.

White Owl opened the discussion: "As you can see, we are in a situation where our days are numbered. If we should ever be under attack, we will be outnumbered and will not have enough horses to create a mobile force. Do any of you have any suggestions?"

A silence fell over the assembly. Only the crackling of the camp fire could be heard. Finally an elder named Man Who Walk Like Bear broke the silence.

"Maybe there is so little to take, no tribe will bother us. I am old and tired. I wish to live out my life here next to the stream where I spent my childhood, my manhood and now, my old age. I can still fish and hunt and the Great Spirit has provided me with all I have ever needed. When I return to the Great Spirit, I will be a contented man."

Everyone nodded approval of what Man Who Walk Like Bear had said, for he had touched their hearts. They too had affection and attachment to their homeland. Calm permeated the assembly.

Fierce Warrior stood up displaying his powerful physique and presence. "We must increase our fighting capabilities in order to defend ourselves. We must recognize our enemies and be prepared to fight. I say, we steal our horses back and all of their horses as well. This will put them on foot, which will make it more difficult for them to attack us. Chief White Owl, I urge you to give me permission to steal our horses back."

Everyone agreed, but White Owl silenced their enthusiasm. "Fierce Warrior, I must deliberate before I give you permission. Meanwhile, One Who Takes Care Of, what are your thoughts?"

"White Owl, I am torn between the choices, so I withhold my opinion. One Who Takes Care Of wants to remain neutral so I can remain witch doctor no matter who is chief."

"Very well, One Who Takes Care Of, I am grateful to all of you for your opinions. Now, I give you my plan. If you are not in agreement with my idea, feel free to disagree and give your reasons for your disagreement."

Chief White Owl continued: "I say, given the military weakness of our situation, we move the village to another part of the mountain. There we will have the cover of the mountain and a situation where the enemy will have to climb up to get to our village. If game is scarce, we can come down to hunt and fish. We can survey the terrain for possible attack.

"If the enemy is sighted, we will lead them into a crevice where our arrows will be concentrated into a small area. If we train every member of the tribe to attain excellence with a bow, and organize this excellence to result in a rain of arrows onto our target, we will be successful in the defense of the village and give the enemy such a defeat as to let all potential enemies think hard before they consider an attack on us.

"Remember, that nearly all of their warriors will be riding a horse because they have to travel so far to get to us. The arrows that kill horses will provide meat to dry or smoke. Each warrior killed will have a bow, a quiver of arrows, a knife, a spear, and a tomahawk.

One powerful victory will strengthen our defenses. This military hardware will be passed down to future generations."

"If we do as Fierce Warrior suggests, that is to raid their village for a few horses," added Chief White Owl, "they will mobilize a force stronger than we can repel. It will mean the end of our tribe."

Everyone nodded their approval enthusiastically.

Fierce Warrior, forgetting his desire to replace White Owl as chief, was stunned at this wisdom. "Chief White Owl has, once again, proven his wisdom. I will do all in my power to implement the plan."

"Thank you, Fierce Warrior. Do any of you disagree with the plan?" the chief asked.

Silence fell.

"Very well, at sunrise, we will send a party of 10 braves with Fierce Warrior as their leader, to the mountains from which our stream originated. Go back to your tipi's to get some rest."

Man Who Walk Like Bear arrived at his tipi to find his granddaughter, age 7, was running a high fever and had a severely swollen left leg. The girl was a treasure to the tribe. Her name was, Girl With The Perpetual Smile. Man Who Walk Like Bear turned and ran to fetch One Who Takes Care Of.

"Hurry, my granddaughter is very ill."

When One Who Takes Care Of saw the girl on the edge of death, he told Man Who Walk Like Bear, "The demons have her under their spell. I will dance the Dance of Fire to overcome the spirits of death."

When the rest of the tribe heard the witch doctor's chant, they gathered around the tipi and prayed to the Great Spirit. The thought of losing her was like a huge black cloud. After all, she was the sweet soul given to the tribe by the Great Spirit.

The witch doctor chanted for two hours, but to no avail. By this time, she had fallen into a faint.

"Girl With The Perpetual Smile has been lost to the demons," announced the witch doctor. "Go home. Tomorrow we will burn her body so that her spirit can escape to the other world."

When the girl was finally left alone, a young brave, age 13, slipped into the tipi to observe the face of death. Starring at the body, Boy Who Thinks noticed a facial tremor and a slight movement of her hand. "She lives!"

Boy Who Thinks knew the girl would die if he brought the witch doctor back to chant. He had seen some people live and some people die while the witch doctor chanted. When the patient lived, the witch doctor would proclaim, "I have driven the demons out!" When the patient died, he would proclaim, "The demons and the forces of death have won!"

Boy Who Thinks wondered if the outcome would have been the same if the witch doctor didn't exist. But he dare not say anything for his fellow tribe members were in awe of One Who Takes Care Of, and they were a little afraid of the man who dwelled in two worlds.

Boy Who Thinks decided to bring the girl back from the other world by dealing with the problems in the physical world. He looked closely at the swollen leg and discovered a slight bump with a color of brownish gray.

"It's a thistle! It must be a large one to cause such an injury. It is a good thing she is not awake. I will take my knife and open the wound a little wider so I can prod the thistle out above the skin, then I can pull it out."

Boy Who Thinks implemented the plan perfectly. "This thistle is very long. Good, only a moderate amount of blood. She won't bleed to death. Now I must put some pressure on the leg to force out the poisons."

After pressuring the leg, Boy Who Thinks placed some leaves over the wound to stop the bleeding. Then he carried her to the stream and held her in a floating position. The cool water quickly reduced the swelling and the fever.

Satisfied that the girl would recover, he carried her back to the tipi and laid her down.

"Boy Who Thinks, why am I so wet?"

"I soaked you in the stream to bring down your fever and take the swelling out of your leg. You had a huge thistle in your leg. I removed it. The stream solved all the problems."

"Thank you for saving my life."

"It was the Great Spirit that saved you. The Great Spirit created the natural laws of the universe. I just obeyed them. It was the laws that saved you!"

"I am grateful that you understood the natural laws."

"The tribe thinks you are dead. One Who Takes Care Of has pronounced you dead. Everyone will be happy to see you alive again. I must be going. Do not be afraid, for the Great Spirit has smiled upon you. I look forward to seeing you tomorrow. It will be such a surprise when they all see you walking."

To the astonishment of the entire tribe, Girl With The Perpetual Smile was walking and laughing, with only a slight limp. She appeared perfectly healthy. She told everyone how Boy Who Thinks saved her life. The news spread quickly throughout the village.

The witch doctor was furious that Boy Who Thinks had accomplished what he had not. His position as witch doctor could be compromised if he let this go without explanation, so he called for a pow wow that included the entire tribe.

"I have requested this assembly to warn you of the grave dangers Boy Who Thinks has caused us. He has interfered with the natural process when he tried to help Girl With The Perpetual Smile. He has angered the demons in the spirit world. They will put a curse on our tribe. We will have no peace."

The witch doctor continued: "I have ventured into the spirit world. I have sat by their campfires where they have told me of their powers. When I travel back there I am welcomed and given a place of respect. It is I who have the power to convince the demons to leave our tribe alone and busy themselves elsewhere. As long as Boy Who Thinks is in our midst, the demons will be stirred and restless. Therefore, I ask Chief White Owl to banish Boy Who Thinks to other places where he will receive the wrath of the demons, leaving our tribe safe and secure."

A dead silence descended on the scene. Everyone waited for White Owl's decision.

"On the coming sunrise, Boy Who Thinks will be banished, never to return."

At sunrise, Boy Who Thinks, with all his belongings, started to walk away from his previous life, when a lone voice cried out, "Boy Who Thinks." It was Girl With Perpetual Smile. Her limp was less than the previous day.

"Boy Who Thinks, I am so sad that you have lost all because of me. The thought of you will bring tears to my eyes,"

"Do not be that way. You are Girl With Perpetual Smile. Your face brings happiness to all around you. The Great Spirit brought you here to be who you are. Do not be someone else. Be grateful for each day and live it to the utmost. I shall miss you and hold you dearly in my heart. The thought of you will bring a smile to my face."

"But, won't you be lonely?"

"Yes, there will be times when I will be lonely, but I will always have my constant companion."

"Who will that be? You have been shunned by all."

"My constant companion will be truth."

With that, Boy Who Thinks headed for the foothills, waving goodbye every several hundred yards or so. Finally, he was gone.

It was rumored that Boy Who Thinks was dwelling in a cave in the foothills. While the majority of the tribe still trusted the witch doctor, some sought out Boy Who Thinks when sickness entered their family circle.

After a few years, more and more sought Boy Who Thinks for their health care. After healing them, he would send messages to Girl With Perpetual Smile. "I am well and lost in the search for truth. The thought of you makes me smile."

And so it is, that throughout history, the descendants of Boy Who Thinks are always demonized and banished by those whose existence is dependent on maintaining the status quo.

(Order *In Search of Honor* by mail. Send check for $27 ($22 plus $5 shipping) payable to Pam Sherburne, 7697 95th Place, Live Oak, FL 32060.)